Oh, Hello Alzheimer's

A Caregiver's Journey of Love

Lisa Marshall

Green Heart Living Press

Oh, Hello Alzheimer's: A Caregiver's Journey of Love

ISBN Paperback: 978-1-954493-36-0

Cover photography: Dan Brehant Photography and Cait Fletcher Photography

Cover design: Elizabeth B. Hill

Praise for *Oh, Hello Alzheimer's*

"Lisa Marshall has found joy where none was thought to exist. Most people aren't this honest to their own diary. Lisa Marshall is an open book—a book you won't want to put down. In my travels across America for CBS News, I have yet to meet a more compassionate person than Lisa Marshall. She will show you how to make the most of an Alzheimer's diagnosis. She will also show you the way to true love. Diagnosed with Alzheimer's in the prime of his life, Peter Marshall was dealt a horrible hand. Yet, he may be the most happily married man I ever met. His love was so deep, it become an instinct. This isn't just a book about Alzheimer's. It's a book about how to love, from the woman who mastered the craft."

—Steve Hartman, CBS Evening News

"Lisa's poignant and unfiltered perspective of life as a caregiver is thoughtful and informative, while being a devastating front row view to the realities of Alzheimer's and the ripple effect on families. Her unwavering love and respect for Peter is tangible throughout their beautiful story."

—Kait Hanson, TODAY.com reporter

Lisa opened up a world that no one wants to know about, let alone live in. Their story shined an authentic light on all the crevices of this devastating disease. Lisa's example gives me hope each and every day as I navigate my own caregiving path. I am eternally grateful to have witnessed her strength, compassion and commitment to Peter, with amazing love, patience, and respect. This is real life for too many of us.

—Heidi Kroft, Caregiver

"Lisa's journey as a caregiver for her beloved Peter as · he struggles with younger-onset Alzheimer's is one in which many people will be able to relate. Her brave storytelling sheds light on the tremendous need for increased awareness and support for the more than 11 million Alzheimer's and dementia caregivers across the country. This book is a testament to their dedication, generosity and strength in the battle against this devastating disease."
—**Ginny Hanbridge, Executive Director, Alzheimer's Association Connecticut Chapter**

"Lisa Marshall is simply amazing. I've been a licensed social worker for over 25 years—working primarily with the geriatric population and currently as the owner of CEU Creations—providing required continuing education trainings for helping professionals. Lisa has presented for us many times. The techniques and tips that she shares for 'hands-on caregiving' are absolutely invaluable and truly life-changing in many ways—not only for the person with dementia, but for the caregiver (as well). In addition to sharing practical tips/tricks, Lisa has an incredible zest for life and ability to find and share joy in any situation. Her enthusiasm is contagious and all who learn from Lisa will carry her wisdom and joy with them. She is unforgettable and her book is a 'must-read' for all caregivers and anyone who works with people with dementia.
—**Anne McSweeney, LCSW President, CEU Creations**

Dedication to Peter

My Dearest Peter,

I love you much (most beautiful darling)

more than anyone on earth and I like you more than anything in the sky (e.e cummings)

You have given me your life and shared your children with me, whom I love, and you have loved my children with all your heart. Together we cradled our grandson, even though you were a child then.
You are a teacher of grace, kindness, and generosity.
I have felt incredibly loved, so fully and deeply by you.
My heart bursts because of you.
You lift me, always.
You ground me, always.
You challenge me, always.
You make me a better person, always.

Ours is more a feeling than words. The best ice cream cone, the perfect wave, the warmest sunny day, the best night's sleep, the most relaxing afternoon, the hardiest of laughs, the most agonizing sorrow.
I am the luckiest woman in the world. I was loved so intensely by you.
Thank you for loving me so relentlessly every single day, more than anyone on earth.
I have tasted true love because of you.

Love Always and All Ways,

Tart

Acknowledgments

My heart swells with love and everlasting gratitude to so many who helped me through this journey. First and most importantly, Peter, who loved me so tenderly until our last day together. Peter made it easier to care for him in the hardest of times because he was so incredibly loving.

To my beacon, my guiding light, Sarah Brehant. My courageous daughter shined so brilliantly even though she too was grieving. She tossed her feelings aside to help me with every emotion, decision, and crisis. My respect for her is immense.

I will be forever grateful to Adrianne DeVivo, Dementia Specialist at the Center for Healthy Aging, for guiding me around each next corner, and truthfully showing me what was coming.

The Alzheimer's Association has been endlessly supportive and I have made lifelong friends from our experiences together.

To Robin Clare, my writing coach, friend, and spiritual counselor, I feel enormous pride to have received your attention, encouragement, and guidance during the intense process of writing this book.

Without the tireless support and generosity of so many friends and family, I would not have been able to care for Peter so patiently. Thank you for your tremendous dedication. And to the thousands of followers on the blog, thank you for constantly lifting me up with encouragement.

Table of Contents

Foreword

I didn't know Peter Marshall before his diagnosis of early-onset Alzheimer's. I didn't know the sarcastic, funny, gentle, kind man, the husband and father, and friend that his family and friends knew. But I did see glimpses of that man as I worked on a story for the *Hartford Courant* in the fall of 2019.

Peter and I were runners, and we decided to run together that fall, maybe once a week, wherever Peter decided he wanted to go around his home near Andover Lake in Connecticut. After he would take me on a route involving the numerous hills around the lake, he would always return home to his wife Lisa and exclaim dramatically, "She tried to kill me!" Once as we labored up one of the inclines, he saw a woman walking and told her the same thing as I rolled my eyes and told him this was his route, not mine.

We joked and laughed a lot. One day I discovered I had a pocket in my running skirt where I could carry a phone (which I liked to do since I had no idea where we were going and wasn't quite sure if Peter did—even though he always did). I said to Peter, "Oh my gosh, I have a pocket," to which he replied, in a girlish tone, "Oh my gosh!"

So he was still in there, his personality occasionally shining through the plaque and tangles of Alzheimer's clogging his brain. I was never sad around Peter because I never knew the former Peter, the brilliant engineer who solved intricate problems but now struggled to put together a coherent sentence. I only knew the Peter I knew, funny and mischievous, a man who liked to be outdoors and active, a man who loved his wife very much and knew deep down that she was helping him, even if he couldn't express his thanks.

11

The greatest part of this story, which I immediately grasped when I met the Marshalls for the first time in September 2019—is the love story between Peter and Lisa, a love which endured for 20 years through sickness and health. Even when Peter had bad days or Lisa thought she couldn't take the frustration and heartbreak of Alzheimer's anymore, that love kept them afloat.

People would say to me, as Lisa chronicled her daily care of and interactions with Peter on her Facebook page: "How can she do that? I could never do it." It wasn't easy. There were horrible days and there was heartbreak, again and again—the days when Peter didn't know who she was, the day he couldn't make it down the stairs and she knew that the end was near for her beloved 56-year-old husband. Let's also not forget they made it through a pandemic, with limited contact from family and friends through much of 2020.

But Lisa did it her way—honestly, the only way she could do it—and has emerged on the other side, certainly not unscathed but still able to smile and laugh and find joy in the world. And she wrote this book. She's a wonderful writer, as evidenced by her Oh, Hello Alzheimer's Facebook page, which was what initially attracted me to do a story on the Marshalls—her honesty, her realness, her anger, and her pain mingled with tenderness and love.

Of all the stories I have done, this is easily the one I became most involved in and along the way, long after the story hit the paper, I became friends with Lisa and Peter. I miss Peter and our runs and walks. But I believe he and Lisa served a purpose to educate people about and bring awareness to the ravages of Alzheimer's in a meaningful and personal way. And I know he would appreciate that.

Lori Riley, August 2022

Introduction

After the reality had set in that my husband was diagnosed with early-onset Alzheimer's Disease at the young age of 53, I wanted to scream from my lungs, "Look at this! Look at what is happening to us! Someone help us! I'm losing my soulmate!" It was a cry for help, and I was begging for a rescue. A rescue that never came. Peter died three years and eight months after diagnosis. While the diagnosis was devastating and could have overpowered me, I knew that I had to understand the disease and what to expect. Being Peter's caregiver would require enormous research, but there was little available as I tried to find information.

As our experience grew, I decided to start a blog entitled *Oh Hello Alzheimer's* to offer readers the chance to peer into our world and get a firsthand look inside our private walls. I began to share the raw emotions of receiving the diagnosis and its unfairness. The horror of knowing there is no cure for Alzheimer's and the panic of slowly losing the love of your life. People have asked me why I started the blog, and I believe it was an answer to my cry for help above. I am writing this book to share our experiences and the knowledge and wisdom I learned during this devastating time to support caregivers of loved ones with Alzheimer's.

In the beginning, I didn't believe her promise to steal every ounce of my husband. Alzheimer's, this wicked bitch, immersed herself into our beautiful love story and she was uninvited and unwelcome. Wearing my Wonder Woman cuffs I fended off her warnings with a carefree laugh assuring her, she has the wrong strong man. Her claw marks are indelible on my heart and my cuffs are dented and battered; I am bruised. Yet, our memories are protected by our powerful commitment to one another, our bond, our love, and devotion and she will never chisel them away. And in the end, all we need are our memories; the bitch has not stolen them from me, and they are glorious and painful at the same time.

Through the years of caring for my husband, Peter, I discovered many tips and tricks for dealing with the unique nuances of early-onset Alzheimer's. Many of these tips apply to all forms of dementia and I discovered many people were hungry to feel part of this learning community. What surprised me were the life lessons I learned along the way that now, on the other side, help me to live a more joy-filled life.

When I began writing, I would read each entry to Peter asking for his permission before publishing it. Peter's dignity is of utmost importance, so his permission was paramount. Many of my posts are wrought with emotion as I depict something that happened or a way that Peter or I felt. When reading the words to Peter I often struggled through, choking on my own words, sobbing at the disbelief of it all. One day, I struggled to read the words I would publish, my shoulders shook in disbelief and tears fell in my hands as I hid my face. Peter knelt on one knee behind me as I sat at the dining room table reading. He rubbed my back as I cried and said, "It's ok. It has to be done. It has to be you."

Peter was right and his words ring in my ears. His words gave me permission and courage and a passionate voice to evoke change and guide others. The story of our journey has ended with Peter's death. I've written this book for caregivers and families struggling with Alzheimer's and other related dementias. It's a continuum of Peter and my fierce commitment to help and care for those behind us. I hope to help by offering guidance, support, and hope on the other side. The struggle and daily grief are unbearable, but my experiences are real and relatable. This book was surprisingly difficult to write, emotionally.

The research of combing through over three years of blog posts was grueling. Repressed memories and experiences were dusted off and relived so they could be told robustly. This book had to be filled with truthful experiences no matter how painful they were for me to rediscover. Readers expect it and deserve it. *Oh Hello Alzheimer's* connected a community of people who belong to a club we never wanted to be a part of. Egos were checked at the door, and it became not only a depiction of our beautiful love story but a safe place to ask questions and find the bravery to advocate for a loved one. I hope that caregivers find this book an extension of that space, a road map for your dementia journey.

Peter has given me his permission to share our journey and use my voice to help others. This is Peter's gift to the world.

Much Love,
Lisa

CHAPTER 1

Diagnosis Day

It had been over a year of tests and pokes and prods, images and spinal taps, cognitive crap and fears, head scratches and questions, and wonders. We were referred to a first neurologist whom I ultimately fired for his lack of grit to get to the cause of Peter's decline. I found him to be pompous as he threw his hands up with no explanation. He lacked the empathy I expected. When I asked for a referral for a second opinion, he was extremely unhelpful, and I ended up researching neurologists on my own. I learned through discussions with other caregivers, that this is not uncommon.

What Dr. Neuro Number One did do was refer Peter to the Hospital for Special Care for extensive cognitive testing. The goal was to find out Peter's cerebral ability as well as his deficits. Peter was scheduled to perform these tests for six hours the first day and another four hours the next day. Imagine being asked questions until you cannot come up with an answer for a solid six hours. Peter must have felt so inept to be pushed over and over to his limit. Peter came home after the first day and approached me in my home office. He announced that he would not be going back for the second day of testing. He had tears in his eyes. I stood up and held him and let him tell me how frustrating it was to fail over and over and over all day long. He was deflated and defeated and exhausted.

"Would you feel more comfortable if I went with you tomorrow?" I quizzed. Peter reluctantly agreed after a bit of coercion. The next day I took the day off work and accompanied Peter for his second day of cognitive abuse. It was grueling to watch and shocking to see this highly intelligent man floundering with the most basic of questions. I was astonished and so grateful I was there to witness it.

"Peter's reading comprehension is that of a fourth grader and his math scores are on a sixth-grade level," the doctor gently told us. It was surreal and I felt my eyes blinking hard to understand his words. How could this possibly be my math-whiz husband?

I'm an incredibly positive person, placing everything picture-perfectly in its flawless little place. Every emotion in tidy organization, with only enough honesty to mute the pain of *WHAT IF? What if this is serious? Surely it wouldn't be,* I remember thinking. Our love story is too grand to be tarnished. Nothing could penetrate our bond or prevent our dreams for the future. Right? My confidence was shaken after our visit, and I was rattled. I was feeling vulnerable at the thought of our perfectly perfect life being compromised.

When we visited Dr. Neuro Number One to discuss the results of the bloodwork, MRI, and extensive cognitive testing he was flippant. He had no idea what was wrong. "We have a baseline now. I'd recommend retesting every year to monitor the decline." This did not sit well with me, and I felt my inner Annie Advocate bubbling up. Peter could not tolerate days of cognitive torture again and I wouldn't put him through it. "I think we need a second opinion" I tried to suggest gently, but I bruised his ego. Dr. Neuro Number One, stood up, clammed up, and instantly had his hand on the doorknob. He refused to give me another neurologist's name and literally told me to google it. Dr. Neuro Number One was fired that day.

In the following days, I started researching and looking for a new neurologist. Reading reviews and profiles trying to select someone I felt may be able to help us forge ahead to a diagnosis. I finally found a new

Dr. Neuro about an hour away and felt confident as the hospital's reputation is superior. It had been over a year of jumping through the insurance hoops of getting another referral and finally an appointment with Dr. Neuro, I requested all records be sent to the new neurologist.

There was one final test Dr. Neuro ordered for Peter, a spinal tap, or lumbar puncture. This test would look for proteins called beta-amyloid and tau. Experts believe that a reduction in beta-amyloid protein in spinal fluid could be a significant clue that the protein tau, could be present in the brain. Tau has been associated with neurofibrillary tangles and an increase in Tau has been linked to Alzheimer's disease. Peter handled the test well and did not suffer from the common headache associated with a lumbar puncture.

We waited the remaining days or weeks until April 30, 2018 arrived and we both anticipated a quick and easy appointment. 14 months and 16 days after Peter saw his primary care physician on Valentine's Day, we drove the hour to the neurologist's office; our moods were light as we bounced around within our boundaries of denial. Just another adventure together, a lovely day off to spend with one another. Peter's attitude was the same as it was during the Valentine's Day visit to his primary care physician the year before. He was not convinced anything was wrong but was happy to appease me and help my mind rest. We listened to '70s music and sang off-key together, holding hands as Peter drove us to face our fate.

Peter and I, neurologist, physician's assistant (PA), and fellow filled the exam room. It was the follow-up appointment, the bearing of truths of all the testing and torment. I had done precisely no research on Alzheimer's because it wasn't that. It couldn't be that. It was something else. Something they'd prescribe a pill for, some quick treatment and that would be the end of it, back to our perfectly pretty life! Dr. Neuro sat on the edge of the exam table in the room, seeming apprehensive and serious, hands clasped, and he breathed in a breath and paused before he spoke. The PA and fellow stood completely still and respectfully quiet behind him. Peter and I were perched on chairs opposite Dr. Neuro. His white coat was neatly pressed. His name was carefully stitched in deep ocean blue. Peter's knee bounced at a furious pace now, and I wore my magic marker smile to hear the big news. Our hands were clenched together, and our moods were more serious in the sterileness of the moment.

Dr. Neuro leaned forward, arms on his knees, and he stuttered a bit. He looked at Peter and then carefully looked deep into my eyes with the utmost empathy. Gently, he delivered the next words in slow motion, at least that's how I received them. The image of his eyes is burned into my memory. Dr. Neuro's words were encased in a feeling of sorrow that I didn't understand. The words rolled across his tongue so very cautiously as if he were apologizing. He was so very sorry to be the one to deliver this horrific news. Then he paused, waiting for our reactions, our questions, but there weren't any. I was blank and unaffected by the news, completely ignorant about how our lives would spiral swiftly for the rest of our days together until the end of us.

Most of Dr. Neuro's words whizzed past my ears, apart from these few: 'Early on-set Alzheimer's'.

"Oh!" I remember thinking, almost relieved, "Everyone has that. Where should we go for lunch?"

Lisa's Lookback

In retrospect, I'm grateful I didn't do a lot of research before our diagnosis appointment. Not knowing was a gift to protect my heart and allow the information to come to me as I was ready. My heart was preserved for just a little while as I gathered information and came to the realization our Cinderella story was on borrowed time. The Alzheimer's bitch was coming, and she was coming fast. I thought we would have more time and never imagined she would steal my beloved Peter so quickly.

Questions to Ponder

1. Were you or are you prepared for the diagnosis?

2. Is it easier to research before and know what's coming or ease into the facts?

3. Would you have done anything differently before the diagnosis appointment?

Bravery

She was never quite ready.
But she was brave.
And the universe listens to brave.

-Rebecca Ray

CHAPTER 2

The First Signs, Before Diagnosis

The beginning signs were easily ignored or brushed away and as they grew in merit, my dirty little secret did too. If I didn't talk about it and address these forgetting things, they weren't real. Peter was very intelligent and able to easily disguise the voids in his memory for a long time. He developed coping tricks to help inspire his memory into action.

Peter was examined by a psychologist as part of the Social Security Disability approval process. It was a lighthearted hour-long appointment and Peter and I laughed quite a bit as we talked about the nuances we had experienced so far. It was the early stages before it became scary and real. We liked the doctor and felt comfortable speaking candidly with her. We explained some of the coping mechanisms we had in place, and she was impressed by Peter's ability to help himself. He would set alarms on his watch if he needed to be somewhere. Peter couldn't remember Alexis's name and so I typed her name on a piece of paper and taped it to the wall above the device. Another sticky note was adorned on the front door that read, "Phone Wallet Keys" and eventually we added, "laptop and lunch" to the list.

I'd open the refrigerator only to find the lunch I packed for Peter resting on the shelf after he had left, or his phone or wallet lying on the counter in his absence. He would call me once he reached the city to tell me he didn't have his phone so if I needed to reach him, I should call the office. The frequency of these forgettings increased and Peter's nudging mechanisms soon became ineffective.

Several years before our Alzheimer's diagnosis my dermatologist determined that a suspicious spot on my lower back was basil cell skin cancer. The plan was to visit a local plastic surgeon for the excision, and I was very nervous about the procedure. Peter, of course, would leave the office and meet me there for the midday appointment to provide his usual sweet soul-soothing and handholding. Except he didn't. He forgot. He never showed up and I braved the surgery alone. I went back to work, and we met at home that evening when our workdays were done. We had dinner and watched television and I felt no need to mention the appointment because I knew when he found out he would feel such agony, thinking he had let me down I couldn't bear to tell him. Later that night, as I undressed to change into my pajamas, he saw the bandages and darted to my body, his big hands gently touching my back. Our eyes met and he knew. Peter pulled me to him carefully and rocked me in his arms and when he pulled away from me, tears streamed down his cheeks.

The incision healed and several months later we were visiting friends, staying overnight. As I undressed for bed, my back faced Peter and he spied the three-inch mark on my skin. He came to me and gently touched it, kissing my shoulder, and caressing my scar, he quietly asked, "What happened here?" The clues kept coming and I kept ignoring that they were connecting to the worst nightmare of our lives. Old things seemed new to Peter, and what I thought were engrained memories were a challenge for Peter to recall.

The simple act of pumping gas is not so simple if you cannot remember the five digits of your zip code for the processing of your credit card. Peter would carry a sticky note in his wallet with our zip code written on it, another coping tactic. Things were added to the note in the coming months when his brain failed him; our anniversary which was the door code to enter our home, his birthdate, and our address. The note was smudged and well-worn from enduring all the ins and outs of Peter's wallet.

Words began to escape him, and I felt a lump in my throat the day he described "the thing we get on to travel, we take our suitcases, it goes in the sky." My heart raced and when given the answer "airplane", Peter smiled and laughed and brushed it off making fun of himself. Chalking it up to getting older, of course. These word voids were happening more and more often, and I would offer the word as gently as I could. Peter's answer was always, "Yeah, yeah, yeah!" as if he knew it all along.

Lively gatherings with longtime friends most always included reminiscing about past times together or discussions of mutual friends and Peter began not to be able to keep up. These memories were vivid to the group but would be fuzzy or nonexistent for Peter and it was becoming obvious to those closest to us. The squinted, quizzical eyes of friends and their furrowed brows made my heart sink further. The best of friends had the best of intentions and pulled me aside to ask kindly if something was wrong. If the closest of friends had been brave enough to express concern, how many friends said nothing? Who knew? Were they judging? My secret was out and suddenly I knew with my whole being that I alone would need to be his fierce advocate. Our friends were now holding me accountable for Peter's care and I would need to hold myself accountable as well. Peter would never call his physician on his own, nor would he be able to communicate the struggles he was experiencing or know the questions to ask. He was not capable of advocating for himself.

Valentine's Day, 2017 was the day I first took my Valentine to his doctor. That was the day our love story would begin to end. That visit was the start of the grueling work of cognitive investigation which Peter would come to despise with fury. Peter remarked to his primary care physician with a shrug, "She says she's noticed things for four or five years."

A quick battery of cognitive tests challenged Peter immensely and he gave up even trying to answer most of the questions. It was difficult for me not to blurt out the answer to help him.

Peter was the handiest man I have known, able to design and build challenging projects in our home. Now he could not tell his doctor what tools would be required to hang a picture on a wall. He could not draw the face of a clock showing 11:05. He repeated, "I don't know" to many questions, laughing it off for the duration of the appointment. Even when the doctor tried to make the answers multiple choices he struggled. It was a shocking realization that left me feeling panicked. My goal was to leave the doctor's office with orders for bloodwork, an MRI, and a referral to see a neurologist. We left with those things along with the doctor's words ringing in my ears, "The scores are alarmingly low for a man with Peter's education."

The doctor's words played on repeat in my mind and I started to worry about our financial future. The only time Peter and I weren't together was when he was at work. I had no idea how he was handling his day-to-day duties. Peter managed a team of independent and self-motivated employees, and Peter himself worked solo often. But what was he doing? Certainly, his co-workers were noticing his deficits and how long would it be before his boss would address his non-performance. He had been an employee of Conning for 18 years, one of the many long-timers. His mind was always sharp, and he thought outside the box, prodding others to think there, too. Peter was an analytical ponderer, always probing and investigating a better way, the right way to do something.

He oversaw the risk management and compliance department and needed to stand his ground very firmly when salespeople or even his bosses would push Peter to bend the rules. How was he handling this pressure?

Knowing his future at work was in jeopardy because he could not possibly be performing to his own par, I decided with the advice of my attorney, to immediately send a letter to Peter's Human resource department. The letter included Peter's diagnosis from his neurologist and an explanation of his possible non-performance. Management and HR gently looked under the hood of Peter's duties and carefully peeled off layers of responsibility until there weren't any. Later, I learned that Peter would spend hours in the common areas just looking over the city, and eating his lunch. I spoke with Peter's HR team over the phone on several occasions. We checked in and compared notes and finally, the time came to meet in person to discuss the details of short-term and long-term disability. The day of that meeting was Peter's last day of work. The team was kind from day one and remained compassionate and helpful throughout the rest of Peter's life.

Sending Peter's diagnosis to his HR department gave me such a sense of relief. I had been so afraid that he would lose his job which would have a huge impact on us financially. Peter carried our medical benefits, so that was a big concern as well. If I hadn't notified HR, Peter could have lost his job and we could have lost those benefits along with his short- and long-term disability insurance. There was now a medical reason for the lack of performance they were surely seeing. The frequent phone discussions were helpful to both me and Peter's HR department to keep a pulse on his capabilities. Everyone was concerned about Peter's comfort level along with his effectiveness as a Director of Risk Management and Compliance. It became clear quickly, that Peter needed to step away from Conning.

Peter did not understand what happened at the meeting that Friday and we were planning on a trip to our vacation home that day. When we arrived there, I made some dinner and popped a bottle of champagne for us. I filled our glasses and told Peter I had a surprise for him. His eyes widened, he grinned, and he listened intently. Choosing my words deliberately I shared the big news, "You never have to go back to work again, you're retired!!!!!" Peter threw his head back in laughter as he grabbed my hand, pulling me hard so I landed on his lap. He squealed, "Really? Are you serious? How did you do that?!" He was incredibly relieved.

Lisa's Lookback

The earliest signs in my best recollection were four or five years before Peter visited his primary care physician at the beginning of 2017. Each warning on its own meant nothing, but as the symptoms started to fit together, the puzzle grew clearer.

I was in denial for those years. Peter was struggling so hard at work hiding his deficits, that he immediately had a huge decline when he finally retired. I attribute this to his intense relief of not having to keep up the unbearable charade. Peter could relax and just be himself. He was home. He was safe.

Questions to Ponder

1. Were there signs that you dismissed?

2. Were you in denial about the clues you were given along the way?

3. Looking back how long did you see symptoms before taking action to seek a diagnosis?

The Constellations

*For the first eight years of our relationship, Peter and I
loved each other from afar, traveling from Harrisburg to
Hartford every other weekend. Peter loved to surprise me, and it
was not unlike him to have wine and candles ready, Norah
Jones swooning in the background.*

*I remember vividly one Friday night that he was
jumping out of his skin to present his newest surprise, he was
always such a romantic! Shortly after my arrival, he grabbed
my hand and took me to the bedroom and I was thinking,* Geez
Dude, I just drove five hours, let me unwind a sec!

*The lights were on, all the lights! Peter instructed me to
lie down on the bed and he was grinning ear-to-ear. I was
hesitant but trusting so I complied. Peter closed the bedroom
door and told me to close my eyes and I heard him clicking
lamps and light switches to the off position. He urged me to
KEEP my eyes closed and I did.*

*"OK!" he announced excitedly, and I thought he might
start jumping up and down clapping! "Open your eyes!"
It was beautiful and as I write this, I'm overcome with
emotion remembering just how beautiful he was. Not only had
he bought glow-in-the-dark stars for the ceiling, but he had also
made a grid with string across the entire ceiling and plotted the
constellations precisely as they are in the night sky.*

*The room was completely dark except for the stars
overhead. It was brilliant and lovely and romantic and so
totally Peter. His love for me has always been so gallant and
attentive and he has made me feel so loved every day. I'm so
fortunate to have incredibly unique memories like these, and I'm
well aware of how special our love was.*

CHAPTER 3

Going the Distance

People were often curious about how our storybook love affair began. Even after 20 years together, friends would roll their eyes and tell us to get a room. Our entire relationship was so filled with love and attraction that we couldn't stand to keep our eyes and hands off each other, even in public. There was something magnetic about the energy of our romance and people frequently quizzed us about how long we'd been together or how we met. We met when we were married to other people.

Peter's family of four moved in across the street from my family of five in Harrisburg and it didn't take long for a bond to form. Often, the nine of us played and dined and partied even vacationed together, creating memories that would last for our lives. We were neighbors for five years until his family of four moved back to Connecticut, where they began.

Peter and I often watched over the brood of children after five pm while our spouses worked their respective jobs. My driveway was sloped and fun for riding bikes and Peter's had the cool basketball hoop. Neighborhood kids hung around often, and Peter and I had a bird's eye view from my front porch. We became the best of friends.

One day, after years of friendship, Peter and I sat on my porch, and he told me that he had been offered a job. He explained all the pros; increase in pay, better benefits, and challenging work. The only con he revealed was that it was in an entirely new field. He currently worked as a fire protection engineer. Peter was concerned about learning the new industry of finance, but they hired him for his analytical mind and were creating a position for him. The canvas was his to paint.

He was asking for my feedback, and I was elated to give him two thumbs up. I was very excited that he was being challenged with this new opportunity. My head was nodding affirmatively, and Peter was smiling like the Cheshire cat when the other shoe dropped. After he had my buy-in, he told me the new job was in Connecticut. Shortly thereafter, Peter's family of four moved away. Lives were gotten on with separately and kids continued to grow, careers were nurtured, and our roots dug deep where we were and eventually both marriages failed.

Sometime later, Peter and I reconnected by phone, chatting on and on like old friends do, feeling as though we had just spoken the day before. One call led to another and another and they grew in length and depth and flirtation until the decision was made to get together. Peter drove the 326 miles, from his door to mine for a visit that would be the beginning of the steamiest long-distance relationship in the history of mankind. In my humble opinion.

It was all there, the delight, the butterflies, the nervousness, the high school thrill, and we could not keep our hands and lips off one another. Our conversations were challenging and fun and the playfulness was nonstop, and we quickly fell deeply in love. It was hopeless and it was lovely, and our hearts were singing. The depth of our love grew quickly and strengthened, and nothing could keep us apart. Except for death.

My three children were older than Peter's two children and we had no intention of moving one set of siblings out of state away from their respective other parents. So, we continued the 326-mile trek every other weekend for eight years. We alternated the drive, so we were each only burdened with traveling once per month.

We had shared custody of our respective children and so our weekends alone together were private, playful honeymoons to say the very least. We incurred five speeding tickets, one car accident, and two flat tires, rushing to be in each other's arms during our courtship. We counted the days and the hours until the next time we would see each other. Cell phone plans were ridiculously expensive then, charging by the minute, so Peter would pull his truck up to a payphone and roll down his window pulling the receiver inside. Using all the spare change he had collected, he would feed the phone until his last coin was gone and our conversation was cut off. We were never ready.

When we were apart, I would purposely lie down to take a nap, closing my eyes so that I could sleep only to dream of him. Even now, I feel this way. Just to see him, breathe him in, smell him, feel him. To see Peter whole and healthy in my sleep is a vision I never want to wake up from.

We wore a path between Connecticut and Pennsylvania and jumped into each other's arms every eleven days as if we'd been apart for months. My heart would pound, and my palms would sweat when I saw his truck pull into my driveway. Many times, one of us would surprise the other by arriving hours early, a day early, or even on an entirely off-schedule day. The delight was euphoric! Peter and I often joked that one of our surprise trips was going to backfire and we would find ourselves at each other's empty houses, still five hours apart, trying to surprise the other! Fortunately, and miraculously, it never happened.

There were many surprises as we both tried to outdo each other. Unexpected trips, romantic dates, lovely letters, unexpected gifts, and packages! Peter was much better at designing these wonders than I ever could be. One of the most unique surprise packages I received must have taken Peter hours to prepare! He knew I loved the cereal Raisin Nut Bran, but mostly what I loved was the raisins. They are simply delicious. I reached into the mailbox to find a package from Peter, and I was never disappointed by his thoughtfulness. I carried the coveted package, practically skipping into the house, and per Peter's usual, he had used an enormous amount of tape to keep my anticipation brewing. I grabbed the scissors and began the task of opening my latest treasure. Cutting the last of the tape and unfolding the flaps of the box, I squealed with glee as I pulled out a quart-size Ziploc bag filled with just the raisins. Peter had bought two boxes of my favorite cereal and plucked the sweetest prizes out just for me. The bag was heaping. What did he do with all those bran flakes?

Peter's surprises were countless, as was his compassion and the way he adapted to my needs. Our schedule was similar for each visit, one of us arriving at the other's house on Friday night. Each Friday felt like we had an eternity of time but on Sunday morning we would wake up dreading a departure. We struggled to unravel our limbs and get out of bed. Peter's leaving had such a profoundly negative effect on me, that I started negotiating with him to stay longer and longer. I couldn't bear the panic.

Finally, I was buying him a work outfit each Sunday so that he could stay in my arms until four AM. My prince would get up while it was still dark, dress and we would kiss and kiss and kiss saying our goodbye. He would drive directly to his office, arriving by nine AM. Eventually, Peter just started packing his work clothes and staying until the wee hours, the last moments until he had to leave for his five-hour commute to work. And we would begin again our countdown until our hearts and lips would meet once more. My panic attacks disappeared, as it was easier for me to simply fall back to sleep as Peter slipped out in the night. The anxiety never did return until many years later when I knew that Peter was preparing to leave me for the final time.

Lisa's Lookback

Enduring our eight-year long-distant relationship cert-ainly had its ups and downs. Anticipating being together was glorious but saying goodbye became harder and harder over time. I suffered from panic attacks when Peter would leave me after our magnificent weekends together. I learned tricks and tips to help myself cope with the panic of being away from him. I knew that I had to have something exciting, or fun planned to distract me from his absence. I encouraged myself to face the fact that I had to relearn those techniques as the end of Peter's life grew nearer. I knew he would leave me for the final time, and I knew I would panic.

Questions to Ponder

1. How did you meet your loved one?

2. Are you grateful for your time together?

3. How can you celebrate your time together?

CHAPTER 4

The Proposal

Peter was the master of surprises and relished in pulling off one of his unexpected treats, even if it meant the surprise was not getting what I wanted. It was my birthday and I absolutely love my birthday. I'm a social butterfly who collects genuinely kind friends and great-hearted people. I love to talk to my friends and receive their delicious birthday energy. Connecting with my friends and my entire family in one day makes it the best day ever, every year! We had planned a long weekend trip to Block Island, a tiny little island off the coast of Rhode Island which isn't an island at all. We took Peter's truck on the ferry, and we stayed at a darling bed and breakfast overlooking the ocean. The romance was ever-present.

We had been together five years and had discussed marriage. Even though we wouldn't get married until we could live together, we felt a commitment was appropriate. Our long-range plan was to help all three of my children out of the nest and into college. Once that milestone arrived, I would sell my beloved home where I raised my babies, leave my big fat job, and abandon my cherished friends and family. After, I would move to Connecticut to marry the love of my life and become as I frequently joked, an evil stepmother to Peter's two children. I never thought twice about all the changes that would happen and I never regretted it for a single second. I would do anything for this man, without hesitation.

Since we were celebrating my birthday, and enjoying a longer than usual weekend, and the commitment conversations were in place, I felt the stars were aligned. I was certain Peter would propose. It was going to be perfect. I was giggling, imagining every possibility of when and where he would ask me to marry him. The beach, the bar, the bath, the bed. All my friends had been put on notice that this was the weekend, and everyone waited with anticipation for the news! Peter and I were surrounded by so many folks cheering on our Cinderella story and we were all holding our breath for Peter's proposal.

Peter and I drank and ate, shopped and laughed, and loved and loved some more. The weekend was divine, and I waited impatiently for my big moment, but Peter never asked me to marry him. My heart was heavy as I packed up my suitcase and I felt disappointed, but we had made some fantastic memories, I reminded myself, trying not to let my disappointment show. Peter suggested we take some pictures together on the Jetty before getting on the ferry. Just what I needed to pull me out of my sappy mood.

We strolled hand in hand to the rocks and Peter had his coveted camera. He found the perfect rock for me to position myself belly-down on, leaving plenty of room for Peter next to me. He turned on the camera's timer, darted toward me, and leaped to my side for the picture. It took a few tries to capture the perfect pose. That photograph, that perfect pose, would be Peter's favorite picture for the rest of his life. He would laugh so hard each time it appeared. He loved the picture so much that he even uploaded it onto the dash of his truck so each time he drove he could reminisce again.

The perfect picture, and what was so funny to him, was that I had splayed my empty ringless hand out on the rock in front of me to show the world that Peter did not ask me to marry him. The naughty, devilish smile that Peter wore in that photo was my favorite part. Peter had one-upped me. He would never offer up a surprise when

I was expecting it. Peter and I never spoke about my deflated expectations, but he knew.

We left Block Island on a Monday and traveled to a small cottage Peter's parents were renting in Rhode Island. We stayed the night there visiting, playing cards, and eating delicious seafood. We adored our times with Peter's parents and always stayed longer than we anticipated and as parents, they adored time with Peter, too. Tuesday morning, we drove the hour or so back to Connecticut, and from there I drove back to Pennsylvania, unengaged.

It was back to reality and our countdown began again until Peter would make the trip to Pennsylvania for our next honeymoon weekend. Work and kids and their extracurricular activities kept us busy and distracted until our next rendezvous. On Thursdays, Peter and I did not have our children as they were with their respective parents. Occasionally, on Thursdays when we couldn't wait the eleven days, we would meet halfway, each of us driving the two and a half hours to the Cliff Park Inn.

A quiet, charming Bed and Breakfast nestled on a sprawling golf course. The restaurant was as quaint as the rest of the mansion, and the food was delicious. The rooms were spacious and tastefully decorated and some of the rooms had large, jetted bathtubs for two. A gigantic porch wrapped around the inn, and it was dotted with several rocking chairs that overlooked the greens. We loved the property and felt lucky it was located precisely in the middle of our two homes. When we rendezvoused at the Cliff Park Inn, we would have dinner, stay the night, and leave early enough to drive in opposite directions to our offices.

After the Block Island birthday weekend, we went back to work on Wednesday and by Thursday morning I couldn't wait. I closed my office door and picked up the phone, nervously dialing Peter's number. My heart was racing in anticipation of hearing the sexiness in his voice. He always answered the phone with a deep slow hello I can still hear today. My goodness, that man could turn me on.

"Hello yourself," I said. "Can I buy you dinner tonight?" I invited. Peter paused for a moment then eagerly agreed to my offer. We both made a quick lunchtime run home to gather clothes and overnight necessities. The clock dragged on for the rest of the workday until we could finally drive toward each other.

Once we were reunited, we were seated at a quiet four-top table in the corner of the smallest room in the three-room restaurant. Diners were scarce and we had plenty of privacy for eye gazing and kissing over a bottle of wine. Dinner was delicious and the server was happy to bring our food at the slow pace we were enjoying. We were the last pair to leave, and the manager locked the door behind us as we stepped out onto the wide porch. I walked ahead of Peter, aiming for the entrance to the staircase that led to our room and the bed I could not wait to get into. Peter stopped me, asking if I wanted to enjoy the rocking chairs for a little while before heading upstairs. I glanced at my watch and deciding ten o'clock was early, I agreed. There really is nothing like enjoying a rocking chair on a big old porch on a beautifully moonlit July evening.

I sat down on my chosen chair, and Peter sat in the chair to my right. I was feeling happy from the company and chatty from the wine and began yammering on and on about something. I recall Peter perching on his elbow on the arm of his rocker. He wore that devilish grin, his body turned toward me oddly in the chair. He looked boyishly cute like he was loving me and laughing at my gibberish. I was mid-sentence when I realized he was wearing that naughty smile for a reason.

Peter interrupted my blather. "Do you think you could put up with me for the rest of your life?" His two fingers flipped my hidden engagement ring up from his palm. He knew he had surprised me, one-upped me again. I would never have expected him to ask me when I was the one who invited him to dinner. I buried my head in his neck and I cried, not even looking at the ring. It was the perfect proposal, the perfect surprise, and Peter delighted in it.

Peter had run home at lunchtime for his overnight things and grabbed the ring as well. He later told me he had bought the ring a few months before and was just waiting for the precisely perfect moment when I wouldn't expect it. He nailed it!

When I could compose myself and stop blushing, I pulled my head away from Peter and he slipped the ring on my finger. Soon after, we headed to the bedroom to celebrate. As I was getting settled, Peter pulled out what appeared to be a ring box. He went on to tell me that it was the box my ring came in and it was special. "It lights up," he told me. "Try it" he suggested, tossing the box from where he stood on his side of the bed. I caught the box and opened it up. There was no light. It was a pair of earrings that identically matched my engagement ring. Another Peter-style surprise.

Lisa's Lookback

Peter was the consummate friend, boyfriend, fiancée and ultimately husband and I adored him so passionately. As a couple, we exuded an energy that everyone loved and were never shy about showing our love in public. Often people would comment about our Cinderella Story and I dismissed their noise, thinking everyone has this. It wasn't until we were well into Peter's disease that the comments were so frequent that I started to realize just how special our bond was. The common comment was that some people never find a love like ours and it started to sink in and I began to believe it. Looking back, I'm so very grateful that I had the 20 years I did with Peter, and I feel like the luckiest girl in the world to have been loved so intensely by Peter.

Questions to Ponder

1. How is your relationship? Does it need a sprinkle of spice?

2. What are you grateful for in your relationship, and does your loved one know?

3. What can be done to strengthen your bond?

Conquer Your Fear

*Embrace the unknown
and act despite your fear.
Empower yourself with knowledge.
Encourage yourself to be brave.
Demand determination
to prepare for your future.
Conquer your fear.*

CHAPTER 5

First Steps After Diagnosis

The diagnosis itself was overwhelming. Knowing there is no cure and your loved one is going to die no matter what you do is daunting. So, what do you do? I'll share with you the steps that I followed and what I put in place to help us along our journey as well as protect me in the future.

The most important step was to look at anything legal and for that, I needed a professional with special expertise in this area. I needed an elder law attorney. Even though Peter was only 53 and did not qualify for senior citizen benefits, I chose an elder care attorney as we would approach the end of Peter's life and need the same guidance, no matter what his age.

Not knowing how long Peter could work and when I would need to retire concerned me. What did our financial future look like? Would we be able to afford in-home care, or long-term care in a memory care facility if necessary? What would my financial future look like when our journey with Alzheimer's was over? I needed to educate myself and find answers to my questions, so I confided in our financial advisor, Peter had been diagnosed with early-onset Alzheimer's disease.

Between our new elder care attorney and Ray, my long-time financial advisor, I learned the steps I needed to take to protect our current and future financial position. These tasks are tedious and grim. No one wants to think about them or carry out the monotony of doing them, but they must be done.

First, I reviewed our wills. Years before, Peter and I had created our wills using an online service which ultimately proved to be inept as the laws vary from state to state. It was comforting to have a conversation with our attorney and understand what was missing from our wills and what needed to be added or changed, instead of simply haphazardly checking boxes on my laptop. After our initial meeting, I felt secure knowing we were in qualified hands.

As part of refurbishing our last wishes, we appointed executors of our wills. In the event that we died at the same time or I also became incapable of making these important decisions, we needed to appoint someone who we trusted to carry out our wishes. We chose two of our sons, one for each will. They were happy to carry the responsibility if needed.

I met with my financial advisor at length to discuss the insurance policies Peter and I had in place. Fortunately, he had the foresight years before to suggest additional life insurance. Peter's employer offered life insurance, but it was not sufficient for our needs since my current employer did not offer these benefits. We bought an additional policy for each of us, to at least pay off our mortgage, in the event something unforeseen happened, like Alzheimer's. The beneficiaries of the original and new policies needed to be considered. The question now was, were they still pertinent? Did anything need to be changed?

My children urged me for years to purchase long-term care insurance which I politely ignored for a long time. They had watched their paternal grandfather decline from ill health and dementia, witnessing the hardship on their grandmother. Luckily, they had long-term care insurance and 24-hour in-home care, covered by their policy. Ray, Peter, and I agreed with the kids and we bought a policy for each of us. The policy was a life insurance policy with a long-term care rider. That meant if we continued to pay the premium when I needed to file a claim for long-term care, the amount reimbursed came directly from the life insurance policy. For instance, at its peak, Peter's cost of in-home care was $6,000 per month. The policy was capped at a $3,000 reimbursement per month. That $3,000 was taken off the top of the death benefit after Peter died.

There were stipulations and the policy was expensive, but it was well worth it. The policy would not begin to reimburse care costs until Peter could no longer handle two of his activities of daily living on his own.

Activities of daily living include:
1. Bathing
2. Continence
3. Dressing
4. Eating
5. Toileting
6. Transferring (to and from chair or bed)

I often thought losing the ability to perform these six activities would be so far in the future that I would have time to prepare mentally and emotionally, but it came upon us quickly. I didn't even realize we had arrived until someone told me, "Peter will qualify, he can't bathe or dress on his own." It's like when you fall asleep on a long trip and wake up just before you get there and think, "We're here already?! That was so fast." I was stunned.

I immediately contacted the insurance company to discuss filing a claim for Peter's long-term care insurance. After nine weeks I was overwhelmed with the amount of paperwork they required as proof of Peter's disability.

There was paperwork for me, forms for the agency that provided Peter's caregivers, requests for medical records from the primary care physician, Peter's neurologist, and so on.

I put my head down and filled out their paperwork, hopeful that once they had every required piece the claim would be approved. Weeks went by and I kept following up, but each time they wanted more. Every time I received a letter hoping for good news it was just a request for something new, another roadblock.

Finally, I received the final medical record they were waiting for from Peter's neurologist and I was elated! The approval meant I would be reimbursed for a caregiver 30 hours per week! Someone to help with the showering and shaving and dressing and watching so I could focus on enjoying my husband. After all, isn't that what I'd been paying insurance for all these years?

After receiving the letter of good news, the phone rang. It was the insurance company. I had just come from a two-hour hair appointment, the only two hours of respite in thirteen days! I was relaxed and happy and answered the call anxiously listening for the great news of approval.

Nope. The case was presented to the board of doctors and it was not approved because Peter had not had cognitive testing or an MRI since 2018 when he was diagnosed. There was no proof of decline.

After an angry conversation with the insurance rep, my choices were to pay thousands of dollars out of pocket for an MRI to show brain atrophy or put my sweet husband through more cognitive testing. I wouldn't do it. He couldn't take it. The emotional toll it would take on Peter was not worth any price. By the time I hung up, this woman had had the worst day at work ever. I was sobbing uncontrollably, yelling, and slinging profanities for her lack of compassion. She promised that she had advocated the best she could on our behalf. I felt alienated and alone and exhausted.

When this process began months before I reached out to Yale. Peter had previously participated in a 12-month clinical trial which included MRIs and frequent cognitive testing. They had the precise information I needed to support my insurance claim, but they would not release it. I'm not one to take no for an answer, especially when pushed into a corner. I called again, crying, and explained that this was my last resort, begging them to please help me.

Ultimately, they provided the insurance company with the twelve months of data they obtained which includes monthly cognitive testing and three MRIs. The claim was approved, and benefits were paid, but the road to fruition was exhausting. As the caregiver for your loved one, I highly recommend being diligent about not only the paperwork but continually following up with the insurance company and meeting their demands to ultimately get your claim approved.

Peter's employer offered the benefit of short and long-term disability. These benefits were worth every penny. They are typically not expensive, and they offered us financial security after Peter retired. I highly recommend opting into disability benefits if your employer offers them. Our policy considered any other income we were receiving and reduced the amount of the other income, which was Social Security Disability (SSD). For instance, if the long-term disability policy was to pay out $5,000 per month, and we were receiving $2,000 from social security, the long-term disability would only pay $3,000 per month. SSD is an exhaustive process but necessary. Another tedious adventure, but once you get through the paperwork and the approval process, it's done, and it's retroactive from the day of diagnosis.

Peter was no longer capable of making these legal

or health care decisions for himself by the time we received the diagnosis. He was not able to understand any of the insurance jargon or disability verbiage. Being appointed with power of attorney for Peter was critical. Often, a copy of the notarized power of attorney was required to access information.

Acquiring power of attorney for Peter prompted me to think about my abilities. What if something happened to me and I became incapacitated? Peter was not able to handle my affairs and so I assigned the job to my son. I also designated Peter's son secondary power of attorney for Peter should I not be able to handle the responsibility.

There were end-of-life decisions to contemplate.[1] These are very personal and may sound grim but they need to be discussed and implemented proactively. We needed to answer the very personal question to resuscitate or not resuscitate. Provide nourishment or not. CPR and intubation, or not. Putting our health care directives in writing and assigning someone to make sure they were adhered to was important. This person can be different from whomever you assigned power of attorney, or it may be the same person.

Medicaid is tricky but offers benefits to those who cannot afford to pay for care for their loved ones. There are strict guidelines and income requirements to receive said benefits. These rules should be studied and discussed with an elder care attorney to fully understand them. Both loved one and spouse are entitled to only very low asset levels before being able to receive the benefits Medicaid has to offer.

Ask your attorney about these limitations and what assets will and will not be included. Taking your loved

---

[1] See this article on advanced directives by Dr. Geoffrey Hosta, https://www.washingtonpost.com/opinions/2019/11/28/doctors-are-torturing-dementia-patients-end-their-life-its-totally-unnecessary/

one's name off your combined assets could be pertinent. Also, remember there is a five-year look back. Medicaid will research your financial history for the previous five years looking for these changes. To be safe, I removed Peter's name from our mortgage and refinanced our home.

Always wanting to be proactive rather than reactive, I decided to explore my plan B. Plan A was always to keep Peter home, but as he became more agitated and combative I needed an emergency plan. The Alzheimer's Association was gracious in providing me with a list of questions to ask memory care facilities. I began the arduous task of touring eight facilities, scrutinizing their every detail. Because of the list I was provided with, I was well equipped to ask questions I wouldn't have otherwise.

The Alzheimer's Association provided me with a plethora of information throughout Peter and my journey. The topic of care out of the home vs care in the home is unfortunately controversial. If you're not caring for someone with dementia it may be easy to judge the caregiver. It's not easy to make either decision, to place your loved one in a facility or to keep your loved one home. The decision is extremely personal and your loved one's care is the ultimate deciding factor.

These decisions are grueling and may seem grim, but they are necessary. Usually, after the laborious work is finished, you can rest easier knowing you're protected. By being prepared, you're taking something off your plate so that you can aim your focus toward your loved one with less distraction.

Lisa's Lookback

It was difficult dealing with all the nuances of insurance and social security, but once I plowed through it, it was done. I'm thankful I had the wherewithal to handle the tasks. What do elderly people do, who may not be as sharp as they once were? Even as a fifty-something-year-old person, I was so exhausted simply taking care of Peter that these tasks were completely overwhelming. There were times I could've handled phone calls more diplomatically, but my patience was worn so thin from lack of sleep that I couldn't control my outburst. Perhaps a plan needs to be implemented. A designated person to help caregivers navigate the paperwork necessary to receive the benefits he or she is entitled to.

Questions to Ponder

1. Do you feel prepared financially now and in the future after your loved one's Alzheimer's journey has ended?

2. What can you do now to protect yourself and your loved one?

3. What can you do now to be proactive, rather than reactive, regarding how and where your loved one will be cared for?

Find Joy

*Keep your face to the sunshine
and you cannot see the shadows.
It's what the sunflowers do.*

-Helen Keller

CHAPTER 6

Find Joy! No Regrets!

I adopted these mantras early on in our disease, after diagnosis, and recommend them to everyone whether you're affected by Alzheimer's or not. Life presents moments and minutes and hours and days of opportunity, and we instantly choose what to do, and how we react to them. Optimism can be scarce when faced with adversity that has only the saddest of outcomes, but why waste even the briefest present moment? Look for joy, seek it out, invite it into your heart and joy will stifle sadness almost every time. I reminded myself if I wanted to have no regrets, I'd have to live in each moment and be mindful to not do anything that I'd regret.

Often Peter and I would sit quietly for hours on the front porch while dirty dishes were stacked in the sink and hairballs glided on my floors inside. Bathrooms were dirty and beds were unmade. Enjoying those front porch moments and making those memories, was so important for my healing after Peter's death. I can't say the same would be true about doing the dishes or sweeping the floor or making a bed. I knew the chores would be there later, but the hand I was holding would not.

Finding joy in the current moment, prioritizing the days and front-loading memories became my mission and I vowed to have no regrets. I lived by these rules keeping them constantly present in my every reaction. I kept my promise to myself and feel peaceful now about how I cared for Peter during our journey. We were consistently faced with new challenges as Peter battled to stay connected to the world. He was confused and combative and agitated and I knew it was not Peter but the wicked Alzheimer's bitch. Her talons gripping tighter and tighter, Peter's awareness and understanding slipping away faster and faster.

It was easy for me to feel impatient or frustrated, but as with anything practice helps improve and so I would practice tempering those feelings. And I improved. When I felt these emotions, I would take a deep breath and remind myself of my vow of no regrets. I was frustrated and impatient with Alzheimer's, not Peter. My heart could not, would not, allow my mouth to be cruel because the ramifications were so extremely torturous to me. The consequence, hurting Peter's feelings, would pain my heart. I simply could not bear to wound him or make him feel less than. Bruising his vulnerable sweet soul was never worth the release of my harsh emotions. Taking a breath gave me pause to find a gentler solution, a kinder reaction, and remember the tragic result of not being compassionate to my prince.

I reminded myself frequently that Peter is not giving me a hard time, he's having a hard time. This helped to keep things in perspective and the more I practiced, the easier it became. Through the months and years, I moved things from the important column to the not-so-important one, chores mostly. It's a cathartic and necessary exercise if you genuinely want to find joy and have no regrets. I found myself continuously asking if what I was doing was truly important, or if there was something more meaningful Peter and I could be doing together.

I planned and planned anything and everything I thought would bring us joy, keeping in mind Peter's abilities or lack thereof. We traveled, bought a vacation home, walked and swam, kayaked, and enjoyed life immensely. Until we couldn't. I took a million pictures and videos so reminiscing would be clear and easy later.

We visited friends and family often and the bonds of our army became increasingly strong, and I knew as I needed them, they would come.

In the beginning, Peter was generally happy and in a good mood and Zoloft usually helped him be his normal content self. However, as progression commenced Peter was acutely aware that something was wrong, and his shortfalls could make him sad. He would cry sometimes, apologizing, thanking me for my care. He knew he was sick; people began treating him differently, and he was no longer my rock he had been so proud to be.

His memory was failing him, names and faces becoming increasingly blurry. Tasks were harder to accomplish alone. This herculean man could do little self-sufficiently without at least asking for guidance. The neighbor's mail would be brought in with ours, packages collected that did not belong to us. Confusion mounted about where to put the trash, the blue bin or the green. Peter's independence and pride were vanishing.

As his disease progressed, emotions became erratic, and I never knew which Peter would be in front of me. Sometimes sad, sometimes pensive, angry, lost, brooding or fearful, and most certainly confused. Each of these emotions needed to be managed carefully and thoughtfully. One day, his sadness was sparked, and he began to cry after watching a beautiful and touching wedding video of our son Sam and his stunning bride Olivia. We both cried as it tugged at our hearts and we were so happy, and we watched it again and cried some more brimming with pride.

Feeling as though we needed a distraction, I changed the subject to wrapping presents for our Grandson trying to shake it off with happy dancing, music, and silliness. Peter's tears wouldn't stop coming from his heart and he withdrew to another room. I know that feeling all too well and so I halted the wrapping and silly distractions. I went to him in the dark family room.

"What's wrong? Can you tell me? Are you very happy or very sad?" I asked slowly and gently, so he could comprehend my words. He couldn't or wouldn't and it didn't matter. It could be a hundred things and we've felt them all separately and together so I asked him if I could sit next to him. He nodded that I could, and he wiped his wet face and rubbed his eyes with the heels of his palms. Sitting next to him, I asked if it was ok if I sit very close and he smiled and nodded again. I draped my legs over his own crossed legs that were resting on the table. I slowly unfolded his closed arms and held his hand, resting my head on his shoulder and he cried a little more. I cried, too.

We sat there together in the dark wallowing in our pity party for two and the tears continued. Peter never did, or never could tell me precisely what he was crying about but it didn't matter. Sometimes you need only to help someone cry.

As we were reminded in the wedding video we just watched, my daughter-in-law shared these words, "Today I promise to give you all my words when needed, and share in silence when they are not."

Lisa's Lookback

My only regret is that I didn't connect Peter's symptoms earlier. If I had started the process toward diagnosis when signs first appeared, I could have implemented these mantras sooner. I was in denial. Was I patient with him? Was I kind? Or was I outwardly frustrated? When Peter retired, I rifled through the boxes of things he brought home. I found a notebook I had never seen before with a note taped inside written in Peter's hand. The paper read, "I wish I could go back in time and find you sooner, that way I could love you longer."

Questions to Ponder

1. How do you respond to the array of emotions you and your loved one feel?

2. What is truly important in the remaining days together?

3. How do you prioritize what's truly important?

Caregiver Burnout

*Taking care of myself
doesn't mean
'Me first'.
It means 'Me, too'*

-L.R.Knost

CHAPTER 7

The Four A's of Self-Care

As a little girl, I often snapped, "I can do it myself" to my parents or siblings when they tried to offer assistance. An independent, type A, do it myself-er, I assumed the same stubbornness in the beginning days of caring for Peter. I quickly learned that many emotions needed to be dealt with before I could confess that I did in fact need help. After years of the same grueling groundhog day, I experienced a level of exhaustion that was so heavy it was nearly debilitating. There were nights I would finally get Peter into bed only to be too depleted to even take my clothes off for my own slumber. I couldn't wash my face or brush my teeth, and I literally threw my daily wear contacts on the floor after peeling them off my eyeballs.

I had sized her up, arms crossed, jaw in hand, this bitch who calls herself Alzheimer's. For the first time in my life, I could not strategize a victory plan. Before retiring to care for Peter, I was an accomplished professional advertising salesperson. The revenue goals that needed to be achieved were clear and I relished in being victorious. Savoring the thrill of being number one, I worked smart and hard to bring my clients success and earn their trust. The delight of growing these business relationships and feeling proud of my accomplishments motivated me immensely. Now retired, I knew that I would not succeed in this chapter, there were no goals to conquer, and no proverbial mountain top after the hard effort of it all. I would not get to call myself the winner in the end nor would I feel the slightest twinge of accomplishment along the grueling way. However, along the grueling way, I developed coping skills to aid in my self-care, and ultimately be a better caregiver to Peter.

There are 168 hours in a week and caregivers frequently work them all, keeping one eye open, until we no longer can. Exhaustion sets in, tears flow, and perhaps we become resentful or sharp-tongued. We are afraid. Afraid of the future, afraid of every decision, afraid of failure, we fear the guilt we know is coming. I remember feeling guilty about taking an hour to get my nails done with a friend or lying in the dentist's chair not wanting to talk to my hygienist because I needed to hurry back to Peter's side. I would run out of the hair salon with wet hair, feeling so terrible that I had already been gone too long. It's incredibly important to take care of yourself, so you can take care of your loved one before you burn out. You will be a more patient caregiver, and ultimately your loved one will receive kinder gentler care if you are kinder and gentler to yourself.

Often friends and family ask, "What can I do to help? "or "Please let me know if you need anything?" Learning to accept help was a big hurdle for me and as I researched, I found I was not alone.

Samantha Maltrou, of The Soul Therapist, shares five reasons that we don't ask for help:[2]

1. **You are protecting your pride.**

2. **Your way is the only way.**

3. **It feels comfortable to stay uncomfortable.**

4. **You are building your tribe and protecting others.**

5. **Worried about what other people think.**

---

[2] https://thesoultherapist.com/five-reasons-we-dont-ask-for-help/

People want to help, they truly do. Doesn't it feel terrific when you have helped a friend or loved one? This notion resonated with me the most as I felt I was giving something back while accepting help. After giving some thought to how I was feeling, I knew there must be others feeling the same way. People want to help they just don't know how. They're not mind readers and I found that once I began to accept the help it was easier than I anticipated. You cannot do this alone, the work is too heavy, and your loved one needs you to be healthy so you can take care of him or her. Perhaps the first thing a caregiver needs to fully accept is that this is not a job for one person, but a tribe of people you surround yourself with to get through.

After this discovery, I developed what I call the FOUR A'S OF SELF-CARE to help me enlist in my army in a way I could accept emotionally.

1) **ACCEPT**: Accept help when someone offers something, anything. This will encourage them to ask again and get you in practice for saying yes more often.

2) **ASK**: Ask for help before you need it, being proactive rather than reactive after you've unraveled. When we wait too long, our thoughts become insurmountable, and we begin to feel alone and sad. Before burnout begins, enlist someone to help.

3) **ARTICULATE**: Articulate precisely what you need. Perhaps you have a personal doctor appointment and you cannot take your loved one along? Maybe you simply need a nap to recharge? Does the dog

need to be taken for a walk? Does a phone call need to be made that you simply cannot get to? A small errand, like the post office?

4) **ACTUALLY**: Even after developing this theory of good intentions, It was hard for me to kick start, so I needed to somehow hold myself accountable. When someone asked, "Please let me know if you need anything" I made a demand on myself. Instead of offering the usual empty promise, "Ok, I will" I made a difficult demand of myself. I responded differently, with just one word. "ACTUALLY." That one word caught my friend's attention, and they perked up, excited to hear how they could be of assistance. By saying, "actually" it held me accountable to ask for something I needed. The first few times were cumbersome, and I soon realized I needed to have a mental checklist of some things that I could always use help with.

Here are a few things I always kept on my list:

- A meal for my freezer. Often by the time dinner time rolled around I was too exhausted to cook. Going out to dinner was becoming too confusing for Peter and too tiring for me.

- An hour or two alone in my house. This was by far my favorite ask. Friends would come and take Peter for a walk or a run or bowling or out for lunch. The quietness of having the house to myself was heavenly. Sometimes I would blare my favorite music and dance around. Most times I cleaned up Peter's piles of fidgets and photos and shoes and things he insisted on displaying on every surface. I prefer everything in its place, so this gave me great pleasure to clean and feel organized again. Peter wouldn't notice, he'd simply get everything out again, but I enjoyed a few hours of tidiness.

- An hour or two away from the house, perhaps lunch with a friend, a manicure, or a walk, anything!

- Can you run to the store for me? It became harder each day to get Peter in the car, to the store, through the store, back in the car, and home again. Having someone pick up a few items was incredibly helpful.

- Take the trash cans to the street. Early on, Peter was able to maneuver one of the trash cans and we did the task together, but eventually, he could not understand what to do and would usually rifle through the trash instead. If he did manage to pull the can to the street, I worried about the cars and his safety. Imagine trying to haul two large trash cans to the street yourself while trying to keep a child out of harm's way. Eyes dodging back and forth between task and toddler. Peter, somewhere between unaware and feeling inept.

- Can you have a glass of wine with me and just make me laugh? Laughter is lovely medicine.

Please take good care of yourself and conserve your energy! A little goes a long way! A hot bath, a face mask, a manicure, or an hour to read a book alone, can make a huge difference. When I was diligent about my self-care I held my head a little higher, my stance was a bit taller, my patience stretched a little longer and my energy level lifted. But moreover, I felt such a sense of community, an army of people not only loving me and helping me, but loving Peter as well. And isn't that beautiful?

Lisa's Lookback

It is nothing short of astonishing when I look back at photos of myself and compare them to a recently taken picture. The contrast shows such a horrifying truth about the difficulty of watching someone disappear that you love deeply. My skin tone looked gray, my eyes lifeless, and my entire face seemed to sag as if matching my spirit. I was so immersed in loving and caring and doing and I truly thought I was handling my self-care well. I was not and I could not see what others saw. Friends and family urged me to take better care, take a break, and by the end, insisted I at least walk outside the house to breathe some crisp December air. This role is all-consuming and I thought I was doing my best to take care of myself, but looking back I should have practiced what I was preaching a bit harder. Now, I constantly receive comments about how fresh and alive, and different I look. The main reason I wrote this book was for other caregivers to help ease their stress during the most difficult task they'll ever be challenged with.

Questions to Ponder

1. Do you have a mental list of things you need help with?

2. If not, what could you delegate to lighten your load?

3. Do you need to practice asking for help and do you have a mental list of people to call on.

Can

Alzheimer's disease puts caregivers and her victims through the gamut of emotions. Gratitude is a big ask when everything is so intensely hard and you're watching your loved one die in front of you knowing there is no cure. Yet.

While writing this manuscript, I had to read every written word I posted on my Oh Hello Alzheimer's *blog. The task was grueling, but as I combed through my posts I found this reminder. A reminder to be grateful, wherever we are, for the joyful things we have rather than grieve those things we don't.*

Oh Hello Alzheimer's Blog Post

Lighten up! I want to tell the world, to stop complaining! Life is amazing and good and it's exactly what you make of it. Stop focusing on what you don't have or can't do and focus on what you do have and can do!

Peter has Alzheimer's. Peter doesn't have cancer and a month to live.

Peter can't go to the grocery store with a long list. He can go get me that one damn thing I forgot that I need for the recipe I'm making right now.

He can't read everything anymore, but he can read the greeting cards at the store and pick out the perfect one for me.

We don't want him driving long distances to unfamiliar places, but he can go pick up some things from our daughter's house while I tackle something else!

He doesn't always remember where they go, but man can he do the dishes!

Oh, Hello Alzheimer's

He doesn't understand the difference between the recycling bin and the garbage bin, but he takes out the trash and he can drive it to the dump!

He can mow the lawn and he can sweep the deck and water the garden, so what if he doesn't remember how to do math or Sudoku? Who needs it?

He can't remember most people's names, but he knows their faces and their hearts.

He can't speak like he used to, but he can gesture and listen and understand.

He can paint and clean and check in on his parents and he can pick up all the dog poop! YES!

He can kneel and talk to a smiling dog or a little kid and it makes him so happy.

He's helpful.

He's cheerful and friendly.

He's so kind.

And he laughs and he's funny and witty and sometimes flirty.

He can hold my hand. He can hold my heart. He can melt my heart just by looking into my eyes.

I'm the luckiest girl in the world."

CHAPTER 8

Understanding the FAST Scale

According to the Alzheimer's Association Facts and Figures Report[3], "more than 100 years ago, Dr. Alois Alzheimer described specific changes in the brain that are now known as beta-amyloid plaques and tau tangles. Today we know that Alzheimer's is a progressive brain disease that's marked by these key changes and thought to impact memory, thinking, and behavior.

"What goes wrong in the brain? The brain has three major parts: the cerebellum, cerebrum, and brain stem. Each one plays a role in how the body functions. The cerebrum fills up most of the skull. It's the part of the brain most involved in remembering, problem-solving, and thinking. There are about 100 billion nerve cells (neurons) throughout the brain that transmit messages for us to create memories, feelings, and thoughts. Alzheimer's disease causes nerve cells to die, which leads to brain tissue loss, or shrinkage, and causes a loss of function and communication between cells. These changes can cause the symptoms of Alzheimer's disease such as memory loss: problems with thinking and planning; behavioral issues; and, in the last stage, a further decline in functioning, which can even include swallowing."

During the three years and eight months from Peter's diagnosis to his death, we experienced every one of the symptoms of Alzheimer's. Each of these behaviors presents different challenges for the caregivers. I constantly struggled to find ways to keep Peter safe and

---

[3] https://www.alz.org/alzheimers-dementia/facts-figures

busy and happy during this stage.

There are two different documents describing the stages of Alzheimer's that I used throughout Peter's illness. The first is called the FAST Scale, or Functional Assessment Staging. The Center for Healthy Aging supplied me with this report when I was in denial. I remember thinking, "We don't have this kind of Alzheimer's. This is not for us." However, I relied heavily upon and found myself constantly referring to the FAST scale to see which stage we were in and if we had moved from one stage to the next. It describes seven stages, some broken out into several subsections as the disease progresses. The second document was provided by the Alzheimer's Association and is known as the Alzheimer's Disease Continuum. There are three stages, mild, moderate, and severe. You can find these detailed charts at the back of the book.

One thing I learned is that nearly all caregivers have the same unanswered question on their minds. This is a question that cannot be answered by any medical professional. The burning question? How long?

"How much time, Doc?" I want to ask them all, all the doctors, specialists, and those who have suffered as caregivers before me. How much longer do Peter and I need to endure this ambiguous rancor, this punishment? The charts were both helpful and frustrating as some stages seemed to drag on forever. I would refer to them when Peter exhibited a new behavior, almost hoping we had started to advance to a new stage. Secretly, there were days, especially in Peter's advanced stages, when I hoped it would end quickly. Often, there would be no evidence we were moving through the horror at all, just sitting still in a nightmare we couldn't wake up from.

A day with our grandson, Sonny, was delightful, but cloaked with sadness as well. Celebrating one child's development, mourning another's childlike decline. This disgusting disease is a demon of the darkest kind, weaving her tentacles around our hearts squeezing just enough. Just enough to make me want to leap from the tallest of buildings, eat those never wake up berries, and close my eyes while driving too fast. But there they were, looking back at us, those young, blinking questioning eyes. Our children and our grandchildren. I needed to stay strong, to endure and tell them the stories they haven't heard and share in the laughter and memories and all the vulnerable and excruciating painful days to come. I must take care of myself for them.

Lisa's Lookback

Alzheimer's disease is a marathon, not a sprint, and there were days I did not think I could hold on. Ironically, the days I reached for the FAST scale and found we had dipped our toes into the next stage, were almost comforting. Even as I faced the horrific grief of Peter's ensuing death, watching him struggle and decline was worse. Some days I just wanted it to end, for both of us. Peter was no longer my husband, my lover, my partner. The quality of his life was dwindling at an unfathomable speed. Every day he was becoming a younger version of himself, a child.

Questions to Ponder

1. How did it make you feel when you were able to place your loved one in a specific stage?

2. Have you ever felt as if you wanted the disease to progress more quickly so the journey would be behind you?

3. Did you find that your loved one wavered back and forth between stages?

CHAPTER 9

FAST Scale Stage Four

It had been about a year since diagnosis and Peter was in stage four of the FAST scale, Mild Stage per the Alzheimer's Association. The nuances of the disease were plentiful and staying on my toes was paramount. I wanted to be prepared for anything and so I was proactive in reading everything I could get my hands on. I needed to learn what might happen or could happen, so I was ready to respond appropriately, being proactive rather than reactive. This is easier said than done, but with practice, I became an expert.

My normal pace is more like a scurry than anything else. I don't allow even the tiniest bit of extra time, but I loathe being late, so I've perfected how long I have to get somewhere and fit as much as possible into that time. Until stage four. Peter always called me out on this because when I'm ready, I'm ready and I'm walking out the door and I announced five minutes ago that we would be leaving at precisely this time. He would laugh as I was flying past him and shake his head.

Once we reached stage four, things became different and life required me to slow down and expect the unexpected and that happened frequently. I learned to allow some extra time on my way out the door as Peter may need some help or have a question just as I'm leaving. It's those times when I didn't leave a little buffer of time, that I became flustered because I was going to be late. Peter would most certainly feel the abruptness in my attitude, a painful consequence I loved to avoid. I never wanted Peter to feel anything but happiness and joy. Allowing more time to get out the door, meant one more kiss, one more pinch, one more smile, and a little more time to love and be loved.

It was of utmost importance to me, that Peter remained confident. He sometimes had an incredibly difficult time coming up with the words he wanted to say or keeping his thoughts to communicate from escaping. As his thought process grew more sluggish, Peter would give up and say, "It wasn't important anyway."

"But oh, my darling prince, it is." I would urge. "You see we're not giving up that easily and I'm interested, genuinely in what you have to say. It's what I first fell in love with, your mind, and the way you challenged everything I said and argued with me to prove a point. I'm interested so try and try and try. Together we'll get it."

It took great patience and often Peter would get interrupted during a conversation because people didn't understand that he needed TIME to process what he wanted to say and most likely it wouldn't come out correctly. I would explain, "If we don't interrupt and we cue him with eye contact and smiles and head nods and interest, he'll get there. We may need to play charades for a bit. We may need lots of guessing, but we'll get there. Please don't interrupt. Eye contact. Smiles. Head nods. Silent encouragement. Struggling is nature's way of Strengthening. Let's keep him strong. Let's keep him confident."

I'm fast-paced and I'm a hundred miles an hour and my brain is constantly at full throttle. I'm a thinker and I do things quickly. If I'm not multitasking, I'm most likely bored. I found it difficult sometimes to stop and slow down enough so that Peter and I could communicate effectively. I would come home from work rambling on and on, flitting about and he probably only understood about half of what was coming out of my mouth at warp speed. I was out in the busy, fast world and needed to adjust to Peter's speed every day after work. He listened so intently every time.

When I needed to communicate or task Peter with something, it had to be slow and one single thing at a time, one step at a time. "Can you please fold the laundry and take it upstairs" didn't work anymore. Those are two separate tasks and he most likely wouldn't remember the "take it upstairs" part without me asking if he had done it. It wouldn't even be a reminder; it would be a brand new request as though I'd never asked him before.

I learned not to bother to tell him about upcoming events until the day of. He wouldn't remember so I thought of them as surprises. I'd look forward to the day of the thing so I could tell him and *then* we'd share in the excitement together!

At this point in our Alzheimer's journey, we were managing pretty well, better than many others I spoke with. I'm confident it was because we always loved each other so carefully. I think of couples who don't have a unique precious love story like ours and wonder how they manage and cope and care for each other. Life was good, despite the wicked Alzheimer's bitch that loomed over us, and we seemed to be laughing a lot.

Another day, per my usual, I was rushing out the door to go see a client and Peter asked, "will you help me get it started down there first?" He pointed down the road. After gesturing and playing our daily game of charades I realized that he needed gas and wanted me to help him. Peter did not understand that I was going to be late if I went to the gas station with him, he was losing the ability to understand time. Of course, I would help him, happily.

We stopped at the door, and I reminded him of the note he asked me to put on the door frame to help him remember those three important things we all grab without thinking:

PHONE, WALLET, KEYS

The words were on a bright pink sticky note and were cues for Peter to be prepared for his day. The note worked great until he no longer knew what those words meant. I pointed to the first word and Peter said "phone." He pulled out some keys from his pocket. A ring which held all the extra keys to who knows what and not the actual car key at all and said, "Is this my phone?"

I said, "No, those are your keys. Do you know where your phone is?"

"I think it's in the gun." He said pointing to his car. These were the moments when I needed to be stone-faced and calm and try not to let on that I was scared. Scared of what was next. Afraid of how quickly the Alzheimer's bitch was taking him from me. The mixed-up words and gibberish conversations were happening more often and I despised watching him struggle. Eventually, we found his phone, wallet, and keys precisely where he had taught himself to put them so he wouldn't forget. In the kitchen drawer.

Our routine was pretty similar on weekdays. After work I would come home and make dinner, music hummed in the background, Peter was most likely sitting on one of the island stools while I buzzed around in front of him. We tried communicating about our separate days, independently, which was becoming more of a challenge. Communicating was an exhaustive chore. When you're not experiencing the same events or don't see a thing then you have to rely on the story that's being told to paint a picture.

The first words Peter lost were nouns. Imagine if stories no longer had nouns. No person, place, or thing. No person's name. No names of places. No names of things. You're only allowed to use pronouns and descriptive words to talk about your day. For instance: Today, I went out to lunch with my friend Sue because I was in Bloomfield meeting a client, Cindy. Cindy and I talked at length about our caregiving experiences. Her son has epilepsy so she understands the struggles. After lunch, I went to Georgina's to meet with my client George and his son Nico to go over their new menu. On the way home I stopped at Highland Park Market to grab some bread and creamer and turkey to hold us over another day. I called our son, Zach to see if he and Priscilla, his wife, wanted to meet at Market Grille for dinner.

Try it without nouns:

Today I went out for XXXXXXX with my XXXXX XXXXXX because I was in XXXXXXX meeting a XXXXXX, XXXXX. XXXXX and I talked about our XXXXXXX XXXXXXXX. Her XXXX has XXXXXXXXXXX, so she understands the XXXXXX. After XXXXX, I went to XXXXXX to meet with XXXXXX and his XXX, XXXXX to go over their new XXXXXXX. On the way XXXXXX, I stopped at XXXXXXXXX to grab some XXXXXXand XXXXXX and XXXXXXto hold us over XXXXXXX. I called XXXXXXX to see if he and XXXXXXX wanted to meet at XXXXXXX for XXXXXX.

Nouns. Without them communication is difficult, and a struggle, and we played daily games of charades until we were both exhausted. After dinner, we would usually watch something on TV and sit quietly holding hands, snuggling, and enjoying an episode of something. Sometimes I would smile and pretend in the peacefulness of the quiet when we don't have to talk, that everything was ok.

Things were not ok and the only promise was that they were going to get worse. I was working in my home office when Peter came in. He leaned down and kissed me and asked, "what am I going to do today?" So I asked him. "What are you gonna do today?" He gestured and said something resembling "mow the lawn" and off he went. I heard him get the weed wacker out and I was so excited because we had walked around the yard the evening before talking about how long the grass had gotten.

I was in my own world of work for three hours. I remember thinking it was taking him a long time to trim the edges of the yard. What a thorough job he must be doing! I smiled to myself. Leaving to meet a client, I went downstairs to the kitchen. Peter was there, sweating and full of those little bits of green grass, white tube socks up to his calves, work boots on his feet. I explained that I needed to go see a client as I grabbed a water bottle and an apple at my usual hurried pace.

Peter reached for my hand, "Oh, Tart!" I approached to give him my full attention. "I was doin' it and doin' it and doin' it," he said, as he made the motion of the weed wacker cutting. "Then I knew I could use the other one." He gestured pushing a lawnmower. He took me to the front door to show me. My jaw dropped. He had spent three hours cutting half of the grass in the front yard with the weed wacker. He had forgotten he could use the mower.

During this stage, Peter began forgetting things that I told him and he had always just responded as though it was the first time he had heard it even if it was the fifth. It never bothered me to repeat things for him. In fact, if it was something fun or exciting I delighted in seeing his face light up over and over again! I got to surprise him multiple times! But changes came and soon Peter developed an irritation with me. He would snap at me when he didn't remember something I had told him several times,

"You never told me that."
"Why didn't you tell me?"
"I wish you would've told me."
"See, you don't tell me things"
"OH! I didn't know that if you'd tell me..."

I knew it well and practiced the number one rule of Alzheimer's: Never argue with a person with Alzheimer's. I just responded with, "oh, I know I forgot to tell you" or "oh, geez I'm sorry" or something else that diffused his irritation. Imagine how very frustrating it must be to feel this way.

I wanted to help, and I wanted to make things better. I wanted to make the wicked bitch go away and I wanted my husband back. But that would never happen, so we felt the feels together and we felt the feels alone, separately. I had many advantages over Peter. I could call my daughter or my sister or my friend and be candid about how fucking mad I was because I couldn't find the salt because it was in the refrigerator. Or rant about being sick and tired of having to look for his wallet or his keys and why the hell can't he pick up his phone when I call. How many tracking devices can one person have?

Peter did not have the cognitive capacity to pick up the phone and shout and yell and scream to his daughter or his sister or his friend and be candid about how fucking mad he is because he lost the salt because he put it in the refrigerator or complain that he was so sick and tired of having to look for his wallet or his keys and why the hell couldn't he ever remember how this damn phone works he must've been thinking. *Also, what are all these square tiles attached to all my stuff?*

Can you imagine for a few precious moments how incredibly frustrating it must be for a person with Alzheimer's? Imagine not being able to formulate the words to share a funny thing that happened or explain what you did earlier in the day or discuss your feelings or ask for help doing something specific. However frustrated I was, Peter must have been a million times more frustrated. Here's my little piece of advice, take it or leave it. Try, try so hard, with all your might to remember this. Do whatever you need to do to let off your steam and get your frustrations out so you can be as patient and positive as you possibly and humanly can. Please don't take it out on your loved one. Words are like toothpaste you can't put them back.

Love is patient and love is kind but sometimes love is mad and tired and hangry and grumpy and irritable. Love is also forgiving. One day, my fuse was short and I had explained things over and over, exactly the right amount of times to be a bit sharp in repeating them one more time to Peter and I immediately felt regret. It sits with you for a bit, stinging, reminding you that you're weak and you should be better and stronger and kinder and for Fuck's sake it's not his fault. My patience usually remained intact and I was able to stop what I was doing to listen, really listen. I could repeat things over and over and over if need be but I'm human. Was I ever impatient? Absolutely! Did I ever lash out at Peter? Of course! I had to work hard on the forgive myself part. If you're a caregiver, forgive yourself and get back to it. Love yourself. If you're doing your best, you're doing a phenomenal job!

Emotions were volatile and unpredictable during this phase. Several times I found Peter alone, crying uncontrollably. One morning I was running just late enough to quicken my pace as I chose my pandora station for my shower and I burst into the bedroom with my face in my phone. Peter was standing in front of his closet staring and I passed him on my way to grab a work dress from the closet and then I heard it. The sniff. I stopped. I waited to see if it was just a sniff or if he was crying.

There it was again. I went to him; his back was toward me and I physically had to turn him around and he was indeed crying. I held him and asked him what was wrong and per usual he said nothing. I reminded him that we don't do that, we talk about things and get them off our chest. And he did.

It was the usual answer "I can't do things myself" and he cried a little harder hearing himself admit it. We held onto each other, arms wrapped around as far as they could go. It was the kind of embrace that makes you stop and hold your breath and your mind races wondering what you can do to make things ok. I could feel his stomach contracting with each cry and his fingers slowly reaching farther around me to try to touch one another. That desperate embrace, almost a panic, burying his head in my neck and allowing the tears to fall on my skin.

Peter pulled away and promised he was ok, so I took my shower and moved on to getting ready to leave for the day when I heard him sniffling. I went to him again and he blinked the tears back. Again he promised that he was ok and then he gestured pointing at his face and said, "If I wanna do this bubbling stuff about you and me I can... Sometimes I gotta do it. It's ok." He gave me a little push, back to getting ready. Watching your loved one in pain is one of the most horrific things I've ever felt. The heartbreak was unbearable some days and I want nothing but to take this horrible disease away from him. *Fuck you Alzheimer's, I hate your guts.*

Fear was another emotion that Peter exhibited throughout his disease. He was extremely concerned anytime I was away from him. Fearful I was not coming back. Afraid I would leave him. He came to me putting his face in front of mine so his breath was warm on my skin and he whispered, "I'm afraid you're going to leave me."

The lump in my throat grew fast and large and I thought I might suffocate on his words but instead, I whispered back, "My Love, I'm trying to keep you as long as I can."

Lisa's Lookback

Peter stayed in stage four for a long time relative to the other stages. It felt like an eternity, it felt so cruel, but actually, it was just a preview of what was to come. I'm thankful now, that we stayed there so long. Compared to the rest, four was bliss. Peter could drive, we could still communicate, he was continent, he was independent enough to be alone. We were still able to enjoy a partnership. I hope I was grateful. I hope I was kind. I hope Peter felt loved.

Questions to Ponder

1. Are you able to be proactive and ready for the myriad of changes your loved one will present?

2. How will you remind yourself to remain grateful?

3. Can you commit to your loved one that you will continue to be compassionate, that you will remind yourself that your loved one is not giving you a hard time, they are having a hard time.

CHAPTER 10

Sex and Making Love

Peter and my sex life was hot and steamy. Enduring an eight-year long-distance relationship meant our libidos were in overdrive by the time one of us was heading towards the other. Sweaty palms and butterflies were commonplace, and we could not wait to see each other. Often, bags were dropped just inside the front door as we locked lips, hands roaming, hearts pounding, we were breathless. Frequently, we headed directly to the bedroom after the 11-day abstinence. Our passion was raw and real and undeniable and there was no stopping the coming unity. Clothes were left in a trail as we unbuttoned and unzipped and dropped shirts and pants, panties and bra, and collapsed onto a bed to reunite physically, mentally, and emotionally. We would make love until we were exhausted and hungry, falling on our backs sweating feeling whole and complete once again.

That's certainly one example of our sex life, but Peter taught me a beautiful lesson about making love. During one of Peter's visits to Harrisburg, we turned on the gas fireplace and spread out a blanket in front of it. We gathered wine and glasses, cheeses, and fruits. Pillows were piled high and the perfect music swooned us in the background. We laughed and talked and played backgammon, scantily clad for all of it. We fed each other hand to lips and we kissed and explored each other's mouths, and we laughed on that blanket by the fire for hours.

My heart raced in anticipation of what was to come and finally I couldn't wait. "I thought we were going to make love?" I asked Peter.

His reply will stay with me for the rest of my life. "We are making love." He said and then he slowly placed a grape he had peeled for me in my mouth as he smiled. His eyes were taunting and twinkling. My heart exploded with love.

During our eight-year courtship our desire for sex and making love grew and we couldn't keep our bodies or our eyes off one another. Friends knew we were always that couple who didn't care what anyone thought about our public displays of affection. We were proud of each other, and we cherished the limited time we had together. Little did we know just how limited our time would be.

One time we were out for a ride on Peter's Harley, just sightseeing, enjoying the New England countryside. We weren't far from his house, fifteen minutes or so, but the rumble and the ride and my arms wrapped around his body had us both feeling frisky. Before I knew it, we were pulling off the road, hoisting our legs off the bike, and heading into the woods. We didn't care. We walked hand in hand without words, knowing exactly what the other wanted and we found what we thought was the perfect spot. No one was around, we were in a secluded area of the woods and anticipation was high. It didn't take long for things to heat up, and it also didn't take but a split second for us to stop cold. What we thought was a remote area of the trail turned out to be more well-traveled. Another couple came upon us as we held our breath and our pose. They caught a glimpse and did an immediate about-face and walked out the way they came. We never could stop laughing about it whenever one of us recalled that day!

Nothing was taboo and we delighted in exploring and pleasuring each other in any way. We were open and game and loyal to each other's intimate happiness. We were eager to discover ways to thrill one another and not shy in introducing new ideas. We celebrated life and love and happiness and togetherness physically and emotionally every single day we were together in those early days. We were insatiable sexually and intellectually. We could not get enough of each other's company. It was not uncommon to pull off to a side street on our way home from a fabulous dinner to make love in the truck. We simply could not wait until we got home.

Eight years later, the countdown was finally over, and we were spending our last night in my home in Harrisburg. Most everything was cleared out of the house, except an air mattress in the family room and a few last-minute items we'd throw in the truck. I had raised my beautiful children here and had lived at this address for 17 years. I was extremely attached to the memories that were made in this home not only with my children but now with Peter and his children, too. The last eight years had been filled with anticipation of finally being married and together in Connecticut.

It was a warm end-of-summer night and Peter had surprised me with my favorite splurgy champagne and some shrimp cocktail. We decided to head to the back corner of my property and enjoy one last firepit fire. We finished our bougie bottle of champagne, and Peter said a familiar Peter saying, "one tastes like another" so we popped the second bottle.

We took the shrimp outside to the firepit and Peter grabbed a blanket. As I spread out the blanket Peter went back inside and soon emerged with a lamp and an extension cord. He met me on the blanket and the night was lit by the crackling fire and the living room lamp. Peter peeled every shell off every shrimp and hand-fed me until I was full. He knew exactly how to make love to me without touching me sexually. I wanted him constantly. The night crept on, and we made love outside just a few feet from my neighbor's house, protected by only a six-foot fence. We woke with the sun, snuggled together under a blanket. The fire had gone out. Peter was a hopeless romantic and I knew he would miss this house, too.

When we were settled in our Connecticut house, Peter was 44 and I was 43. The honeymoon continued and our jobs were the only thing separating us now. I worked from home as a professional salesperson, Peter worked in finance in an office in Hartford. I was often home when Peter arrived home at 5:30 and I remember vividly the feeling I would get when I heard his truck pull into our driveway. I would listen intently as he came into the house and tiptoed up the stairs trying to scare me. It was the same every single day. He would approach me, my back to him, he would move my hair and kiss my neck. I craved it and yearned for that kiss every day. That kiss was the segue from work to play.

We settled into our routine over the next couple of years and we became comfortable, and our daily lovemaking became twice-weekly sex. We were cozy and happy, satisfied with each other's timing until Peter's forgetting began. Looking back, it was one of the first signs I ignored. Peter was somewhere around 48 when the fighting started. I feel certain now, it was mild cognitive impairment.

According to the Alzheimer's Association's 2022 Alzheimer's Disease Facts and Figures Report[4], people with MCI due to Alzheimer's disease have biomarker evidence of Alzheimer's brain changes plus new but subtle symptoms such as problems with memory, language, and thinking. These cognitive problems may be noticeable to the individual, family members, and friends, but not to others, and they may not interfere with individuals' ability to carry out everyday activities. The subtle problems with memory, language, and

---

[4] https://www.alz.org/alzheimers-dementia/facts-figures

thinking abilities occur when the brain can no longer compensate for the damage and death of neurons caused by Alzheimer's disease.

By the time Peter went to bed he was exhausted, falling asleep on the couch every night. By the time we went upstairs, he fell asleep as soon as his head hit the pillow. I was left awake and wanting and angry. If I had only known what was happening, I would have handled it so very differently. Instead, this became the only thing we ever fought about. Did he not want me anymore? Was he not interested? I confided in my closest friends that I thought Peter may be having an affair. My brain tried to believe it, but my heart simply couldn't. There must be some other explanation. I would find out years later there was indeed, an explanation.

We began to argue weekly about why Peter was no longer interested in having sex. He was romantic, kind, and affectionate, but the heat, the passion, was now only initiated by me. Did I no longer turn him on? He swore every time we discussed it that he loved me in precisely the same way he always had but was just tired and once he belted out, "I forgot about it!" He always rose to the occasion, but why did it have to be me initiating all the time? It turned out he truly was forgetting. Peter was exhausted from the daily charades and hiding and disguising himself. What a torturous way for my prince to live and now I was poking him, too. I wish that I had known he was sick then.

We continued on this way, and I had resolved that I would just be the initiator of intimacy, after all, he never turned me down and we accomplished the same precipice in the end so why not? I just adjusted. As time went on and Peter declined so did our sex life. Many of the fun ideas dissipated and it was more of a get the job done motif. But still, the job was getting done. Then one night, after diagnosis, we made love, and something was very different. After an appropriate amount of time, I dismounted and scampered off to the bathroom. When I returned, I leaped back into Peter's warm arms and as he wrapped them around me, I realized he was crying. I sat straddling his body and leaned into his face asking him why. "I think I did something wrong. Something I wasn't supposed to? Did I hurt you?" he cried. My heart sank into my stomach and tears seemed to fall right out of my eyes, knowing we had reached a pivotal point. I promised Peter that he did nothing wrong, and he had my full permission, and we are married and in love and it was all very beautiful. Peter was not convinced. That night was the beginning of the end of our sex life.

His reaction scared me, and I was concerned this would be the new norm and so I stopped initiating and so the sex stopped, and Peter's cognitive decline continued. How could I continue to make love to my husband when he was so confused about what was happening? A few more months went by, and Peter did not initiate, nor did he seem to miss that luscious part of our relationship and so I tried to forget it, too. The thought kept nagging at me though, did I want that to be my last memory of our delicious lovemaking life? I didn't.

COVID was rampant and we had canceled four trips in 2020. We were both now retired and free to do what we wanted, go where we wished. But the pandemic halted travel and paralyzed everyone. I knew I had a brief window of opportunity where it was safe to travel if we were careful, and Peter would still be cognitively awake enough to be able to enjoy what I was planning. I decided to go for it. What the hell did I have to lose at this point? Peter's body was still very physically fit, he could still handle some reasoning, he could feed himself and he was very affectionate towards me. I knew he loved me as much as he ever did.

I planned a trip to Portland Maine, it was October

2020. I would drive. We stayed at a charming inn overlooking the water. Our room was on the third floor, and we climbed the stairs, breathless from our masks and the flights of stairs by the time we arrived in our room. The room was quaint, adorned with the perfect essentials, the bed looked cozy, and the bathroom spacious. Our room had a door that led to an adjoining porch. Again, we were on the third floor. Peter was in a phase of increased confusion so the extra door concerned me. At home, all the outside doors now had triple locks for safety. In the event Peter tried to get out of the house, the three locks would be too much for him to comprehend and he would be kept safe inside. Here, at this inn, there were no extra locks so I would need to keep one eye open the entire time to be sure Peter did not wander off. I was very concerned about the porch door since we were three floors up. I decided to stack the luggage and coolers up against the porch door, so it appeared to be just another wall and the tactic worked. It was a shame we couldn't enjoy the night air on the porch overlooking the water.

I knew in my heart that this would be our last trip together, and Peter would not be able to tolerate a location change again. I worried he would not be able to handle the next three days. We shopped and visited lighthouses, hiked, and found seafood restaurants that satisfied my cravings. I pretended nothing was wrong and Peter followed me around like a puppy. Peter's vocabulary and ability to string sensible words together had declined to a point that he seemed more comfortable saying nothing. This made it easier for me to pretend nothing was wrong.

It was October 2020, fourteen months before Peter died. At this point in our journey, I had secretly switched Peter to drinking nonalcoholic beer, as he seemed to be increasingly confused when he drank alcohol. I however was drinking more than ever. I had packed several bottles of champagne along with Peter's favorite alcoholic beer and I had a sexy plan in mind. On the first day, we explored the area and soaked in the culture falling into bed exhausted. It felt wonderful to be together, away from home, navigating a new area, and still able to do so. The weather was chilly, but the sun heated up in the afternoon and we sat on the rolling green front lawn of the inn. We shared a bottle of champagne and rested our heads on the rocking chairs enjoying the warmth of the sun on our faces. The forecast for the following day was promising rain, so we took advantage while we could.

The weatherman predicted perfectly, and it poured all day. We drove into the closest town for lunch by a fireplace and planned on stopping in several shops as we made our way back to the inn. After the first boutique, we changed our minds as the wind was turning our umbrella inside out and the rain was sleeting sideways. It was time to put my plan into action. We returned to the inn and ran from the car to the warmth of the inside. We were drenched as we climbed the stairs to our room. We would most certainly need to get out of our wet clothes. I opened a bottle of champagne and closed the blinds and turned up the heat. I found some sultry music.

We quickly finished the bottle of champagne and popped another, laughing and flirting. Peter seemed giddy and it had been a long time since we were tipsy' together. My heart was full and I felt the old anticipation of wanting to feel the heat of our naked bodies. It had been months since we had made love and I hoped Peter would not react the way he had the last time. Manufacturing my last love-making memory with my prince, I led him to the bed. Peter and I were both relaxed from the champagne, our hearts were connected, and I felt close to him in a way I hadn't in a long time. Our husband-wife relationship had turned into a mother-son connection over the past year, so it felt heavenly to be connected as lovers. We made love, and it was exactly as I had hoped. Peter was present and aware and responsive and best of all happy. After a quick rainy-day nap, we woke and made love again for the very last time. We were euphoric as we held each other so tightly under the warm blankets. This memory was beautiful, sensual and a loving last memory that I will cherish for the rest of my days. I promised myself it would be our final time.

Lisa's Lookback

Making love was such an important part of our relationship, I simply could not risk Peter being upset or feeling as though he had done something wrong. Manufacturing our final time allowed me to choreograph many of the details so Peter felt safe and loved and satisfied. It was a gift that I cherish still and deciding never to have sex again was the right decision for me. Many caregivers experience a different scenario. The caregiver has been thrust into the parent-child relationship, yet their loved one is still interested in sex. It can be an awkward situation, unwelcome even. There is guilt involved with not accepting sexual advances and saying no. In my opinion, it's extremely personal, but you need to permit yourself to say no if you no longer want to participate in intimacy.

In contrast, when your loved one no longer wants to be intimate, caregivers may feel a loss and grieve that warmth. The void can be deep and finding approaches to fulfill your sexual desires are complex. Perhaps something as simple as a facial or a massage can fill the space where human touch was such a big part. Shortly after Peter died I found myself weeping uncontrollably during a massage. I was overcome by the loving touch of someone else's hands on my body.

Questions to Ponder

1. Have you considered how you will handle the sexual part of your relationship should you no longer feel comfortable participating?

2. What memories are you going to make if you continue to say yes when you feel awkward?

3. Are there other ways you can make love with your loved one without having sex that are just as fulfilling?

4. If your loved one no longer wants to engage in intimacy, how do you manage your own frustration emotionally and sexually?

5. How do you seek and receive affection during this time?

6. How do you make love to yourself without having sex?

CHAPTER 11

Clinical Trial

After Peter's diagnosis, I reached out to a research group at Yale Neurology that I had found online to see if there were any clinical trials that he might qualify for. There were not. I called aninegain, and again, and again, desperate for help and hope and healing for my prince. At the end of 2018, about months after diagnosis, Yale called and invited us to attempt to qualify for an upcoming study. This process consisted of an initial meeting in the clinic. Peter and I sat in the large conference room for the explanation of the trial. An actual quiz was presented to ensure Peter understood what was explained to him. There were consent forms to sign. After that, the dreaded cognitive testing.

It's always the same or similar questions that make Peter plummet into a frustrated and angry mood. What's the date? What day is it? What year is it? Who is the President? What season is it? Where are you? Count by sevens backward beginning at 100. Remember these three words, I'm going to ask you to recall them later. Draw a clock that reads 10:50. Copy this shape, usually a cube. Follow the pattern and write the next sequence: A1, B2, C3, etc. The questions and the length of the testing were excruciating for Peter.

Peter would score higher if the administrator of the testing was patient and kind and encouraging. Unfortunately, not everyone was, and then he would just shut down and stop answering the questions. He came out of the room and sat quietly next to me. The doctor came out and explained that Peter did not qualify for this clinical trial as his score was too low and his disease was too advanced. She explained that there may be other trials in the future and they would contact us if anything came up. I felt her words pierce my hope like a balloon, too fat with air. The sharp reality was seeping in: there was no cure for Alzheimer's disease. Peter and I walked somberly out to the car for the hour-long ride home. We wept with disappointment.

A month later we received a call about a different trial. I mentioned it to Peter and he immediately blurted, "NO! I'm not doing it!" He didn't want to endure the frustration of the cognitive portion of the trial. He said, "it's degrading!"

I decided a walk may help our moods and we were halfway through our three-mile walk. Gently, I brought up the trial and carefully discussed the reasons why we should consider participating. Peter's mood softened and by the end of our walk, he reluctantly acquiesced. Throwing his hands up, he agreed and in his language said "for you!" as he pointed a finger in my direction. I knew he was not happy. I also knew he would do anything for me.

May 25, 2019

13 Months After Diagnosis

I scheduled our visit and did not tell Peter. We woke up in the morning and I said, "Get in the shower, we're leaving for Yale in thirty minutes." He barely talked to me the entire ride as he was angry about going.

Upon arrival, we did the song and dance of explanation, consent, and quiz, and then it was time. We sat in the waiting room waiting for the test administrator to collect Peter. We were nervous and hopeful. Peter kept going over the questions he knew were coming. He'd ask me "What month is it?" "What's my birthday?" etc. He was shaking, his leg was bobbing, and he had tears in his eyes. As he blinked them back, I thought, "Shit! I shouldn't be putting him through this."

But my instincts kept nagging me to do everything I possibly could for him, with no regrets. I wanted to leave no stone unturned, leaving absolutely no doubt that I had been a good caregiver and provided Peter with every opportunity. I needed to be guilt-free as a caregiver, knowing I did everything I could to give him a beautiful life. The demands I placed on myself to walk away with no regrets exhausted me to a degree I hope to never experience again.

The test administrator appeared, and Peter walked away from me in slow motion to be very brave and answer those stupid questions. When Peter reappeared, the first thing he said was, "She was so nice. She gave me lots of time." He was very thankful and relieved, and he was smiling. We waited only five minutes and received a hearty thumbs up! Peter was one of ten selected at the Yale location, one of 254 nationwide in the study!

This study required two pills to be administered per day. Fifty percent of patients received a placebo. Fifty percent received the real drug. The study would last for one year. Peter started taking the trial drug on June 15, 2019. Those two little pills were a daily dose of hope: hope that our future plans would remain intact and that Alzheimer's would not win. We left the office and I swear we were walking on air! We grabbed each other in the elevator and released our tears of hope.

June 21, 2019

14 Months After Diagnosis

We made the hour-long trip to Yale for our first appointment. Peter was anxious about driving to unfamiliar places and I was happy to take the wheel. His driving was starting to make me uneasy, too. I felt Peter's nervousness as he thought about the cognitive testing he was about to endure. He didn't sleep well the night before and he tossed and turned throughout the night.

I had made the mistake of telling him the truth when I should've just left some details out. The confirmation call had come and I was told it would take three hours and there'd be a lot of cognitive testing and a physical workup.

I was faced with a choice. Tell Peter, to prepare him, that he would be undergoing the dreaded cognitive testing and lots of it, or just wake up that day and tell him to get in the shower. The cognitive testing wasn't as important at this point because Peter was accepted into the study, they just needed to determine a baseline. It was no longer pass or fail, but Peter didn't see it that way.

A valuable lesson I learned through my years of caring for Peter was that it was ok to withhold information if it was going to upset him. Lying became easier each time the words spilled from my mouth, but ultimately I was protecting Peter from his own anxiety. By telling Peter the visit would be more than three hours I was trying to relieve my own anxiety to my partner. But Peter had not been my partner in months, and I was alone in most decisions. He was not the same man or partner I married.

Since the day I met Peter, he always had the answer, to every question anyone asked him. He was worldly and smart and handy and knows something about everything. He was so reliable. He was the guy who has that thing you need when you're camping or on vacation. Whether it's a bungee cord, a safety pin, a Band-aid, a ratchet, a charger, tweezers, or some other MacGyver made-up thing, you could always count on Peter to have it. Smart. Clever. Resourceful. Reliable. Funny.

The answers were no longer there. A list of more than two items was confusing. Directions with more than a step or two were too much. Imagine, the white coats with their shotgun mouths firing question after question until you fail. For hours. Of course, he was nervous.

Peter couldn't understand that this wasn't a test but just a day to determine what he could do and couldn't do. He was irritated and mad and he swore and called one doctor a bitch after she asked him how many nickels are in a dollar. He said, "I think they're going to kick me out." I explained and explained but sometimes you can't change a person's mind or perspective when they start down that obsessive path and sometimes redirection is the best course of action.

I came to learn that lying was ok if it was in Peter's best interest and the lie wouldn't harm him. Going forward I spared Peter the details of the visits. The anticipation was too grueling for him.

June 22, 2019

14 Months After Diagnosis

We tried not to get our hopes up, keeping our expectations low. We hoped that we were helping in the name of science to find a cure for Alzheimer's or at least something to slow down the disease. Peter started by taking one pill every day for two weeks to see how he tolerated it. He tolerated the pills well and his dose was increased to two per day. The most common side effects included headache, fatigue, dizziness, and nausea. Peter suffered no side effects.

What is this drug, named BHV4157? We had a 50/50 chance that it was the drug and not a placebo. We spent most of the three hours apart, speaking to the same doctors, but separately. They needed a perspective from both of us. It was the first time I met Dr. Mary Margaret and I liked her immediately although, the first five minutes of her interaction seemed disingenuous. She quizzed me about our family and my career, likes, and dislikes. She was curious about Peter and my relationship. The sterile initial conversation was merely a preface to the interview. The doctor explained that she would be asking me questions about Peter's capabilities from my perspective. The session would be recorded. The answers would be something like "always, most of the time, sometimes, never." Very gray.

She asked questions like, "If you gave Peter a list of three or four items would he be able to shop for them."

"Never," I replied.

"Is he able to drive outside of his neighborhood?"

"Always."

"Now tell me about an event that happened in the past week in as much detail as you can." She explained that she would prod Peter to remember the event and ask him to recall details as well. She then asked me to describe an event that happened a month ago in as much detail as possible.

The session lasted probably thirty minutes and some of the questions were very gray and hard to answer but I got through them easily until she asked, "Is Peter wetting the bed yet?" I remember the question ringing in my head. I remember feeling as though I should look around the room for someone else. I felt certain that was not going to happen to Peter! I stuttered and heard my voice answer defensively and very clearly, "NO!" with an undertone of "why the hell would you ask me that?" And that word "yet" made it an entirely different sentence.

July 18, 2018

15 Months After Diagnosis

We went to the clinic for Peter's second visit. They took all the usual bodily fluids and asked him the questions. The questions he rants about in the elevator on the way down as we're leaving.

"Do you feel sad, do you want to harm yourself?"

The questions irritated him and it was a bit comical how he ranted about them. "NO! I tell them every time."

After participating in the trial for four weeks, I saw no improvement in Peter's cerebral abilities.

August 20, 2019

16 Months After Diagnosis

I'm not sure what I expected truly, but I had tremendous hope and joy when Peter was accepted into the clinical trial. After all, scientists have been finding cures for all sorts of diseases for hundreds of years so why not Alzheimer's? Why not this clinical trial? Why not Peter? Someone had to be the first person to be cured of every atrocious disease before there a cure was discovered.

We drove an hour to spend twenty minutes. Peter gave up his fluids, promised he wasn't suicidal, and we exchanged empty bottles for new ones filled with pills. It was all very anticlimactic. I expected more fanfare, instant results, or an immediate and significant difference. There was none of that.

September 30, 2019

17 Months After Diagnosis

The twelve-week appointment was more like week one and we were there for more than two and a half hours. As per usual I didn't tell Peter about the appointment until the morning and there was no way in hell that I was clueing him in on the length of the appointment. He would know there was going to be cognitive testing and he would anticipate it and he would be grumpy.

There was the usual fluid collection, the "are you going to kill yourself" questions, the dreaded cognitive work, and then the meeting with the psychologist. Peter called her the mean lady. He couldn't articulate why she was the mean lady, but he didn't like her.

I met with the mean lady first, Dr. Mary Margaret, who I thought was delightful, but then again, I wasn't frustrated by her interrogation. She sprayed me with her bullet-like questions.

"Could Peter handle an emergency?"

"Rarely."

"Could he go to the grocery store with a list of four or five items?"

"Never."

"Can he make small household repairs?"

"Rarely."

"Does he know his date of birth?"

"Never."

"Would he know what day of the week it is?"

"Rarely."

"Would he know what month it is?"

"Rarely."

"Could he add a column of a few numbers?"

"Never."

"Would he know his address?"

"Never."

"Would a stranger know that something was wrong with Peter?"

I responded right away with a "yes," but she amended the question and reframed it.

"If he didn't speak?"

If he didn't speak no one would know, would they? It's not like he had chickenpox or was wearing a cast or had an eye patch.

When Peter was not feeling confident or

comfortable, when he didn't feel safe, he remained quiet. He would nod and smile and interject a laugh at the appropriate time. Of course, he seemed fine. Peter told me he could tell when people were uncomfortable around him and that broke my heart.

December 24, 2019

20 Months Since Diagnosis

"We're going to Yale for your MRI today." It wasn't a lie, but it wasn't the entire truth. The study included two MRIs over twelve months. We also would attend the usual visit including the grueling memory questions, and the meeting with the mean lady. Dr. Mary Margaret, AKA Mean Lady, asks the questions in this manner: "Could you remember a list of two or three items without writing them down? Usually, sometimes with physical help, or never?"

For many of us unaffected by this unforgiving disease we could easily think about the three choices and promptly answer. For Peter, he was still processing the question when he was offered the choices. I imagine he processed each choice slowly and by the time he did so, he forgot the question. No wonder he felt frustrated.

After our three-and-a-half-hour tour, we headed back home. We held hands as I drove and, I knew he was still mad. I wanted to acknowledge that he was mad and that it was ok that he was. Instead, I turned up the music and soon he was whistling, and his mood had softened.

We didn't talk much about the visit, but Peter did say the mean lady wasn't as mean as she usually was. I told him it was because I told her, "You're the best husband in the world and I'm so lucky to have you." He grinned and pushed me playfully and said, "Shut up." We laughed.

One of the questions the doctor asked me was if

Peter could operate a small appliance. She used the examples of a microwave, a toaster, and a vacuum. I honestly didn't know. He hadn't needed to use any of those appliances recently.

I was curious so I asked Peter to vacuum the furniture with our small handheld vacuum. Peter brought the vacuum downstairs and unwound the cord, bent down on one knee, and started with a vacuum motion on the chair. He looked at me and said, "Why isn't it working?"

I said, "You have to plug it in." He laughed, plugged it in, and did the task perfectly!

April 7, 2020

23 Months Since Diagnosis

We had completed nine months of the one-year clinical trial. COVID was in full swing and social distancing had become the norm. Peter was scheduled for his last three-month appointment which of course was canceled. Instead of the grueling questions which confuse and frustrate him, we simply got a phone call from a doctor to go over the depression questions. Peter answered them and laughed afterward as he always does.

The facility sent his next batch of pills overnight, which were the final doses of medication. I use the word medication loosely as I feel certain he was taking the placebo. There had been no evidence of improvement, no positive swing in cognitive brightness, simply a steady, swift downward decline. Often I thought we should just stop the study. Peter was confused about how to take pills and needed remedial direction to complete the steps. I'd place the pills in his hand, and tell him to put them in his mouth, he may or may not chew them before I could hand him the water to wash them down. Typically he would be confused about what to do with the glass of water and I found the pills melting on his tongue more than once.

Why then? Why continue if I felt he was getting the placebo? We were invested in helping the medical community and perhaps the Alzheimer's community including those not yet diagnosed. I felt committed to this mission. If I couldn't help Peter, perhaps I could help someone by continuing to participate in this study.

July 23, 2020

Two Years and Three Months Since Diagnosis

Due to Covid, we hadn't been to Yale in over seven months, and we were due for our last visit, the longest visit, which would last some three hours. We woke early and I pushed Peter into the shower, promising I'd buy him a coffee and a sandwich on the way. Scooping up his dirty clothes off the bathroom floor so he wouldn't put them back on, I laid out an outfit that would work for both the clinical trial appointment and golf later that night. Why struggle with Peter's clothes twice, right?

When he was dressing, he asked me, "What for?" and I responded, "the doctor" and that was the end of it thank goodness. No tension or fidgeting or madness on the long drive to New Haven.

When we got off the elevator on our floor it hit him. "I've been here!" he said rolling his eyes. I promised him it would be the last time and he snarled at me.

As the doctor asked me all the same questions she had asked me all year", I realized immediately that my answers were different now. One yes or no question, in particular, stuck with me. "Would someone sitting at the next table in a restaurant know there was something wrong with Peter?" I had always responded by saying that if Peter didn't speak, then no, they wouldn't, and she'd always responded with ok.

This time she responded differently, and I understood the question fully. She responded, "So not by the way he was eating or by his posture?" Clear as a bell now, and I think even as wide-eyed as I am about this disease, I lived in a bit of denial for my protection.

Eventually, Peter would lose his ability to cut his food and ultimately feed himself. He would begin to walk hunched over and finally not be able to walk. I had not fully prepared myself for those milestones.

When we were finally finished and in the car, Peter could not wait to tell me what he had done! He was excited and could hardly speak through his bursting grin. His body was wriggling, and he explained in his fragmented language that when he felt frustrated he pushed his chair back and said, "Nope. I'm not doing it!" Proud as a peacock to have a say in his day! Good for him.

Yale offered us an additional year of this trial with the guarantee of getting the drug, rather than a 50/50 chance. Peter and I discussed it briefly and we politely declined.

Lisa's Lookback

I was so desperate for help and hope during these months, that I underestimated the trauma we would endure. It was as if I would take a peek around the corner of what was to come, only to pull my head back quickly to not see. The Psychologist's questions gave me a glimpse, helping me to prepare for our tragic future. Knowing the frustration that Peter endured during the study, today, I would not put him through it again. However, in 2019, I had hope. To date, I do not know if Peter had the drug or the placebo. We were told we would not know until the study was concluded which could be several years.

Questions to Ponder

1. How do you feel about telling the partial truth or a lie to your loved one with Alzheimer's?

2. Knowing that a cure for Alzheimer's has not been found to date, would you put your loved one through a clinical trial to help doctors gain more knowledge?

3. How do you manage the emotional push and pull of decisions that you have to make on behalf of your loved one?

Waiting Room

Oh Hello Alzheimer's Blog Post

Almost two years after diagnosis, I was sitting alone reading a book in the waiting room of the oral surgeon while Peter was being examined for his wisdom tooth extraction. A woman I presumed to be in her 80s clanked through the door with her walker. Her walker was adorned with flowers and a basket that held some of her must-haves and a younger woman accompanied her and I assumed she was the woman's daughter.

The daughter gently instructed her mother to sit on the brown leather chair and the mother did so and waited quietly while she was checked in. I couldn't help but watch the pair as I felt a connection when I heard the mother speak. The daughter came over and put her face in front of her mother's, softly touching her hand when she asked her if she had eaten anything for breakfast. The old woman replied in a very loud and angry voice, "I don't know. If I did it was toast!" The daughter took the paperwork she'd filled out to the nurse behind the glass window.

When she was checked in, the daughter put her face once again in front of her mother's and asked if she wanted to keep her jacket on. The mother in a softer almost childlike voice asked, "Is it cold?" The daughter told her she might want to put her sweater on if she took her jacket off and she decided it was best to keep the jacket on.

The daughter sat next to her on a sofa and the mother fidgeted and said, "I want to sit next to you."

The daughter explained, "I think it will be hard for you to get up from the sofa."

The mother seemed sad about this and reached her hand over to touch the daughter's hand.

The daughter held her mother's hand tightly and assured, "I'll be right here."

And the mother smiled a mother's smile.

The daughter realized that the mother's fingernails were long and promised to trim them for her when they got home and the mother said quietly, "You do everything for me, I'm sorry."

And the daughter replied, "I don't mind at all." And smiled.

There I was, in the company of them, and another older couple and I became emotional. I don't think they noticed, or at least I hope they didn't, and I brushed away the tears, but they kept coming. I couldn't decide if I was crying because of this kind and genuine unconditional love I had witnessed or because I recognized that this would be Peter and my future, or perhaps both. May we all learn to be so kind and patient following the example of the daughter in this writing.

CHAPTER 12

Love Me Tender

I didn't know it had a name, but it's real, and caregivers despise it. It's called "showtiming." I've experienced this best-behavior phenomenon with our children, our grandson, and now Peter.

Our grandson Sonny, exhibits the very best behavior, his sweetest, dearest self, when he's with me each Sunday and I don't experience his naughty, temper tantrum side very much like his parents do. Because they are very safe, and Sonny trusts them. No matter what behavior he demonstrates they will tolerate and love and care for him. Like a child who unexpectedly moves swiftly from one emotional mood to another, the Alzheimer's bitch sets up our loved ones to experience the same intense fluctuation in mood.

Up to a certain point in the disease, those who suffer from Alzheimer's are able up to to be on their very best behavior when the time calls for it. Laughing and verbalizing and nodding and pretending with such precision that we as caregivers feel as though we are insane. As caregivers, we begin to question our judgment and our reality. For example, caregivers hear comments like, "He was great!" "He's getting better." "Wow, he was really communicating." "He's not as bad as I thought." And on and on. When Peter was returned home, it would be similar to the child who just came home from school or daycare with a glowing report.

When it's showtime our loved ones can perform! These little and big people can hold it together for periods long enough for parents and caregivers to be judged as liars. I was dumbfounded and experienced feelings of guilt or insanity that my every day did not look like this at all! I want to stab you in the eye for saying it. I remember thinking, *Come home with me to experience the truth, please. Spend a month, week, a day even*.

The wicked bitch knows when to be pretty and proper and well-mannered and when she's done with her beautiful show of etiquette, the tantrums begin, the exhaustion shows up, and the moody mood swings rear their head. And guess who gets to see that and clean up after her? Guess who gets to handle those delusional breakdowns from fatigue? Caregivers are left picking up the pieces of their so-called fabulous and lucid day. Please know that on the other side of the short-lived niceties is weariness and collapse and confusion and exhaustion because our loved ones have used every single ounce of bravery and energy to play the part they still realize they should.

The takeaway for me is that Peter felt completely safe and comfortable enough with me to reveal his vulnerable feelings. He trusted that I would be there to help him through these difficult and overwhelming emotions.

If you met my husband in the early stages of his disease, it's true, you may never know that he had Alzheimer's. He was generally quiet, a speak when you're spoken to sort of gentleman. He succeeded at being part of a conversation by nodding and smiling and interjecting an appropriately placed "yes" when needed.

But if he was asked open-ended questions needing to tell a story or deliver details or recall a memory, he would fumble. As he declined, we often couldn't connect, and we gave up, frustrated. Peter wanted so desperately to be understood and I wanted so desperately to understand him and I confess that sometimes I didn't have a clue what he was trying to tell me. In the later stages, I pretended to understand so he didn't feel the desperation. The best practice for communication is to meet our loved ones where they are, even if it means pretending to make them feel heard and safe. Feeling secure is always better than feeling frustrated and trying desperately to be understood.

Oftentimes, people, including me, would yammer and chat and cackle and joke in groups of two or three or more while Peter faded quietly into the wallpaper. We would visit friends in their homes or invite them to our home. Our visits had become more and more infrequent due to the disease progression. We'd be catching up with each other, knee-slapping and belly laughing while Peter watched trying to keep up with the conversation. He kept quiet enough not to be noticed because no, he couldn't quite keep up, much less interject or say a witty thing. How sad for Peter to be physically present in the room, but not able to comprehend the conversation going on around him.

When these moments happened, we walked away feeling fulfilled and, if asked about Peter we'd say he had a great time because hadn't he? Of course, he had. But did we pay attention or engage him or even bother to ask him any little thing or even have the patience to wait for the answer? Or help...him...find...the...words...he's...trying to use...to ...tell us...something?

What used to be a stimulating, socially engaging conversation had become a struggle and a challenge. So, he was faced with the choice to either join peers in conversation, trusting friends would be patient, or remain quiet and feel left out. Sometimes choosing to be quiet was easier. Peter felt alienated in these situations.

Sitting on the couch quietly one night, tears welled in my eyes the moment the words came out of Peter's mouth. In the middle of his sentence of word salad, emerged three words strung together that instantly broke my heart. "I'm thrown out," he stated, feeling discarded and ignored and unimportant. I couldn't help but question my behavior. Did I do something insensitive to make Peter feel obsolete?

It's scary and awkward sometimes and we don't know how to act or what to say. Our loved ones still have feelings and want to participate in our conversations. We need to take a moment to ask questions and engage them. Slow down, look in their eyes, and perhaps place a hand on their arm to make them feel included.

Peter told me once, "I can tell when someone's uncomfortable around me."

It was clear the person we were conversing with wasn't comfortable and certainly hadn't educated themselves and spoke to me about Peter while he was standing right next to us. He was ignored as though he wasn't even in the room, with no attempt to make eye contact. It hurt my feelings and I immediately grabbed Peter's hand and brought him into the conversation.

People with dementia have feelings and are often more sensitive because of it and not only can they hear you, but they can feel you! Engage them with your voice and body language. You won't regret including them, but you may regret excluding them.

I set my intention to have no regrets. If I wanted to have no regrets, then I could not do anything that I would regret. I tried to not let a moment pass that I could help or comfort or distract, console or guide. Peter had more and more episodes of withdrawal, and the tide seems to take him farther out little by little, but our hearts are tethered. I could feel his distance and could've easily chosen to ignore it, letting him pace or roam or stare off or sink deeper inside of himself, in confusion. After all, he was busy and safe, and aren't those the most important things? But our hearts were tethered and I felt the tug.

Busy doesn't always mean happy or content and if I let moments like this pass, uncared for, just because I was tired or drained of energy, I would have regretted it for the rest of my life. When Peter was distant and so far away, I would put my hands on his face and look into his eyes and smile telling him, "I love you so much." I would kiss him and kiss him and kiss him until I felt his cheeks rise in a smile. I would hold him and scratch his back and pull him back to shore. This work, this use of energy, resulted in his magical laughter and that was my reward!

Someone once asked me, "Are you always patient? How do you do it? I feel like a terrible caregiver." Her questions and confession took me by surprise and made me stop and think a good long time about it. Was I always patient? No. But I was patient most of the time. I reminded myself that Peter was very sick, his body just didn't know it yet. I could feel the impatience starting, the anxiety of Peter not understanding the simplest of words or instructions coming out of my mouth. My frustration, his frustration, the repeating over and over and over, and the exhaustion.

The pressure bubbled and that's when I needed to take inventory. Taking inventory of what was causing my distress. Typically, it was one of a few things. Either I was trying to accomplish a bigger task than I should while caring for Peter, or I was rushing too quickly, or trying to fit too much into our schedule. My agenda was selfish and if we weren't enjoying the task together, why do it?

The cure for impatience is simple. It's kindness. Kindness trumps everything. When I felt it coming, I simply stopped what I was doing and do something kind for Peter, even if it was just a few kisses or a back scratch.

I would feel happier, Peter would be redirected, and we would have slowed down and whatever I was doing didn't matter anyway! If I hadn't stopped to take inventory and resort to kindness, I may have snapped at Peter in a hurtful way. My sweet, thoughtful, gentle man. How could I forgive myself if I had growled at him for not understanding? Hurting Peter's feelings would be the cruelest consequence I could endure, as he deserved only love.

Dignity and respect were of the highest importance to me while I cared for Peter. He was the gentlest man I've ever met, and he showered me with his chivalry every day of our relationship. I was made to feel like a queen every day. As things changed and the alarming things happen more frequently, I tried to adapt easily without reaction and love Peter with all my heart as he has loved me:with the utmost respect.

Peter had become confused about where to sit in the car. Back seat, front seat, driver's seat? Until our trip to the pharmacy one day, he understood my instructions over the roof of the car and comprehended my gesturing to the front seat. After picking up a prescription, we walked to the car hand in hand. Separating at the front of the car, I jumped in the driver's seat and peered through the passenger side window, but Peter was not there. A. couple had just pulled up in the spot next to us.

Peter appeared on my left at my window, confused, and so I opened the driver's side window and told him where to go, pointing to the front seat. He abruptly turned and walked around the back of the car and promptly opened the back door of the car parked next to us. The female driver was getting out of the car at the exact time Peter was getting in her car. I jumped out of the driver's side and sped to our new neighbor's car gently guiding Peter out, assuring the alarmed woman that everything was ok.

"I don't know what I'm doing," Peter promised her, with a grin and a shoulder shrug. From then on, I became the gentleman opening Peter's car door. Events such as this must be handled carefully and with a light heart. Terse words or arguing serve no purpose when helping a person with Alzheimer's disease. You must simply join their journey and meet them where they are, gently. Arguing causes tremendous stress for both caregiver and loved one.

Sometimes it's hard to know what to do or what to say to someone who has Alzheimer's. They are still the same souls we know and love. Just love them. Love them like you always have. Maybe just a little more.

Talk to them and don't treat them differently. Help them to feel useful and normal. Don't avoid, but rather engage them in conversation. Be patient and give them time to come up with the words they are trying so desperately to find. Speaking loudly has little effect, other than perhaps scaring your loved one as they are not deaf, just slow to process. Speaking in a baby voice or as if you're speaking to a child may make them feel small. Speak clearly and slowly one sentence at a time so they have time to process before introducing another thought.

Throughout our journey, when Peter was still able to go out to eat, I carried business cards with a message printed on them, "Please be patient, the person I'm with suffers from memory loss." When the server approached our table, I would hand over the card saying, "do you take this coupon?" The server would immediately read the card and acknowledge the message, knowing Peter may need some extra time when speaking or have some unusual behavior. This secret communication trick ensured Peter would be treated with respect and not made to feel differently.

There were times when Peter would lash out when I was hurrying through a project or pulling us out the door. "I don't know what you're doing!" He might bark. Or "You never tell me anything!" or "Why didn't you tell me that!" after I had repeated something several times. I reminded myself to remove my emotions and soothe my hurt heart, as it was not his fault, Peter simply didn't remember. His sharp tongue was forgiven immediately because I knew this was not Peter speaking, but the disease. Try not to use words like "Remember?" because your loved one doesn't remember or surely, he wouldn't lash out. He's frustrated because he feels like he's in the dark, not informed about things because he simply doesn't recall.

Peter was always a sensitive soul, emotional, and certain things made him cry. He loved to love. He loved being in love. Thinking of our children and our grandson could evoke tears. A movie, a song, a post, a book, or a photo album, would all make him cry. He's the sweetest person I've ever met.

One night something triggered the tears, and I don't know what it was, but I heard him sniffling, so I stopped what I was doing and went to him to share in his moment. Not knowing what the tears were about, happy or sad I waited, and he buried his head in my shoulder and said, "I'm sorry about all this."

I don't think he often thought about the future and what this disease had in store for us, but he was thinking about it on this day and he was feeling cheated. We knew what was coming but we didn't dwell on any of it. We lived every moment the best we could. But this was different, and he wanted to think about it and he wanted to dwell on it and sometimes that's ok.

I asked him then, "Are you scared?" as my eyes filled with heartbreak. He blinked away the tears and looked at me and answered, "No, because it's not close." And I believed him. These painful moments seemed to come more frequently, each one as painful as the last.

We always sat next to each other on the couch to the right of the end table. We snuggled and held hands while watching TV until we didn't. Until the day Peter, out of the blue just decided to sit on the other side of the end table, on a different couch. While we were just three feet apart, he felt very far away.

I remember that sinking heart feeling, and I feel it now as I write. I met him where he was, joining his journey, and just breathed through another new normal. Imagine a small child, who loses the hand of his mother in a crowd and is surrounded by the great big scary world where nothing seems familiar. The child looks around slowly at everything, turning around in a circle searching desperately for something recognizable. Frightened. Alone.

This is how I imagine Peter felt one night while we watched TV on our new separate couches. I not only saw the fear in his face, but I physically felt it. Out of the corner of my eye, I saw him staring at me. Returning his gaze, I felt his fear immediately. Standing up, I moved slowly towards him, grabbing a blanket on my way. I lifted his right arm and snuggled underneath it, putting my head on his chest. I told him I loved him and promised him I would keep him safe. Peter wrapped himself around me so tightly, that I felt his body shaking. His lip quivered and he said so clearly, "Please don't lose me."

Lisa's Lookback

I set my intention early in our journey to have no regrets about the way I treated Peter. I have no regrets. He had a difficult time tolerating the quick flux in his emotions. He truly just wanted to feel safe, and I realized almost every one of Peter's emotions stemmed from fear. If Peter was anxious or lashed out, or sad, he was frightened about something. Keeping this in mind helped me to be very patient and kind and helped Peter get through the scary feelings.

Questions to Ponder

1. Have you experienced showtiming with your loved one? Were you able to move through the feelings of anger that accompany this phenomenon?

2. How do you manage your own emotions while constantly soothing your loved one's reactions?

3. What do you say to friends or loved ones who are not treating your loved ones appropriately?

Please Stop Calling Me Strong

Oh Hello Alzheimer's Blog Post

Two years and six months after diagnosis

Please stop calling me strong because in reality I'm always falling apart just a little bit and my heart is forever aching and longing for normalcy. Every glimmer of lucidity is a spark of hope that things could be right again, and get better, but they never will.

Caregivers are thrown into this role without training, with no preparation, no education and I just wing it every day and I'm just a woman deeply in love clinging desperately to familiarity. But life changes constantly every single day and we adapt and figure it out and clutch to something recognizable and somedays don't even find that.

Caregivers cope. We struggle. We learn to accept help and even ask for it which makes us feel weak. My eyes open in the morning and I wonder what the day will bring, and my head is heavier and harder to lift with each dawn.

Smiles are mostly painted, and my heart is shriveling, and I am not strong, I am withering, but doing my very best to muddle through the day without any catastrophes. I'm silently screaming and pulling my hair out, scared to death of the future, afraid of the stories I have read and heard, and find it overwhelming to imagine these visions as our reality. But they will be. They are.

Each week the fear heightens as his abilities decline and I am called upon more and more and he understands less and less, and I am not strong. I don't want to be strong. I want to fall apart and drop to the ground and sob and scream and punch, and I am not strong. I am very afraid.

CHAPTER 13

Please Stop Calling Me Strong

The Alzheimer's bitch consumed my every thought every single day, always thinking about her, speaking about her, writing about her. There were no days or hours or minutes without Alzheimer's. The air around us was thick with her fervent breath and she was relentless and proud. She persisted day and night, night and day. I did not sleep more than a few hours most nights no matter how tired I was, and I roamed the day with burning eyes and a heart that broke a little more each day.

I felt it necessary to remind caregivers to practice positivity to cope with their daily grief. A year or so after our diagnosis I posted on the blog, *"If Peter forgets a lovely walk on the beach just hours after we've taken it and he can't remember a single moment from a family vacation from five years ago what's the point in making new memories at all. He's just going to forget them, right?"*

The point my darlings is to be present right here, right now in this very moment, and live it. Live it to the fullest with all the spark and love you have in your black and blue heart. Because truly all we have in life that's guaranteed is what we're currently experiencing. There are challenging days and inside those days there are dark moments, but those dark moments don't need to spiral into an entire day.

Feel the feels and then move on. Sit with the emotions and let them wash over you, without fighting or running. Sit with them, breathe in and breathe out and question the rationality. Forcing yourself to stare at your emotions will help you to accept and experience new growth. It's easy to spiral down and allow yourself to wallow in all that is no longer and all that is your new normal but do the work. Do the work of pulling yourself out and grabbing hold of something positive. Do the work for yourself and do it for your loved one.

How? How can you just pull yourself out of the gloominess when there is so much to be gloomy about? Planning and preparing in your mind for these moments will help you to ready yourself.

Here's a coping mechanism that I use to manage my emotions. Make a mental list of your lovely things. I say mental list because we never know when the doomy gloomy darkness will set in and we can't be searching for a list on a piece of paper or the notes app on our phone.

Practice this technique and know just where to look for the lovely things to lift you, ground you, and remind you of all there is to be grateful for! Do allow yourself to feel the pain, I think that's very important to recognize your sorrow and grief and deal but try coping instead of moping and you will feel better.

I'm grateful for many things but the most precious is my family, they are my list of lovely things. When I felt myself spiraling downward, I often closed my teary eyes and envisioned my loved ones, one at a time, until I'd seen everyone. I envisioned each lovely person with their biggest brightest smile or their most genuine laugh. I've practiced this so many times that I breeze right through it now and before you know it, I'm smiling and laughing right along with them.

I don't believe there is a road map, a right or wrong, a good or bad way of handling grief. Ambiguous grief, grieving someone who is still alive, has its own entirely separate grieving process. I found that as Peter lost more of our memories, I missed reminiscing together about them. I would tell him in detail about our experiences and he would hear them for the first time, every time. I delighted in retelling him, as I was reliving them at the moment.

For the caregiver, the Alzheimer's journey can be filled with guilt. Guilt for laughing or having a great time without your loved one while taking a necessary break. Guilt for having a sharp tongue or too little patience. There is even guilt attached to medication choices. Peter needed to be on antipsychotic medication to curb his agitation and combativeness, but the drugs were strong and made him sleepy and listless. I found myself wishing the end would come sooner some days so we would both be out of our misery. During the last few months, our quality of life had declined to such a disturbing existence that I wanted our journey to be over, but I didn't want to lose my beloved husband. I felt guilty for having these feelings, but in truth, I had already lost him.

I ping-ponged around in all these emotions: anger, disbelief, depression, acceptance, denial, and guilt. Faced with making hard and heavy decisions alone that would surely have guilt tugging at my sleeve, pulling me down, down. I began asking myself, "What would healthy Peter want me to do?" The answer was always the same. Peter would want me to take good care of myself and make decisions to protect my health and future.

I arrived at the point when I needed more help than I was willing to ask friends and family for. I felt at peace about hiring professional help. There is a certain amount of guilt associated with relying on friends and family to care for your loved one while you take a break.

I found that hiring a professional was simply exchanging services for money.

I came to this realization one day when I woke up with less patience than usual. My mood was pensive and quiet and frankly, I was sick of being inside, sick of the cold and rain, and sick of constantly caring for and not being cared for. I don't know what triggered it, maybe just all those things layering and layering, stacking and stacking like a tower waiting to topple.

Within my mantras of "Find Joy, No Regrets" I had developed rules to help me keep these vows to myself and Peter:

Rule #1 Be patient and kind.

Rule #2 Teach and show and encourage.

Rule #3 Hold hands and kiss whenever you think of it.

Since it was raining, I decided to tackle the inside chores like cleaning bathrooms, dusting, sweeping and vacuuming floors, polishing hardwood floors, laundry, etc. Typically, Peter would follow me around like my shadow as he wanted to help but he also still understood that he needed to stay clear of my brisk pace. Wanting him to feel needed, I gave him tasks and most of the time these tasks needed to be redone as he'd forgotten exactly how to do them, but I didn't mind, usually.

On this day. I did mind and I didn't fucking feel like explaining and redoing and showing over and over and so I just didn't and he followed me around. The tension was thick, and I was exhausted, and he was in my way and he was walking on the wet floor. I was again watching him smear the dirty dishes "clean" with a dry paper towel and put them in the cupboards and we weren't talking. I wasn't encouraging, and he felt in the way. He felt helpless and useless, I know he did and that was my fault.

There were no kisses, butt pats or loving arm touches, or playful flirts. I simply just didn't feel like it. Looking back on these few hours I feel regret and embarrassment. Often, I set the tone for our day, and our mood and tempo by following a simple guideline; to set a good example for our children and others who may be going through something similar. Epic fail, and I'll never get these hours back and I certainly did not set a good example for anyone.

It's easy to say, get back up, dust yourself off, forgive yourself, and be kind to yourself, but it's not that easy to do when you feel regret. There was no need for me to be stressed or in a hurry and honestly, who cares if the house is clean anyway? I've been looking inward at my behavior ever since and there's only one conclusion and this is by no means an excuse.

Lack of respite. My daughter intervened when she recognized I was getting burned out and made me take some time for myself, offering to stay with her stepdad. I know I'm not alone here. Please forgive yourself when this happens and take time for yourself, even if it's locking yourself in your bathroom to take a bath and paint your toes or read a book or nap or have a private conversation with a friend. Do something uninterrupted, recharge, and be kind to yourself.

Without help, caregivers are on duty seven days a week, 24 hours a day, 168 hours a week. We sleep with one eye open always on watch, always ready for the next unpredictable event. Which, I promise you, is coming.

Being extremely independent, I came out of my

mother's womb demanding, "I can do it myself." I had clutched that notion close to my soul for 53 very independent and stubborn years. I started accepting help, really practicing the art of saying "yes" after a conversation with a friend, Lori Riley, who said, "People want to help. They just don't know how. You need to tell them."

My friend, Lori's words have loudly resonated each time my pride wanted to say "No, I'm good" or "I'm fine." Well, I wasn't good, I wasn't fine and a little help certainly wouldn't hurt. Lori's gift is a great one and has been life-changing for me. I have learned to ask for help because I have learned that helping feels awesome! Changing my mindset helped me to pivot my perspective into a positive frame of mind. Let people help, so they can feel helpful!

The Alzheimer's bitch is relentless and shows no mercy in her appetite for grief, even in the lucid moments she allowed Peter to have. They offer false hope, although they do bring a spark of joy. The inconsistency is grueling; one day not being able to tie his shoe or brush his teeth, the next tying and brushing effortlessly.

Many of my memories were repressed as they were too difficult to face. Writing this book has been cathartic, making me face the things I endured. I read the following words while combing through blog posts and struggled to put myself back in that time that felt so evil and shocking and unpredictable. I had never felt such unreal exhaustion in my life.

This was written after I had moved out of the bedroom and into my office, which had no door, located just outside where Peter slept. This post about my experience with the Alzheimer's bitch was written three years after Peter's diagnosis.

Oh Hello Alzheimer's Blog Post

She makes me feel crazy and everything that is happening is so incredibly and dumbfoundedly unbelievable. Some days I wake up and just count the hours until I can go back to bed. I hear him coming out of the bedroom and my head is still foggy with sleep and I don't want to wake up yet, so I squint my eyes open the tiniest sliver just to allow in the shadows of him. If I close my eyes, maybe he'll go back to bed or go sleep on the couch.

Every single morning is the same damn Groundhog Day except some days are worse and harder and so I pretend to sleep. I try to gather up the enormous amount of energy I need for the day, collecting positive thoughts and mustering strength and pasting on smiles and digging up laughs only to watch my husband struggle.

I'm sick of it. I'm sick of Alzheimer's. I want my life back. My LIFE BACK? What life? What will I be? And so, I decide to BE present and open my eyes and lift my heavy head and drag my weary body out of the bed.

Each day takes a bit more glue to hold it together and I wait for it; the six o'clock clock. Because that means it's ending, the day is ending. I watch the six o'clock clock until the nine o'clock clock comes when I get to lay down after I put his pajamas on and help him brush his teeth, and he's calm, and he's been kissed a dozen times.

Closing his door, I lay my body down and I think, and I think, and I think until the Xanax kicks in, and I feel my brain slow and my body drifting. I don't want to wake up to another Groundhog Day watching my husband struggling. I'm so exhausted from our struggle.

During this period, Peter would wander at night and even though I had placed loud bells on his bedroom door, there were nights I didn't hear him. I was so deprived of sleep and positive stimulation that my body would not allow me to wake. There were days when I could not find joy, I wanted to sleep for a million years and cry for the rest of my life. I knew it was time for a change and I could no longer handle this bitch alone.

As I listened to the advice from Adrienne, a dementia specialist from the Center for Healthy Aging, she said something that I'll never forget. A follower from the blog had recommended I contact the Center for Healthy Aging for support. Adrianne had given me information that changed my perspective, and I was starting to pay attention to it. The realization of the work that we caregivers shoulder, came to light in a way I hadn't understood before.

Adrianne was once again, stressing the need, almost a requirement, of self-care. I reminded her that I took time to soak in the bathtub and enjoy a face mask every Sunday and she laughed and almost scolded, "a bath is not self-care, a bath is normal hygiene, Lisa."

When I heard what she told me next, I wept and I can't explain the feelings I was overwhelmed with, other than it was a realization of just how much work there was to do and how exhausting that work is.

She painted a picture of an Alzheimer's facility that exists in other countries. There are three shifts of nurses or aides or companions caring for the patients, plus someone cleaning and someone cooking every meal, and someone else administering meds. We as caregivers are doing the work of many, 24/7. The work is extraordinarily heavy and it's constant and too much for one person to bear.

You are strong, so strong and brave, you are mighty! Strong and brave and mighty enough to summon help. Please don't worry what others think of your caregiving, as it's none of your business what they think anyway. Follow your instincts and your heart and adopt the mantra of no regrets. Above all else remember to ACCEPT the help people offer, ASK for help when you need it and ARTICULATE precisely what you need. Don't be afraid to have others help to carry the weight as it is heavy, heavy work.

Cry loudly and sob, scream at the unfairness of this catastrophic buffet you sit at, not wanting to eat. Be angry, but at the disease, not your loved one as he is not trying to give you a hard time but having a hard time. Be kind and open your heart to hear others' advice but heed only what serves you. Allow the remnants to roll away.

Try to sleep, although your mind will not allow it. There is a great benefit to closing your eyes and relaxing your tense face and limbs and breathing as deeply as you are able. Try to allow your mind to drift, although you can't, still, practice this. Please know there is hope, please surround yourself with an army for you simply cannot do this alone.

Here are my top seven ways to help caregivers:

1. Just show up. I don't mean unannounced because no one likes that but say "I'm coming over to drop off some..." Even if they're not home you can drop it off. They won't be able to say no, and they will appreciate you.

2. Make a meal that can be eaten immediately or frozen to eat later. By dinnertime, the exhaustion a caregiver experiences is overwhelming.

3. Take the person with dementia out of the house for a field trip if possible. Having the house to myself was heaven.

4. Listen to caregivers vent and cry and complain and let it out, without judgment.

5. Talk about anything but Alzheimer's! I have a long-time Harrisburg friend, Darlene, who called often during our journey to tell me all the funny teenager stories she was experiencing. We would reminisce about when my kids were troublemakers, and laugh. For those few minutes, I'd forget.

6. If all else fails, bring your puppy over for a visit! Puppies cure everything!

7. Remember, "People want to help. They just don't know how." Help them help you.

Lisa's Lookback

I remained stubborn for far too long, worrying about how Peter would handle being cared for by a stranger. The financial burden of hiring professional caregivers was troublesome, and I concerned myself with the silliness of other people's judgment. Why couldn't I care for my husband myself? I was off getting a manicure or getting my hair done while my husband was home with an aide. Yes! Imprint this in your mind as a requirement. You must take time for yourself so that you can offer your loved one the very best care you can: one filled with kindness and patience and love.

Questions to Ponder

1. Why is it that we feel so guilty leaving our loved ones, even if only for your own personal doctor's appointments?

2. Why do most caregivers wait so long to ask for help? Is society to blame for this stigma that caregivers are weak if they ask for assistance?

3. How can you turn off your caregiver's mind and truly relax when away from your loved one?

CHAPTER 14

Hiring Helping Hands

I began hiring caregivers for Peter two and a half years after diagnosis. We started small just so I could get out and breathe for one three-hour stretch each week. After many hours of filling out paperwork, following up with doctors, and completing caregiver reports my long-term care insurance claim was approved. It was a grueling three months, but fortunately, the claim was approved retroactively from the day I first filed it. It meant I could be reimbursed for up to 30 hours per week at a rate of $25 per hour. Immediately, I increased Peter's care schedule to four hours, four days a week, giving me some much-needed time to myself. Sixteen hours off, 152 hours on each week.

My expectations were high and I assumed the caregivers would be conscientious and reliable, interact with Peter and follow the instructions I gave them. I was mistaken and I felt let down and frustrated with the caregivers that were provided. The agencies charged additional fees boasting their employees received extra training in dementia care. After witnessing the quality of their care, I further assumed their extra training was lackluster; perhaps a video that they did not even watch.

Peter was fit and active and required someone to keep him engaged or at least busy to distract him from feeling anxious when I was gone. I provided long lists of suggested activities and games and had extensive conversations about what I expected.

The first caregiver lost Peter. I came home and he was nowhere in sight. Peter had been left alone sitting on the front porch and he wandered off. She didn't even realize he was gone because she was in the house. Fortunately, a neighbor saw him and called me immediately. I fired the woman on the spot.

The next caregiver simply didn't show up. I was ready with make-up and hair and anticipation for a girlfriend lunch. I called the agency after waiting fifteen minutes and by the time they reached the caregiver and got back to me with news that she wasn't working today, my friend was already at the restaurant. I fired the first agency and hired a new one.

I learned to not tell Peter that someone was coming to stay with him because he would withdraw and become angry with me for leaving him. On one occasion, we were in the kitchen and the music was boisterous and Peter was laughing at my silly dancing. Our moods were airy and light. I waited until 30 minutes before the companion's arrival time and then asked Peter, "What do you want to do with Raymond today?" I paused to give him time to respond and he didn't so then I just started rambling in a nervous rhythm suggesting things they might do together.

Peter's body language started to slump, and his arms crossed, and he was no longer laughing, but I continued to sing and dance while I baked, hoping to coax a giggle. I did not.

Peter slowly got up off his stool, went upstairs and he went to bed to pout. When Raymond arrived, I explained the situation and then went up to check on Peter. He was so mad at me that he pretended to be asleep. His arms were crossed, sneakers on his feet in the bed, and his eyes fluttered like that of a faking child. I left.

These are the behaviors that are hidden from most, which is why Alzheimer's disease is so misunderstood. These incredible minds, our partners, are being reduced to children before our eyes. These are the behaviors that cause caregivers intense stress and guilt.

It's very important to take care and take a break, but it is not without a cost.

While Raymond stayed with Peter, I didn't stare at the security cameras I installed to keep an eye on Peter, like I ordinarily did, or dwell on what was happening when Peter was with his caregiver. I took a long three-hour breath and tried to shake off the horrible mood he was in, knowing I would be punished when I got home.

When I returned, Peter was furious and barely spoke to me, but I kept my upbeat mood and immediately took Peter's hand, and out we went for a little walk by the lake. I asked him if he would help me cut the last of the summer's flowers and he said, "No," with a grumpy scowl but then sauntered out and joined me.

While I prepared dinner, he sat at the island, a good sign as he was at least in the same room! I turned up the music and started the silliness and hoped his mood would rise to mine. The energy required to pull him out of a crappy mood was enormous. We ate dinner in silence, side by side and when Peter finished, he leaned over and looked me in the eyes and said, "Thank you." and he kissed me, and all was well again. The energy spent was well worth it, for one more smile and kiss.

The unpredictability of this savage disease is like a pendulum. One day life was a lovely lull and there would be laughter, dancing, singing, hand-holding and kissing, contentment, and I would think, *This is not that bad, truly, I've got this!*

Then the faithful Alzheimer's bitch would keep her promise and swing in the opposite direction. Peter opened the door for the sixth caregiver I hired and after a few minutes, I kissed Peter goodbye, told him I'd be back in a little while and I felt the shift. The chill. The eyes darting. I assured him I loved him very much and I would be back. This was not the first time the pair had spent time together and it had been going well, so I was more at ease.

As I pulled out of our driveway, they were laughing together so I equated it to a moment like dropping your preschooler off crying, but the teacher quickly distracts him and before long they were laughing. That was my expectation for the next four hours and I truly immersed myself in what I was doing and didn't worry at all. I completely relaxed and enjoyed my time off.

Often, I left the house with no plans, fleeing, running to try to escape the horror. I found it difficult to know where to go or what to do if I didn't have a doctor's appointment or hair appointment or plans with a friend. What I did know, was that I needed the break to breathe and try to drop my shoulders and ease my ongoing tension.

Throughout my life, I have seen people dining alone and felt sad for them as though I knew their sorrowful and lonely stories. Sitting in an old familiar restaurant, I parked myself at a dark corner table. This was possibly the first time I had ventured here alone, and I opened my book, sipping my glass of wine. I felt my feet swinging like a child as my legs hung freely from my high-top chair and I had a birds-eye view of all the goings-on. The hustle and bustle and the free feeling of people finally out and about, freer from the pandemic. I even got to witness a first date near me. It was sweet and sorrowful at the same moment.

I was dining alone and it was lovely, truly lovely. I read my book until my meal came and I watched people and felt my shoulders softening. My energy level increased like that of a rechargeable battery. I filled my belly and my heart and left the restaurant with a new perspective on single diners.

I pulled into the driveway smiling ear to ear

waving my arm off at Peter and caregiver number six who were outside. Peter approached my car door and started whispering obscenities about him, telling me, "Don't say an f'ing word about it to him!" Peter was not one to swear, and he was very angry. Peter was paranoid and delusional.

My heart jumped directly into my throat, and I looked at caregiver number six wide-eyed and asked if anything happened. He replied, "He's a little off today." Peter slipped inside and hid in the dining room whispering and warning me with his finger, not to say an f'ing thing and so I again asked the caregiver a few questions about the day.

He said it seemed as if Peter was looking for me all day. Up and down the stairs, pacing through the house, and finally pacing in the driveway. After the caregiver left, I sat Peter down at the dining room table and he was still whispering and looking over his shoulder as though someone else was with us. He proceeded to tell me what happened in his language which I could not understand. I remained calm and listened holding his hand.

Peter was physically shaking with anger and I did not know why. I was shaking with fear. I watched every single second of the security camera's video footage to try to get to the bottom of Peter's anger. I found nothing but a kind and caring, helpful, and encouraging caregiver.

Caregiver number six was the best match for Peter, however, he called out more than he worked. There were eight cancellations that I can think of over six weeks. Excuses included: My wife has a fever, I'm getting the vaccine, I can't drive in the snow, I wrecked my car, My mother passed away, I have a cold, My daughter has a school function, I tripped and hurt my foot. Were they true? Who's to say? I needed someone I could rely on and caregiver number six had become unreliable.

When caregiver number seven arrived I went to a

nearby restaurant and ran into a kind friend. I put my phone away and I did not stare at the inside of my home through the lens of my many cameras. Instead, I was present, living in the moment. My moment. I laughed. I ate. I drank wine and I relaxed. It was the first time in a very, very long time that I felt a little bit like my old self. Before the Alzheimer's bitch changed me, changed Peter, changed every single thing in my life.

For those few hours, I allowed myself to let go and trust that Peter was safe, I felt free and almost euphoric to not be on duty, but off the clock. I thought, will he be upset? Maybe. Probably. Will he look for me out the window? Most likely. Will he be anxious, and pace and pick and scratch? Most definitely. And that is ok. I must be ok with that. This paradigm shift was necessary for my health and my well-being so that I could continue to be Peter's favorite caregiver. This shift did not mean I cared for Peter any less, I was just caring for myself more.

Agencies boast about listening to the needs of the client and making a good companion match. The next person they sent sat at the kitchen island on his phone for three hours not engaging Peter at all, even though he knew I had cameras and was checking in. They then sent a 77-year-old man who played one sixty-second game of basketball and then sat down, exhausted, for the remainder of the four hours.

I found myself questioning my expectations. Was I expecting too much simply asking these companions to show up, not lose my husband and engage him? I now had long-term care insurance approved, but no qualified caregivers.

In total, I hired eight caregivers from three different agencies. Peter's anxiety when I would leave the house was immense and ultimately unbearable for him. He became paranoid and agitated and sometimes combative.

After a ton of self-reflection, I realized that caregivers are not saints and they are not us and they cannot possibly know the things that we know about our spouses. But they can keep our loved ones safe, and our loved ones deserve lots of people they feel safe around!

My internal guide for Peter's wellbeing with a caregiver used to be "safe and happy," then it became, "safe and busy." I ended up being content with "safe." I decided to commit wholeheartedly to letting go.

Realizing the in-home caregiver option was causing Peter increasing anxiety we popped into an adult day care center. I wanted to explore this option and hoped this setting offered more to engage Peter while keeping him safe. Two weeks prior, I hired a second agency to add two more days for a total of 20 hours a week; five days, four hours a day. I needed some help with Peter's shaving and showering and dressing a couple of days a week. They claimed they would call me in a day or two when they found a suitable caregiver. They never called.

I was pleasantly surprised by the adult daycare's program of activities and the comfort level of everyone there. There were many ways for Peter to get involved in music and exercise, perhaps make some new friends and feel connected. The center offered lunch and snacks and would take care of medications and had a nurse on staff until two o'clock.

We took advantage of their complimentary four-hour day to see if the daycare center was a good fit. I dropped Peter off, and it felt like leaving one of our kids when they were small. Wanting to nurture Peter's helpful side, I told him it was a job and he would be helping the staff to care for the older people. He was immediately drawn in and didn't seem worried that I was leaving. I hoped that he felt helpful and appreciated.

When I returned to pick him up my palms were

sweaty, my heart was racing, and I tried with all my might not to get my hopes up. I walked in and there he was, legs bouncing away, he was chatting with his table mate who happened to be our neighbor! Peter was laughing and talking and waiting for snack time.

The staff was respectful and kind and spoke directly to Peter telling them they loved having him and hoped they'd see him again. Peter was beaming! As we walked out, he was waving to everyone and he said, "Bye-bye! Thank you! Lots of fun! Lots of fun!" I nearly cried. I was overjoyed!

The next day I discontinued in-home care and the following day was his first day in daycare! Peter began to attend daycare five days a week interacting with lots of kind people. His brain was engaged, he felt a sense of structure and quality kind care was plentiful!

Peter took the neighborhood senior bus with our neighbor. The bus picked Peter up at nine and returned him at three, giving me thirty hours a week on my own. The guilty caregiver in me must report that I still had 138 hours left in the week to care for Peter. Those thirty hours of respite came at a cost. My emotions were mixed and changed each day or sometimes each hour with a swooning song in my background. Tasks were getting completed productively and were less chore-like when I could swiftly complete them without interruption, feeling accomplished. But then a song would come on, I would miss Peter and feel the guilt tapping me on the shoulder. Shouldn't we be spending every single second that we can, together? The answer was crystal clear now. No.

With the day my own, in my own home, Peter being cared for really cared for, I could relax and deal with the things that needed tending. Peter's brain was stimulated, and he enjoyed a routine, socializing, and even made a new friend.

The time apart allowed me to remember myself, be myself, and preserve myself for our remaining time together. When we were together, there were no chores to be done, only hands to hold and kisses to kiss, and walks to take. There were snuggles to be had and meals to share, time to relish sweetly in our togetherness, instead of just dragging through the day counting the hours until bedtime.

I had more patience, more energy, and more love. When we were reunited in the afternoon, I felt like Peter's wife instead of his caregiver and our smiles could not be contained when we were together again.

The only thing that remained constant throughout our Alzheimer's journey was the unpredictability. Just as I began to lean into our new daycare schedule, Peter's moods became intensely unpredictable. He had adjusted fairly well to the routine, but after six weeks things changed.

The daycare nurse called me to tell me that Peter was trying to escape but he couldn't get out because of the child's doorknob cover. He was intent on staying in the small foyer and not going back into the building with the group. He would not listen to anyone no matter what they did to redirect him. The nurse put the phone up to Peter's ear and I said a friendly chipper hello, and calmly asked him how his day was. He told me sternly that he was ready to go home. I explained that the bus would be there soon and suggested he should go inside and sit down to wait for it. Miracles do happen. He listened. He didn't escape. 911 did not need to be called.

The next day, my daughter invited me to come to lay by a pool, float in the water, and just hang out, the two of us. For exactly two and three-quarter hours everything would melt away! Just me and Sarah. It had been far too long since we had some girl time, and I was excited! I was walking on air, singing a little too loudly and smiling ear to ear!

My hand was on the door handle of the car when the phone rang. I spent the next 15 minutes trying to convince Peter to go back inside the daycare building. He was angry and agitated and very anxious. I got nowhere. I had to go pick him up.

The 25-minute drive was necessary as the first five I fantasized about throat punching Peter, pounding on his chest, and screaming, "You're ruining my pool day!" But then I envisioned his sweet face and I thought about how he must be feeling. Afraid, paranoid, panicked, and scared, and isn't that so very terrible! I simply couldn't bear the thought of it, and I vowed to continue to try to keep him calm and make him feel safe and loved and happy, useful, respected, and dignified.

I wondered how I could quickly adjust my attitude, help Peter feel safe, and change the mood of the day. I was recently enlightened by the words of a new friend who shared with me the advice of her mother, "If your decision doesn't work out, make another decision."

And so, I did. After picking Peter up, we stopped at home, and I put a bathing suit on him and grabbed a second towel. Peter was calm and had already forgotten the horror of his crisis and was thrilled to be greeted by Sarah when we arrived at the pool!

My shoulders had dropped, my breathing had slowed, and Peter and I had just finished devouring our turkey sandwiches Sarah made. Feeling complete and full and satisfied with my decision to make a different decision, I leaned back and relaxed, happy. Peter sat on a nearby chair, and he was calm and content, and safe.

Melting into a chaise lounge, I thought, "At least I don't have to worry about daycare calling!" and then the phone rang. My world changed far sooner than I had expected and for the first time I had no concrete plan in place. I knew the call would come, I was well aware that it would happen, I just thought I'd have more time.

I was out of time and Peter was out of daycare. He had been discharged after three months. "He's anxious and agitated and angry and hallucinating and paranoid and it's not a good fit. He's not happy and he doesn't want to be there. He's disruptive and needs too much one-on-one attention." The owner explained kindly. I agreed with all of it, but the words tumbled down on me like boulders, and I crumbled under them. Just like that, I went from thirty hours of care per week to zero.

I spent that pool day in a panic and I wanted to run away. I cried and I didn't know what I was going to do and I cried more. Peter displayed similar behavior with all eight in-home caregivers I hired who were not qualified to care for him. He was anxious, I was anxious and that's not respite, nor is it care.

These scary delusional episodes started happening more often, and the people on the TV became real to Peter. He would talk to the actors or try to help someone on the TV if they were in distress. He began to hear voices and talk incessantly to someone I could not see. Confusion had a new meaning and Peter's speech was more stuttered and garbled, all in the space of a week or two. These new behaviors were unnerving and caused me great stress to watch.

I placed a call to Peter's neurologist and antipsychotic medication was added immediately. I hoped it would help Peter feel less frightened and more in control. When I spoke to his doctor, I felt heard and comforted when he said, "It will help curb the tantrums."

When you're surrounded by the sweetest, most caring souls you hear things like:
"You can't do this alone."
"You need to take a break."
"Have you considered a respite stay?"
"You need to take care of yourself."

I started to listen.

The year of our diagnosis I suffered a mini-stroke and took an ambulance ride to the hospital. Monitoring my blood pressure daily became the norm and I became acutely aware that the stress was getting to me. No matter how very much I loved Peter, I needed some time off.

I took a three-night respite away from home while our son, Sam, cared for Peter's every need. On the morning I planned to come home I woke up extremely anxious and panicked and I cried the entire morning. I was missing Peter so much that I left for home early. I cried on the way home, and I cried more the moment I saw Peter, diving into his arms.

A painful lesson was learned when I realized what I was missing had been gone for months. As I ran into Peter's arms, I could not and never would be satisfied again. What I was looking for was comfort from my partner. His keen sense of knowing what I needed without me expressing it. Instead, I sunk into a child's chest, grieving the man I married.

Lisa's Lookback

I'm still dumbfounded by the lack of quality in-home caregivers. While my standards may have been high, I don't think the requests were unreasonable. Professional caregivers should be more thoroughly trained to handle the nuances of Alzheimer's disease, specifically, the needs of people with early-onset Alzheimer's. Often these people are physically fit but cognitively impaired. Their needs are unique and very different from older, less active people who are suffering. A more robust training program would help the agencies obtain longevity with employees simply because their caregivers would be retained by clients if they were more invested in the care process.

Questions to Ponder

1. How are you taking care of yourself to stay healthy enough to care for your loved one?

2. Have you contemplated utilizing an adult daycare program?

3. From your experience, what do you think can be done to improve the training of in-home caregivers?

CHAPTER 15

Emergency Two-Week Respite

It was the first time the words came tumbling out of my mouth and the universe helped me with a bad cell phone connection. My daughter Sarah, heard only every other word. The situation propelled me to repeat the words to another person and in doing so, I had to hear the words, too. I was fumbling and stumbling and stuttering and explaining and defending and promising myself. This was not my plan A or plan B, and hardly C and maybe D. I broke down crying hearing my words, thinking about the possibility of placing Peter in a memory care facility.

I found thinking about placing Peter frightening. Keeping myself in denial, hoping I could care for him at home, felt safer and more comforting for my heart. If I allowed the thought of moving Peter to become real, it felt as if we were closer to his imminent death. It seemed with each sharp decline we were undeniably getting closer to that final point. No matter what the decline, caregivers must do what is necessary for both themselves and their loved ones.

I stopped my frantic pacing and plopped down on the couch in defeat. Sarah has been my sounding board and best friend for as deep and long as I can remember and she can be trusted to provide the truth, no matter how hard it is to hear.

She is safe and protective of me, and I entrusted her with my fear sobbing, "How could I ever place him in a memory care facility?" Rambling on, I vowed, "It would only be after my nervous breakdown. I could never. He's so anxious without me."

When something is stressing me out or I am fearful, I find that if I face it and attack it, my anxiety diminishes. The question nagged me. What if I cannot do this, care for Peter at home? I was showing more signs of caregiver burnout and felt a level of exhaustion I did not know existed. There was a very real possibility that in the coming year I may not be able to care for Peter.

Sarah reminded me that a facility has someone who cooks the meals, someone who cleans, changes the beds and distributes meds. There are nurses and CNAs and they are trained in dementia care, unlike me. Like most caregivers, we are thrown into this role without any experience. We put unreal expectations on ourselves and often do the jobs of many to tend to our loved ones.

I was counseled monthly by Adrianne Devivo, a dementia specialist with the Center for Healthy Aging. We would chat for an hour or more about the struggles or stages I was experiencing and she guided me with truth and foresight of what was to come. I needed to be prepared for what could come, no matter how horrific and Adrianne understood that. I shared with her that I wanted to research some facilities and Adrianne provided me with a list of places nearby that she recommended.

It's just shopping, I told myself as I made appointments to tour what could be Peter's future home. I was simply educating myself, preparing, and readying my heart for what if. It took an enormous amount of bravery to take this step as it felt as though it could be a reality one day soon. Placing Peter also meant we were closer to his death.

Sticking with my thought process of, "You don't know what you don't know" I plunged myself into shopping for the perfect facility for Peter should we need one. My eyes were open wider than wide, and I had a million questions, and I took the time and did the work and left my ignorant ego at home.

First, though, I needed to formulate a list of reputable, recommended facilities that I would pose these questions to. Places that were suggested to me by professionals I respected, friends, and family.

My questions were a combination of my own (from overthinking about it), dementia professionals, and the Alzheimer's Association. After making a list and checking it twice, I trotted off to meet and greet people I didn't know and to face the dementia community. The residents were mostly wheelchair-bound, some with heads hung low, some clapping along with music, some staring into space and I connected and understood all of it.

The people I met, ran the gamut of overbearing salespeople just selling a "head in a bed" to very caring people engrained in the fabric of people's lives who they truly cared about and have gotten to know. I toured eight memory care facilities. Eight.

To me, the way the staff interacted with the residents was important, the second most important thing. Some residents lit up when staff called them by name, and they laughed and communicated in their way. The staff knew personal things about everyone which seemed to make them feel special. Their reactions could not be fabricated, and it was evident whether they were genuine or not.

Most importantly was the energy of the facility. I toured some that felt morgue-like and sad and drained of happiness. The residents seemed as though they were just waiting for their turn. The opposite is true of my favorite facilities where the energy was high, and residents were smiling and joyful and participating on their level and you just cannot fake that.

Furniture and carpet don't need to be updated, just clean. Rooms don't need to be large, just sufficient, as we don't want our loved ones spending too much time alone in the room. Facilities don't need to be grand.

But care? Care needs to be grand and loving and heartfelt, and the givers need to be passionate about what they spend their careers doing. When you visit these spaces, you will see it. You will feel it when you do the work to educate yourself and compare. You will see the contrast in care.

I wanted to be doing anything else other than looking for a new home for my husband but should the 'what if' part of this putrid disease show her head, I needed to be prepared. I wanted to be gardening or walking on a beach or holding Peter's hand or anything else, but this was the task and I decided to be very present, rather than go through the motions. Learn and dig and feel stress-free about the decisions I would make.

When researching facilities online, they all appeared to have the same lush landscaping, happy and engaged elderly healthy-looking models, floor plans, overstaffed hallways, and the "base cost." Armed with a list of questions from the Alzheimer's Association, I searched deeper and inquired more. I caught a few salespeople off guard with my quizzing questions.

Many things don't need to be asked as they are answered just by being present in the space and watching, looking, and feeling. But many things do need to be asked and I've cherry-picked my most sought-after answers.

Questions for Care Facilities

1. Is the memory unit locked and secure with no way of a resident wandering off? Who gets access to the code?

2. What type of training has the staff received on dementia? What exactly does that mean? I'm fairly certain we had caregivers in our home who watched a video and considered themselves trained in Alzheimer's. Probe, and don't be afraid to quiz hard here.

3. Who is on staff when, who is on call, and what for goodness sake is the patient-to-staff ratio? What happens in a medical emergency?

4. Are all residents participating in the same cookie-cutter activity or are there options if a resident is not engaged, or perhaps at a different stage? Is the staff perceptive enough to take initiative to make a change?

5. Is it possible to age in place at the facility? I did not want to move Peter to a second facility unless there was an unforeseen medical emergency. Do they offer Hoyer lift services? Hospice services?

6. What is the level of cleanliness? The place doesn't need to be grand and newly renovated, just clean, really clean.

7. What are the additional fees? The room is the base price. Depending on the care your loved one requires they charge you by the level of redirection they need, the amount of personal care they require, or the help they need eating. Continence care is usually yet another increase. An initial assessment will be performed for your starting price and it goes (WAY) up from there as your loved one declines.

8. How often are care updates and assessments done to determine cost increases? Who performs these assessments?

9. Are the apartment/room doors kept open? How often are residents checked on throughout the day or night to be sure they're safe?

10. What is the longevity of the staff? Is the staff turnover high? If so, why? I think longevity speaks for itself! Question the staff on why they love the place!

Many things can be learned by observing. Some facilities offer very thoughtful extras like green paint on the wall where the sink and toilet are or black toilet seats. This helps the residents understand where toileting occurs. Red plates and cups are sometimes offered to help with eating as it becomes more difficult. A colorful plate offers contrast so your loved one can see and manage their food more easily as their vision declines.

And so, I had done the painstaking work to visit these potential homes for Peter. The education, coupled with the fact that I now had zero hours of professional care and respite, placed me in the center of an emotional tug of war. I didn't want to place Peter, but I could no longer handle this task on my own. There was a compromise that I had not considered until it was presented to me.

I received a message from the Executive Director of the facility that was my number one pick because of all the questions answered above. She simply asked me if I would consider a two-week respite stay if she could get it approved. They ordinarily only offer thirty-day respite stays, but as a follower of the blog, she knew I would not commit to that length of time. I agreed immediately through tears of reluctance and arrangements were made.

The employees of the facility came to us, to our home where Peter was most comfortable, to do the formal assessment of his needs. Peter happily went with a staff member to Dunkin' after meeting her just twenty minutes before. That's how comfortable he felt.

We were invited to, and accepted, visits to the unit so Peter could meet and get to know the staff. We had lunch one day and dinner another. To ready Peter's room without him knowing, I had packed several of his favorite things. The Executive Director and I unloaded the car while his Dunkin' friend pretended to show Peter where she works!

The night before the respite was to start, Peter was playing golf and I snuck off to set up his room with familiar things hoping to make Peter feel at home, away from home. Focusing on the task, I snuck into his room which they had thoughtfully prepared, and started unpacking fidgets and clothes and stuffed animals.

One of Peter's nurses came into the room and before long she was helping me cry it out and assured me, they would take excellent care of him. I already knew that, but it was still the most difficult thing I've ever done.

I had placed the last fidget toy and hidden Peter's favorite snacks, pop tarts, and fig newtons, for him to find. I had coordinated his outfits in his drawers and placed his favorite stuffed friends just so. A three am purchase of cloud backdrops now adorned his walls to cheer him, and there was nothing left to do. I swallowed hard to dam the remaining tears until I slipped out the front door unnoticed.

The blog post below was written the day the staff came to our home to pick Peter up for his two-week respite stay. It was two years and three months after diagnosis. This decision to take time off haunted me and the guilt of leaving Peter, abandoning him, overpowered me.

As I write this, I am alone for the first time since Peter and I last kissed. Before he walked out our front door, we stood in the entryway of our home and I wanted to change my mind and my heart was screaming, 'I'm SO sorry!' and I kissed his lips, pausing there for a few moments to record it, and I said, 'I love you so much," as I gazed deeply into his unknowing eyes.

And then we were apart. I sat down with my dog, and I howled, and tears fell, and my shoulders shook. And then I got up and I brushed myself off, knowing that I had done the work and had put in the effort to do everything I possibly could to make this successful for Peter.

I had no regrets and I finished packing the car and drove off to pick up my daughter and greet the beach. It took some time to relax, and my mind continually wandered to Peter's welfare. Was he sad or anxious or confused or happy and entertained?

Peter made it through the day but was extremely anxious at bedtime and could not understand that he was sleeping there. I sent happy videos of myself explaining that he should get in bed and that I'd see him soon, to no avail. The videos made him more anxious.

After working a 12-hour shift the Executive Director drove back to the facility to calm Peter and stay with him until he fell asleep. Not only was she calming Peter, but she was

calming me, assuring me it was a transition, promising it was
temporary. She texted me a few minutes later, 'Sleeping.'

The people closest to Peter took turns visiting him
so that Peter would have a familiar face every day. Some
ate a meal with Peter, some took a tour or played a game
or took a walk, or simply sat and chatted. The pictures
and videos came popping into my day and it warmed my
heart to know he was being loved.

As with life, Peter felt more comfortable with some
staff members than others, and adjustments were quickly
made to accommodate Peter's comfort. He was active and
needed to feel he had a purpose and the staff filled his
need by offering him lots of jobs! Peter helped with the
laundry, and sweeping, and was assistant to his favorite
nurse, he even helped console a troubled resident.

Peter's activity plan was tailored to his individual
needs and the staff created unique things to keep him
busy. Because Peter was only 56, he was much younger
and more active than most of the residents. He got to go
to the driving range and play pool, paint with a squirt
gun, play corn hole, watch movies, and go for walks and
he received a ton of love from the resident therapy dogs.

The reports from his visiting crew of friends and
family were all the same. "The staff is excellent, and Peter
is very well cared for. Peter is bored and yammers
nonstop and seems a bit anxious." This was identical
behavior to what I was seeing at home. I scanned each
picture for evidence of overmedicating or agitation or
anything worrisome at all and there just wasn't a single
thing.

There were times when Peter's nurse reported he
was missing me or wanted to go home but he was easily
redirected or distracted. With each report and photo, I
relaxed more and more, knowing Peter was in excellent
hands. When I was finally relaxed, I started remembering

myself and getting reacquainted with who I used to be. I spent time at the beach with our kids and while I spent my birthday without Peter, I spent it with my good friend Sherri who just happens to be my cousin. Drinks were drunk, toes were painted, delicious meals were eaten and laughter erupted from my belly.

It was important to me to feel all our special spaces and places alone. Our beach house, our favorite restaurant, the beaches, even our bedroom. It was important to me to be present in each one and sit in my fear of it, breathing deeply and asking myself what exactly was causing the panic and making me want to run. I assured myself I was ok alone, and I looked my fears right in the face and did not push them away.

I traveled the six hours to see my family, my father, and my friends and again, be alone with myself. By my last day in Pennsylvania, I had slowed to such a sweet pace that I took myself on a tour of the Airbnb I had been staying at for three days. I lingered and did my best to notice every detail and imagine my host purchasing that just perfect item. I walked barefoot on moss rocks and felt a feather a bird had dropped, and I appreciated the beauty that I was surrounded by.

And I cried. I cried tears of joy for the memories I have been so lucky to make and for Peter and my future memories we would make when I returned. I cried because I miss my old Peter and I cried because I missed my new Peter.

I cried more in the beginning than at the end of the trip because the countdown to seeing Peter had then begun. The planning and wonderment of his reaction when I arrived tickled me and finally, I felt like myself again.

While on respite, I pondered some of our most special moments. Nearly twenty years ago, I wore a red sundress with white daisies and yellow polka dots when

Peter and I went on a date, and he just loved that dress. He'd ask me to wear it and I would until I got tired of it and it was out of style and my ego refused.

He never asked me to wear another thing again, and never asked me before that red sundress. He could never express why he loved it so much, but I was happy to make him happy, and he made me feel pretty when I wore it.

It hung in the very back of my closet for the latter of our eight-year long-distance courtship and I hadn't reunited with it in the previous four or five years. Peter had certainly forgotten about the dress.

We were married in Turks and Caicos with our five children surrounding us. Some of us flew from Harrisburg and some from Hartford and we all met at the Charlotte airport to continue our journey together. I surprised Peter by wearing that outdated stupid red sun dress. When Peter saw me, he threw his head back and laughed running toward me, grabbing me and I felt like the prettiest woman in the world.

Every year I follow my own made-up rule of donating things I haven't worn in the past year. Something tugged at my heart and told me to keep that dress and as I remembered it on the last day of my two-week respite, I ran upstairs to see if it was in the closet. Had I kept it? I had not thought of, nor seen it, in years. To my delight, the dress hung there waiting for me.

After a fitful night's sleep, I got up early in anticipation of picking Peter up. The nurse's report that morning was that Peter barely slept in anticipation of my arrival. We were in sync as usual. My stomach was in knots as I desperately tried to drive the speed limit on my way to him. The day before I had spent hours tackling all the house and yard chores, so it was just right for Peter's arrival. He loved when the lawn was freshly mowed, and gardens were proudly sharing their colors.

Wanting our reunion to be perfect, I dug that stupid red dress out of the very back of the closet, laughing as it should have been donated or burned decades ago, but I couldn't bring myself to do it. I wore the dress, as ridiculous as I felt.

I was holding back the tears as I walked in and there he was, sitting in a chair waiting for me with a bouquet. His expression was disbelief as if he thought perhaps, he was dreaming. We both blinked back tears and held each other ever so gently, our hearts pounding together. Peter's entire body sighed with relief as we were reunited.

The staff helped me pack up Peter's room and load the car. Hugging the staff, we said our goodbyes. Peter hugged his nurse the longest and hardest and as he did, he said, "I love ya." My heart was so full of gratitude and appreciation for the care he received.

"I thought I lost you." "I haven't seen you." "I couldn't find you." Peter repeated with heavy sighs of relief, and I held his hand the entire ride home. We kept peeking at each other smiling and laughing. There were no chores to be done and the day was ours to share. Our hearts were happy, and we were high school giddy just to be reunited relaxing on the front porch. Peter told me then, "You look pretty," pointing to that stupid red dress.

While I was not interested or ready to place Peter in a facility, I'm grateful for the experience and the people I met. It wasn't safe for Peter to stay alone and I could no longer care for him 24 hours a day. I had reached the point where I could not care for Peter alone and I felt Peter should have more people to love him and feel safe with.

Several conversations took place between myself and one of the nurses that cared for Peter during his two-week stay. We entered an agreement and she became Peter's full-time nurse, taking care of him thirty hours a week. We took care of Peter together for the last four months of Peter's life.

Lisa's Lookback

While I never ended up placing Peter in a facility, I'm glad I had the experience to tour so many and learn the things I did. I felt prepared if I could no longer care for Peter at home. The two-week respite was filled with such mixed emotions, looking back I know that I was at my breaking point. I realize that I would not have met our nurse if I hadn't taken the two weeks and the research I did helped me feel comforted that Peter was in great hands. Grace happens when we are most open to receiving it. I can't help but look back now wishing I could have those two weeks back to just be by his side, but I know it was the right decision at the time. Had I not taken that time off, I'm not sure I could've endured the remaining days of our journey with the grace and patience I needed.

Questions to Ponder

1. Can you open your heart and listen to your body, your family, and your friends when you need a break?

2. Would you consider placing your loved one in a memory care facility to take a break for an extended period of time?

3. Have you visited the places that are special to you and your loved one alone, preparing to visit there alone in the future?

The Generous Souls

"Life is kind of like a party.
You invite a lot of people, some leave early,
some stay all night, some laugh with you,
some show up really late.
But in the end, after the fun,
there are a few who stay to help you clean up the mess.
And most of the time,
they aren't even the ones who made the mess.
These people are your true friends.
They are the only ones who matter."

-mypositiveoutlooks.com

CHAPTER 16

The Generous Souls

I've always believed if I surround myself with people who are smarter and kinder and everything better than me and spend the most time with these sorts they will influence me in positive ways and make me a better person. My advice to you is to stop what you're doing, the mad distractions, and to relish the time you can. Spend it with people who can teach you the good things and please, oh please spend less time with those who bring you down or just suck the living life out of you. After all, what else do we have and how precious is this time, this finite time we toss around so carelessly?

This experience has taught me that there are two types of people that fit nicely and neatly into one category or another. They are the givers and the takers. Surround yourself with givers, like the ones I describe in this chapter. The givers of time, compassion, respite, and selfless support.

I will tell the stories of some of the generous souls who helped Peter and me along our journey. I offer these stories not only to acknowledge these beautiful people but to spark ideas for you as well. Ideas of how you can be helped and lovingly cared for if you ask for help. Or perhaps if you're reading this as someone who supports a caregiver, it may offer insight on what they need.

Here are the stories of some of the givers who showed up to help us. These givers were unwavering in their courage and generosity and have given Peter and me a gift I will hold tenderly in my heart for the remainder of my life.

WENDY KOPP

Being the type of person who is ever mindful of my appearance, I rarely go out without makeup on, hair done, and clothes chosen for the occasion. Those things began to not matter. There was no definitive moment, but I realized it abruptly and knew I had reached a low point.

Our sweet neighbor and friend Wendy Kopp had offered to take Peter for a walk and when she came to the door, I caught a glimpse of myself in the mirror just inside. My head was adorned with one of the worst cases of bedhead I had witnessed from a fitful night. My glasses were smudged with who knows what, and my face wore no makeup. I was taken aback by the sight of me in my drooping robe, no bra, and slippers. Who is that, I thought of my reflection. Who had I become?

I watched the pair walk down the driveway and I cared about only one thing. A shower. I took the longest and hottest shower I had taken in months. I stood with my arms stretched out, hands on the back wall of the shower howling as the water hit my back. I sobbed and let the morning's grief run down the drain. My body shook in disbelief until finally, I slumped onto the bathtub floor wondering if I would ever be able to get up. With arms wrapped around my legs, I sobbed not only from exhaustion and grief but gratitude for something as simple as a long, hot, uninterrupted shower.

Wendy took Peter on many walks during his illness offering me the gift of solitude and peace. Peter eagerly joined her as he felt safe and enjoyed Wendy's company.

CINDY BASTARDI

"Come, please come," I practically begged her as I explained that Peter's physical life was growing short, and his cognitive life shorter. If she hoped to see a glimpse of the Peter she knew, the window was right then. What I didn't realize at the time was that I was begging her to come for me, not her. I needed someone who knew me the way she knows me, to bear witness to this horror we were experiencing.

I've known her my entire life, she is my big sister. We finish each other's sentences, we know each other's secrets and we feel each other's hearts. We cry very easily together, even at the mere sight of each other. We spontaneously laugh together and leaving one another at an airport is truly heart-wrenching.

Her four-night visit flew by, and it was relaxing having someone to just be with Peter so I could shower peacefully or not be so 'on' all the time. We cooked every day and filled the freezer with meals that would last for weeks. We drank wine and we stayed up entirely too late chatting and I unloaded all of it. Puked it out of my heart, all my worries, fears, and my intense hatred for this Alzheimer's bitch I could not rid.

"It's worse than I thought, and we text every day," she said to me as she shook her head, tears welling in her eyes. I felt better somehow that Cindy knew. It made me feel strangely stronger, seen, heard, and less alone.

Cindy is thoughtful, perhaps the kindest person I know, and she brought Peter sugary treats for each day, and he loved them. Cindy brought treats for my soul: bath bombs, eye masks, soap bags, and books. The most precious of her gifts was a bracelet with the following quote: "Fate whispers to the warrior, you cannot withstand the storm." The warrior whispers back, "I AM the storm." As I read the inscription, through my tears I told her, "I AM the fucking storm!"

When I dropped my sister Cindy off at the airport to travel back to her Tennessee home our eyes were already red and wet and swollen from the 40-minute ride. We caught a glimpse of each other in the rear-view mirror as I was driving, and we both buckled, and our eyes darted away.

We sobbed at the uncertainty of it all and the grief and vulnerability and helplessness and we clutched each other's shoulders looking at one another in utter disbelief. Cindy walked into the airport and then I was alone again.

CHRIS LARSH

Before diagnosis, Peter began playing golf in a league on Tuesday evenings. He became friendly with the bunch and looked forward to his time on the course. After their round, they gathered in the clubhouse for dinner, and we would be reunited afterward. I enjoyed my time alone, but always loved hearing Peter's stories about his adventures with his buddies.

The organizer of the league was Chris Larsh, a good friend and one of the most generous souls I've ever met. Our kids went to high school and played basketball together. There were often get-togethers before and after the games and we saw each other frequently during those early years before diagnosis. Chris is an incredible golfer and a selfless friend who requires no gratitude or credit for what he's done but deserves plenty.

As time and disease marched on, Peter's golf skills diminished, and changes were made to accommodate his needs. I know there were many adjustments made that I am unaware of, but I'll describe the few I know about.

The league's golfers were paired randomly, and handicaps were assigned based on skill level. Golf handicaps are a number that represents the golfer's ability based on their previous round's scores. The numbers are used to compare performance with other golfers. The lower your handicap the better golfer you are. Handicaps even the playing field so everyone can enjoy a win. If Chris's handicap was two or three, Peter's was twenty.

The first adjustment made was the pairing. As Peter's skill diminished, he needed more assistance and direction on what to do next. The gentlemen in the league rigged the pairing so that Peter was always matched with Chris. Even as I write this, I well up with tears at the selflessness Chris showed in helping Peter every week. Chris guided Peter on where the next hole was, which club to use, and how hard to hit the ball, and encouraged him. Peter came home feeling like a pro because of Chris.

Peter played with the league until the last year of his life, at which point Chris would pick Peter up, take him golfing, and bring him back home. The game became more casual, and it was common for Chris to encourage Peter to drop a second and certainly illegal ball if he shanked his into the woods. Chris was the consummate coach and friend.

Since they weren't playing with the league, which required an annual fee, the pair played weekly whenever the weather was nice. I'd put money in Peter's pocket and tell Chris it was there until Chris confessed it was a problem. The money would fall out of Peter's pocket and distract him, as would the leaves that blew around the course in the fall. Peter was easily distracted and confused by this point. More clubs in Peter's bag, meant more choices and so Chris plucked out the clubs Peter didn't need and we put them away in the closet.

I couldn't tell Peter when he was playing golf until just before it was time to go as he would get nervous and fidget and obsess about all the things he needed. We would do it together, collecting all the important things he had hidden in his coveted hiding spots: A glove here, sunglasses there, hats strewn everywhere. It was important for Peter to have a spinner to fidget with, perhaps two, and of course the clubs and his cart.

171

As dressing Peter became harder, I learned to dress him in his golf clothes in the morning after his shower for that evening's round. Peter wore his sneakers rather than his golf shoes as he would laugh insisting that his golf shoes were his dad's. Peter's father was not a golfer.

At the beginning of the last season, Peter would stand at the front door watching anxiously for his long-time friend. We would take his clubs and cart out to the driveway to be ready for Chris's arrival. By the end of the season, I had to wait until the very last moment to take his clubs outside. Peter had become possessive and paranoid, thinking they were not safe in the driveway. He would take them back inside the house for safekeeping.

When Chris was busy and couldn't get Peter out on the course, he would arrange for another friend, Peter Zimmerman to sub. Chris would prepare Peter Z. with the details and nuances and improvisions that needed to be made. One evening after golf, Peter Z. came in and we took some time catching up over a glass of wine. It was then, through our conversation, that I learned that Chris was not even taking his clubs on the course. Chris had been caddying for Peter the entire last season. What a gift.

After they played, Chris and Peter would go to the clubhouse for dinner. Peter had started having issues with food and another adjustment was necessary. Handheld foods like hamburgers, pizza slices, and sandwiches had become foreign to Peter and he forgot how to eat them. He would try cutting them with a knife and fork instead of picking them up. Any type of meat that required cutting, was too difficult to comprehend. I decided that a salad with some protein would be best and suggested that Chris ask the kitchen to cut everything into bite-size pieces. They were happy to accommodate the request every week. Chris reported that the staff knew Peter and were patient with him and happy to help in any way they could.

Chris took Peter golfing every week until October that season when it became too cold and dark to play. To help you understand the relevance of that timeframe, Peter died just two months later in December. I am forever grateful for the noble gift Chris gave to Peter and for the respite he provided to me.

ZACHARY BRENNER

Peter's ability to do the heavy physical chores he had always taken care of had ceased. I tried to take on and tackle these tasks, but some just were either too heavy and hard or too much for one person. Our son, Zach, just took over difficult duties when he picked up our grandson, Sonny, from our playdate. Whether it was readying the generator, carrying fireplace wood, putting in or taking out window air conditioners, hanging Christmas lights, or just hauling the trash cans to the curb for me, Zach simply took the initiative and knew what I needed to reduce my stress. I'm grateful for his help in carrying the heavy load.

JIM HILLIARD

Many years ago, these two sweet souls met, Peter Marshall and Jim Hilliard. They were very young, and I'll tell the tale as it was told to me. "Peter was nice to me at the bus stop," Jim told me. It was the first day of school in 1979. Imagine someone having such a profound impact that the memory would be so vivid so many years later.

Shortly after in the school year, Peter encouraged Jim to attend the school dance which is not surprising. Peter was as inclusive and kind as people come. As neighbors, they became fast friends, wearing a path that connected their homes and hearts. They played basketball, played in the lake, and got into trouble they shouldn't have.

I met Jim and his lovely wife Donna at high school reunions, but we weren't close as couples and didn't do things socially. That changed one summer after our diagnosis. Peter hadn't seen Jim much over the years but had mentioned him to me and recounted their childhood stories.

One day I received an unexpected message from Peter's childhood friend. Jim's message read, "Hey, I have the next two days off. Could I be beneficial in some way and spend a little quality time with Peter?" I remember blinking hard at the words, surprised by the kindness. This man offered himself, not knowing what to expect, but knowing we needed help.

We messaged back and forth a few times and he graciously agreed to help Peter with a big errand Peter couldn't handle alone. He ended the conversation with, "See you tomorrow. I don't know how to thank you." I asked Jim six months after Peter died to explain precisely what it was he was so thankful for and he replied, "It's quite simple. You shared him with me. Trusted me with the most important thing in your world. All I wanted to do was spend time with him. I don't know anyone else in my life who would have done the same for me. Peter would have! For this, I am grateful!"

Peter and I took an early morning walk in the rain before Jim's arrival, and he asked me a few times what Jim's name was. He didn't remember what to call him, but he laughed when he recalled memories of playing basketball in the neighborhood when they were in high school, reminiscing about cutting through backyards to each other's houses.

Jim showed up, listened, and asked Peter questions. He lifted Peter up and tugged at memories with him and gave him the most precious gift of all. Some of his...time. After that day Jim was ever-present in our lives. Shortly after his first visit, he sent this message, "Please know that going forward, Donna and I want to lend our efforts in any way that may be of assistance." Jim meant that with all his heart and proved it over and over and over through his lovely actions during Peter's illness.

When Jim would offer, I knew I could count on him to take Peter to Home Depot to lug bags of mulch and sand, get the oil changed in the car, or drive him to a road race. He would take a walk around the lake, go bowling or take him to breakfast, lunch, or a brewery. Jim was committed to Peter and me often saying, "I want to help you both," and he did.

Jim never wanted credit and always insisted the thanks should come from him as he cherished every moment he spent with Peter. Jim referred to Peter as, "my dude." When Peter would speak of Jim, he called him "my friend" because he could not remember Jim's name. Those words were usually accompanied by a hand on his heart.

"Peter makes me a better person," Jim would tell me and I agreed, as he made me a better person too. We are all better if we were lucky enough to have shared in the life of Peter.

ROB AND VICKIE LANGONE

Of the many kind gestures we received, two stand out as the most helpful. First, time. Peter was extremely anxious when I would leave the house and he was with a caregiver. However, he was very comfortable leaving the house with a friend. Rob and Vickie would often drop by, and Rob would take Peter out for a few hours so my precious friend Vickie and I could have some girl time together. It was a sacred, uninterrupted time that I cherished. Peter trusted Rob and he walked out the door carefree.

Secondly and equally appreciated, were meals.

Vickie is an excellent cook and would frequently make meals for our freezer. Caregiving is exhausting and by the end of the day having a meal already prepared was such a gift. If you are caring for a caregiver this is a priceless gesture.

Rob had a special gift of relating to Peter. Whenever we spent time together, Rob would present Peter with a new fidget spinner. Rob taught Peter how to spin it and told him, "Peter, I spin mine whenever I'm happy, or sad, or silly or confused. It makes me feel better." Peter's face would light up when Rob would pull out a new brightly colored toy just for him. He coveted those spinners and carried at least one in his pocket every day.

Not only did Vickie and Rob provide meals and girl time, but their constant check-ins and compassion were incredibly supportive. They witnessed some of the hardest times when Peter's behavior was erratic, which I will share in a later chapter. Together they were a constant port of support in my stormy life, whether it was a simple phone call, a joke to lighten the air, or a shoulder to leave my mascara on. The truest of friends.

LORI BRENNAN

Lori was presented to me through her comments on my blog *Oh Hello Alzheimer's*. I loved her energy and after weeks of reading her comments, I messaged her to extend an invitation to meet for lunch. Sort of a blind date for friends. We hit it off right away.

Lori is filled with this insane amount of childlike non-stop energy. She scoops you up into her joyous inferno and sweeps you along without knowing where you're going. This woman provides a carefree sort of out-of-control vibe that may be scary to some, but her manic personality grabs you by the lapels and you are off!

Immersing herself in our world, she provided many things but her claim to fame will always be her field trips. Peter would jump into her car, and they would be gone for hours. The mall, or to Build-a-Bear, lunch, milkshakes, or the aquarium.

They sang in the car and laughed and joked and sent me silly photos and called me laughing hysterically like children and it was contagious. They would come home with souvenirs and smiles, sometimes flowers or chocolate-covered strawberries from Peter to me.

Peter had lovely field trip days, where he didn't need to feel less than, bored or responsible or worried or confused. Lori and I joked that she had become Peter's fairy grandmother. He was exhausted after his hours of fun and one time he laughed and laughed and said very clearly with his biggest smile, "That was so much fucking fun!"

OUR ARMY OF GRACIOUS FRIENDS AND NEIGHBORS

Through our journey I felt showered by so many lovely gestures, as I recall them now, I feel so blessed. Our friend Randy was an earlier riser than me and on more than one occasion I woke to a text reading, "Breakfast is on your porch." He'd drop donuts off before we were even awake.

Our basement was a catastrophe and the hoarding and hiding of scrapwood had overwhelmed the rooms making it difficult to maneuver! The piles of tools and wood and rocks and sticks from outside along with bags and boxes and garbage were tremendous, and I would stand with my hands on my hips wondering where to start. But I did start, and with the help of our friend Amanda Gibson, we moved an enormous pile of wood to begin the decluttering. All the wood stacked neatly in one place, floors open for walking, and more corners to organize! Amanda offered her helping hands and her kind heart.

The mailman brought more unexpected packages than I could count. Puzzles and games and books and fidget toys, blankets, and bracelets inscribed with hope. Flowers were delivered and notes and cards, too. Our neighborhood put together a meal train. Friends and neighbors signed up to deliver a meal on a certain night and there were always leftovers for the freezer. Another neighbor brought dinner every single week.

Most people are good and kind and I had to learn to say yes when the loveliest ones offered to ease my load a bit. Never in my life have I felt such a deep appreciation for acts of kindness. From the depths of my heart, I thank each of these generous souls for giving their time and energy and being courageous enough to stare Alzheimer's in the face. To see through her ugliness and continue to recognize my sweet Peter who was still inside.

Lisa's Lookback

Just a few months after Peter died, I caught a glimpse of a photo of myself from the last month of Peter's life. I stared at the photo in disbelief and began to weep. I cried not only at the horror of who looked back at me but thinking of other caregivers. My eyes seemed lifeless, my skin dull, and my face appeared to sag weighted with grief. We don't realize how deeply we are affected on the front lines of this disease. Caregivers think of themselves last, if at all because we are so dedicated to caring for our loved ones. People want to help, they just don't know what is needed. It takes courage to ask for help, but in doing so you too are providing a gift.

Questions to Ponder

1. What are you currently handling that someone else could take over?

2. Can you shift your thinking about asking for help to knowing that you are providing the giver with the precious gift of time with your loved one?

3. Ask yourself what you would do if you had an hour or three in your own home alone?

CHAPTER 17

Run 169 Towns Society

When I was in ninth grade, I started running with my brother Gary. I was instantly hooked and when Peter and I started dating we would run together. We were content running a three-to-five-mile distance until a family member convinced us to run a half marathon. We trained and ran two half marathons together.

Road races are time-consuming, and I was turned off by the excess time it would take to drive to and from a scheduled race, the anxiety of waiting for the starting gun, and the pressure of my actual finish time. For me, the road races took the joy out of running and I'd rather walk out my front door and go for a run without all the pressure.

Peter felt very differently. Peter began signing up for local races where he often spotted a group of runners wearing the same T-shirts. This tribe of runners belonged to a club called the Run 169 Towns Society. There are 169 towns in Connecticut and the goal is to run an official race in all of them. There is no time limit, you can count runs you've done before joining and the reward is simply the pride of having done it.

Peter decided to join the club and began meticulously searching for races around the state, organizing them into an excel spreadsheet. Together we plotted which races he could conquer on which dates. Some towns had only one single race each year, so those dates were a priority over towns that offered several races per year. The schedule was built around those elusive towns.

Many weekend mornings I would be snuggled warmly in bed and Peter would gently place a kiss on my cheek and tiptoe out the door. No matter the weather or temperature he would run. Sometimes the day's race would be more than an hour away so he would coordinate two races in that area rather than drive to that county on a different day. He was determined to achieve his goal.

Many races were 5Ks, some were five miles, half marathons and Peter even ran a full marathon, training for the 26.2-mile race in tandem with completing all the Connecticut towns. Peter was a spreadsheet master and knew precisely when and where each race was and there were a few occasions he ran three races in one day to complete a county's official races.

As time went on, after Peter was diagnosed, I started noticing little changes. Peter would have a difficult time getting to a race. He could not follow the navigation system and comprehend the map. Thinking it would help, I turned the voice prompts on his car's navigation, but Peter shared that it made it harder for him. That was too much stimulation.

As Peter's sense of direction dwindled, I decided to track him on his phone to make sure he was safe. There were times I would be at home on my laptop looking at a map and track where he was, to guide him to the race over the phone. He was so fiercely determined to complete this challenge, I had to help him attain his goal.

Soon after, Peter started having trouble understanding how to get to the website to find new races that were posted, and he was becoming confused about his spreadsheet. The stress was overwhelming for Peter as he felt he would miss an important race, so I took over managing the schedule and his excel sheet. At this point, he had run 152 towns and had seventeen to go.

The night before a race, Peter would be anxious and nervous, concerned he wouldn't be prepared properly, or wake up to his alarm or make it to the race on time. He would spend hours loading up a laundry basket with extra shoes and shirts, socks and snacks, hats and gloves, and water bottles. Whatever made him feel prepared. At night I would assure him that I had set three alarms and we'd go over the timeline: getting up, driving to the town, and the starting time of the race until he could relax.

Often, he'd wake up hours before the alarm, get dressed, and come back to bed flopping around waiting nervously for his alarm to go off. The stress of not meeting his goal was overpowering him and something needed to be done.

Peter had only six races to go when I decided I needed to step in and ask for help. We have many friends who are runners who were willing to help. I reached out, posting the dates and times of the final races asking if anyone was willing to escort Peter to help him meet his target. When I told him friends and family members would now be driving him to the remaining races, Peter was so relieved his eyes became teary and he pulled me to him. He sniffled, held me, and softly said, "Thank you so much."

The remaining race schedule spanned from August 4, 2019 through November 24, 2019, culminating with the Scotland Scoot. The final challenge was an elusive race, meaning there was only one race per year. Peter was extremely anxious about every aspect of the race, particularly how to get there and how long it would take, even though I would be taking him. He was desperately afraid he was going to miss the race. I decided to try to alleviate some of his angst. We drove to the race site, and we drove the race route. Peter was somewhat relieved, but not completely.

A longtime grade school friend, Jill Lavasseur was the first to offer to be Peter's racing partner. Jill had been a lifelong distance runner and helped Peter train for his marathon which he completed on October 8, 2016. This was a year and a half before his diagnosis. Peter's son Sam came home from Boston to accompany him on race number 164. Hero Jim Hilliard picked Peter up for race 165, and friend Marc Scrivener joined them running alongside Peter for the Griswold Sunflower race. Our community was strong.

Now he had just four races to go. The next race was Kent, which Peter would tackle on August 25, 2019. Here's a peek into Peter's mindset before a race, a blog post from the day of the Kent race.

RUNNING KENT

I can't tell Peter until the night before that he has a race to run. He obsesses, he won't sleep well, and he'll ask me fifty times when the race is. I've learned when there's an important upcoming event to wait until the last minute, or at least as late as I can to tell him, for his own good. We joked about this yesterday when I told him that Jim Hilliard would be picking him up at 6:30 am to run a 9:00 race in Kent.

"Tomorrow?!" he exclaimed. And he did exclaim. He literally pivoted on his heel and went upstairs. I knew what he was doing. He so desperately wants to finish this goal of running all 169 towns and is terrified he won't. He was preparing. Getting every little thing ready. He came down 30 minutes later with a laundry basket about half full of shirts and socks and underwear and caps and a water bottle.

He smiled at me, and I smiled at him and we had a secret little laugh as we were both poking a little fun at him and his laundry basket. Being prepared is certainly better than not being prepared. I looked through his extensive basket and said, "Don't forget you'll need your running shoes."

"I don't have any," he responded.

"Go check on the floor in front of your closet, they're gray and green" I nudged.

He came back down with his shoes, and we looked in the basket again to make sure everything was there. "What about running shorts?" I asked. "I don't have those" he shrugged. We laughed again as I said, "Are you gonna run in your underwear?"

"Shut up," he joked, and he went back upstairs to dig through the piles of clothes around our bedroom. Success! He came down with a pair of running shorts and an extra pair just in case.

He talked about the race and asked questions about it periodically throughout the day and when we went to bed asked what time we needed to get up. I promised him I would set three alarms so we would wake up on time.

The alarm screamed at six and I sat up and told Peter it was time to get up. "For what?" he asked. "Jim will be here in thirty minutes to pick you up for your run." And he popped out of bed.

I urged Jim not to, but he insisted on driving north from where he lives, to pick Peter up only to drive him back down south and then back home. A total of over three and a half hours just driving! Hero status for sure. Three races to go!

Much love, Lisa and Peter

On September 2, 2019 I received a message from Lori Riley, a sportswriter who has been writing for the local newspaper, the *Hartford Courant,* for 30 years. Lori told me that she was interested in writing a story about Peter's accomplishment of running all 169 towns in Connecticut. Lori is a member of Run 169 Town Society and has completed all the towns.

She gave me her phone number and asked me to call her so we could chat. I did not call her. I'm not sure why, I guess I thought she wasn't serious, and the idea would go away, and I was busy, and it was Labor Day and

I brushed her off.

September 30th, she messaged me again. "Do you think you could call me this afternoon or evening so we could talk about a story?"

Hmmm? I guess she's serious, I thought to myself, and I did call her that afternoon.

That call was the beginning of an eye-opening and heartwarming experience that I feel blessed to have been a part of. For the next three months or so, Lori immersed herself into our lives to truly get to know Peter and understand who he was. I never realized how much work and heart goes into a story. I can't speak for other writers, but Lori was all in.

Lori had done the work to prepare for her story with hour-long casual visits accompanied by a photographer, Kassi Jackson. Lori and I had a quiet lunch together, she and Kassi joined us for a meet and greet with our new grandson and they attended rainy race days. All this effort was to gather information, take photos and understand our story. Lori even became Peter's weekly running partner, pushing him to hit the pavement on the cold days he didn't want to.

After Peter and Lori ran, they'd hang around the kitchen for a while cooling down and yucking it up about who pushed who up which hill and Peter was alive and bright. Lori would finish the hot tea she brought and the three of us casually shared the goings-on of the week and she became our friend. She helped Peter prepare for the final three races of the 169 challenge, and continued to run with him after his final race.

Once again, Jim Hilliard came to Peter's rescue and ran him through the finish line of both races 167 and 168 in October. Gentleman that Jim is, he always let Peter cross the finish line first so that in the event they won in their age group Peter would be ahead. Peter and Jim won second and third places respectively in the 167th race, in the category of Men 50-59.

Peter had been working on his goal for five years and he had one race to go! The racing community was aware of Peter's disease, and they were busy planning for his celebration. Family and friends were excited to cheer Peter on, our spare bedrooms were spoken for by out-of-town guests, purple T-shirts were designed and printed, and we were ready! It's customary to wear a tutu on your last run and Peter's chosen blue tutu had arrived. This goal had taken such perseverance and dedication on Peter's part. I was so proud of this accomplishment and couldn't wait to celebrate his victory!

The week before and the day before and the night before Peter's big race, emails and texts, and calls came flooding in with good wishes from those who couldn't attend and excitement from those who could. Anticipation was building and butterflies would come and go, and the energy was positive and high as we were surrounded by so much love.

As the runners walked to the starting line, I followed 20 or 30 feet behind them, walking alone with my umbrella when someone came up from behind and touched my elbow. "Lisa Marshall," he said, and I knew immediately that it was David. He had driven three hours from Albany to support Peter.

"Omg, you're here!" I said.

"I wouldn't be here if it wasn't for Peter! I had to come." On a work trip to Mexico several years ago, Peter saved David's life, pulling him from the ocean when he was unconscious and drowning.

The day was dotted with emotional moments like that one, but the vision of Peter crossing the finish line is indelible. It's seldom that you are surrounded by such gentle souls, such a supportive group of people. Six friends, Jill Levasseur, James Hilliard, Jim Mayo, Marc Scrivener, Kevin Hellbusch, and Mike Reed, declared that they would be running the race with Peter and that is exactly what they meant, with Peter. They ran at Peter's pace. When Peter stopped, they stopped. When Peter ran hard, they ran hard. Together they surrounded him as he accomplished his goal of running his 169th town.

As they crossed the finish in a straight line, the bagpipes played and cowbells clanged, friends and family clapped and cried. Hearts soared with pride of Peter's accomplishment and the compassion of so much support. And hearts cracked a bit at the uncertainty of what would come next in our lives.

From the blog on December 20, 2019, two months later:

Last night as Peter and I lay in bed chatting at the end of the day as we do, we talked about Lori for a good long while. How lucky we are to have met her and how simply she became our friend. She's met all our children, and our sweet Grandson, she's met our closest friends and she's certainly seen me at my worst, right out of bed before a full cup of coffee.

She's kind and she's humble. Her heart is large. She's genuine, fun-loving and she's easy. She's easy to love and we're so grateful to have gotten to know her and proud to call her our friend.

Lori's story will be in the Hartford Courant *this Sunday. I'm anxious to read it. I didn't ask her if I could get a sneak peek before it was printed because I want the whole experience of opening the paper and finding the story and bursting with pride reading about my husband.*

As you read it, please read it appreciating all the time and dedication Lori put into getting to know us to be able to portray Peter as I'm certain she did.

You'll find Lori's story in the resource section at the back of the book. She lovingly describes the details of her friend Peter's big day and I'm forever grateful to have this keepsake. Now and again, I take the laminated copy out of the drawer and read her words. They wake up memories that sleep and I am taken back to one of the best days of my life.

Wendy and Lori, Jim, and Jill continued to take Peter on runs when he was able and on walks when he could no longer run. They were kind and patient and adjusted as Peter declined. I would tease Peter often when one of the women would arrive, "Oh one of your girlfriends is here!" and he would grin a shy grin or laugh. These people made Peter's life richer and I am forever in their debt.

Less than five months later, on April 20, 2020, I posted this passage to the *Oh Hello Alzheimer's* blog:

We were blessed with a very chilly night this week and to top it off a bit of snow. Peter was cold and I suggested he put his robe on that he received at his 169th race and he smiled and went right upstairs to bundle up. He came back without it, and I wasn't surprised he forgot what he went up for, and he came back downstairs not even realizing he had forgotten something.

I went upstairs to retrieve the robe for him, and he laughed when I held it out in front of him. He stood up and put his arms in and tied the belt around his waist. He was proud like he is every time he wears it and he started reminiscing about that day.

He talked about the crown and the rain and James Hilliard and I interjected, "It was so cold!"

Peter's face lit up and he leaned toward me with a huge grin and asked excitedly, "Were you there? Did you see me?"

Lisa's Lookback

The perseverance and determination it took for Peter to complete this challenge is nothing short of a miracle. Looking back on his accomplishment, he continues to push me to be better and follow through even when times are tough. For instance, writing this book. It's one of the most emotionally exhausting things I've done, recounting so much sadness, but I persevere because of Peter's example. He continues to guide me as I often find myself wondering what Peter would do. He continues to inspire me.

Questions to Ponder

1. What inspires you to keep caring for your loved one, even when things are difficult?

2. When you've persevered through your loved one's Alzheimer's journey, what will your reward be?

3. Do you find comfort in your memories rather than just grief?

CHAPTER 18

Reflection Ralph

Lying on our bed, I sunk into the memory foam and took a deep breath, the deepest of the entire day, and exhaled all of it, trying to rid myself of the horror. Eyes closed, arms overhead, I commanded each muscle to relax independently while Peter showered. Basking in a few quiet moments, until I was called upon again for turning off the shower and holding pajama pants open for his step, and helping him to brush his teeth.

I listened to the water hitting the bathtub floor and heard my bald husband emptying yet another bottle of my coveted curly hair conditioner into his palm. I knew it was running through his fingers. I took another deep inhale to remind myself it was just stuff, just conditioner. The shower curtain slid open, and the rings screamed across the metal bar followed by the usual blather, "Where is she? Hello? I don't have anything!" Peter's voice continued to grow louder until he realized he was not alone, and I listened intently to a new muffled conversation. Curious, I snuck a peek through the door to see who he was talking to.

The conversation was real to Peter as he bantered with the new person in the mirror. When he saw me, he jolted, "We were just talking about school."

"Ok, let's get you dressed." I was not sure how else to respond.

Peter no longer recognized the reflection looking back as himself. That memory, since he recognized himself as a young twenty-something now, is gone. The man in the mirror appeared older than Peter. To watch, to immerse in this fantasy with Peter was gut-punching and heart-wrenching, yet comical at times. We named our new friend Reflection Ralph, Ralph for short, and sometimes Peter called him "Raft." Peter didn't know who he was or why he was visiting but Ralph is everywhere, in every reflection; mirrors, appliances, dark windows, whether we were home, in the car, or out somewhere. Ralph was always with us.

When Ralph first appeared, Peter would sneak into the bathroom to speak to him privately and, trying to understand this new phenomenon, I'd ask, "Who are you talking to?" Then one day it happened. Grinning and whispering tiptoeing quietly and motioning wildly for me to follow, Peter summoned me to the bathroom for the formal introduction. The blood rushed from my heart up through my face and I tried to remain calm. After all, Peter was watching my every expression for any reaction, or confirmation. As usual, when I need just a sec to swallow the emotion and slow my mind to think quickly, I gulped a deep breath and drew that magic marker smile with my biggest, fattest sharpie.

Nodding my head, eyebrows raised, I assured him "It's you!" This is not at all what I was supposed to say because that is ludicrous, and we never, never, never, argue with a person with dementia. Alzheimer's 101. Trying to convince a demented person that their reality is skewed will only cause stress to both caregiver and loved one. Simply meet them where they are and join their journey. It's a constant game of pretending. Immediately I backpedaled and told Ralph how nice it was to meet him and suggested the two men get together sometime, joining Peter's reality. Peter was perplexed as Ralph didn't answer my invitation and I suggested that perhaps Ralph is shy and just needs some time. Peter agreed.

One morning I heard Peter in the family room where a very large mirror hangs on the wall. This was one of Peter and Ralph's favorite places to hang out.

Their conversation was quite loud and so I snuck a look to see what they were talking about. Peter's hands were motioning to his friend to come with him, desperately encouraging him, "Come on, you can do it." He continued his compassionate cry to Reflection Ralph, arms above his head speaking emphatically, "I'll help you!" Ralph's quietness and lack of motivation frustrated Peter, but he remained persistent.

Many people who suffer from Alzheimer's or related dementias will become fearful of their reflection. They may not recognize the person in the mirror if they don't understand the expression on their face. This can cause some people to become frightened of their reflection and react with surprise or shock or fear as they may only understand happy expressions. Covering the mirrors or taking them down is a popular strategy. Fortunately, Peter never became frightened of Ralph and he remained a confidant to Peter.

The microwave was another popular meeting place for the pair. One time I was cleaning up the kitchen island after lunch and Peter's face was inches away from the microwave, entranced in a whispering dance with Ralph. Peter pointed over his shoulder at me and was tattling to Ralph. I couldn't quite make out his words but finally, I said jokingly, "I'm right here, I can hear you!" and Peter burst into laughter, bent over at his waist.

Anxiety and fear cloaked Peter often and we learned coping skills to quiet his mind or perhaps just momentarily distract it. As Peter became more restless, I constructed a basket of things, memories for Peter to find and rifle through at his leisure, it's a marvelous way of finding forgotten treasures. He hadn't paid much attention to the basket, but occasionally he would move it from one special spot to another, so he felt its value was great.

He was looking for a golf ball and started searching in the basket. Peter spent almost three hours with the special things, wondering, searching, looking, fiddling, and questioning. One of the items was a small photo album I made for him 10 or maybe 12 years ago. It contains photos of our adventures and on the opposite page, the words express something I love about Peter. For instance, "Your blue eyes are so kind, I simply cannot stop staring into them," or "My favorite memories of us are on a dance floor, whether grass or tile or mud. Twirl me!"

I gave it to Peter as an anniversary or perhaps a birthday gift. It was chucked aside after it was received and who knew it would be so monumental now? Peter brought it to me and said, "I need your help." He was struggling to read the captions. I had trouble reading the words I had written too and sobbed as I read them. I decided one page was enough for the day.

Peter continued to look through the book and he settled for a long while on a picture of us on our wedding day. In the photo, Peter cradled me high in his arms, on a beach in Turks and Caicos and the day is a glorious memory for me but new for Peter. He brought it to me, and I told him about our day in as much detail as he could handle, and we wept together. And then we wept some more.

We held each other so tightly and Peter said, "This sucks!" in a moment of clarity as if he understood what was happening knowing he couldn't stop it or help or change anything. My heart sunk and agony washed over me. Grief.

Peter disappeared and after an appropriate amount of worrying time, I went to look for him and found him in the bathroom, once again talking to Reflection Ralph in the mirror. He was sharing that wedding photo with his new friend and tears were streaming down his cheeks. Peter held the photo up to his reflection, pressing it against the mirror. As he showed our photo to his friend, he told him through his tears about our magnificent day.

I didn't care about what was right or wrong about how to properly handle the situation at that moment and I just ran to him with my heart bursting with so much pride and grief and love. I fell into his arms sobbing out loud, shoulders shaking, melting into his chest and Peter cried with me, holding me so tightly. He promised me then, as he rubbed my back, "Everything will be ok."

Ralph was in every reflection, and he was met with Peter's delight each time he visited. Peter did not recognize his image in photos or videos or a just-taken selfie and my heart ached when I witnessed this behavior, other times I felt thankful. Ralph kept Peter entertained for long periods while I was busy and this unlikely pair had the best times together!

One evening Peter had gone upstairs and was absent longer than I liked and so again, I tiptoed to see what he was doing, and as I approached our bathroom, I heard loud giggling. I snuck ever so quietly around the corner and slowly moved my head so I could just barely see what Peter was laughing at without being caught.

There he was, in front of the big bathroom mirror doubled over belly laughing, a grin sewn on ear to ear, and the water running furiously from the faucet. Peter was taking hands full of water and throwing them at Ralph. The mirror and sink were soaking wet, and I slowly rolled around out of view not knowing whether I should laugh or cry. My husband, my child, my love.

We were so deep into this disease that I could

hardly remember the us, from before we became these people. We were romantic and fun and funny and flirty and full of so much life and hope. We were none of those things now and my beautiful memories were thick with mud. I felt like a stranger to myself and as I looked in the mirror, I could almost relate to Peter's friend, Reflection Ralph. I hardly recognized the face staring back at me. Fearful, I wondered if there would be a day when I would once again be able to see the people that we used to be.

This is not the way I wanted to remember my prince, the love of my lifetime, my sweet friend. Clutching my heart, I cried almost begging that the ugliness this Alzheimer's bitch spat at us will fade and the architecture of our glorious memories will remain intact and return to me again. Now on the other side, I know the answer to this question, as the horrific memories fade and the older happier memories bubble up to greet me.

She has taken my prince, but she cannot take our beautiful love story.

Lisa's Lookback

Watching Peter communicate and confide in and encourage Reflection Ralph was such a bizarre experience, I felt the only thing I could do was inspire the relationship. There were few people Peter could confide in and feel safe with, but Ralph was a reliable pal and Peter knew where to find him. When they were together I could relax knowing Ralph would occupy Peter and Peter was happy. When we were in public, Peter would be surprised by his friend in a mirror. He would point to himself and laugh and exclaim something like, "You?! You're here!" and then delight in telling me his friend had joined us. People may look at us perplexed, but I'd simply smile and touch Peter gently. They understood. It simply became our way of life. I miss Peter and I miss Ralph, too.

Questions to Ponder

1. Are you able to resist arguing to join your loved one's journey?

2. How would you handle this behavior in public?

3. What if your loved one became frightened of the reflection in the mirror? How would you cope and what would you do to help your loved one?

CHAPTER 19

Forgetting Names and Faces

The support I received from people who stayed tuned in to the *Oh Hello Alzheimer's* blog while waiting for the next post was incredible and I didn't expect to feel so enveloped by love. It's one of the selfish reasons I kept writing. Comments came in constantly, people sharing their vulnerabilities and stories, memories, heartaches, and pain.

I've heard some horrifying stories from those whose loved ones passed on before Peter. Have you ever watched a scary thrilling movie with a pillow up to your face? Barely peeking over the top of the pillow so at any moment you can cover your eyes and not see what's happening? That's how I felt about reading those stories. I wanted to see, and I wanted to know what others had gone through so I could prepare for the down and dirty and not be surprised. Also, I wanted to not hear them, read them, or believe them.

During our Alzheimer's journey, I learned to keep a quiet expressionless face when challenged with a new shocking moment, so I didn't alarm or concern Peter about this new behavior. In reality, I could feel my heart pounding through my shirt, my breath quickening, my stomach knotting. The hardest moments for me were the unexpected instances when Peter forgot who I was.

I needed to be an actor pretending in Peter's fairy tale, appeasing his questions with answers he could understand. These answers were not always the ones I wanted to hear from my lips. The following stories are heartbreaking and I often begged for mercy and if not mercy, then grace to be able to guide Peter through the fog.

Peter began forgetting words that included the names of people he knew and loved. Names are words, just labels to identify someone or something. For instance, the word cup identifies something we drink from, and the word car is a thing that gets us from place to place. Peter knew what a cup was, and Peter knew what a car was, he just forgot the label of the item.

His memory needed a little help to connect the emotional dots to people's labels. Facebook profile pictures are excellent for this and are easily accessible at the moment. "Oh yeah, yeah, yeah." He'd say when the dots in his brain connected, and he recognized the person we were talking about. Peter's heart was huge and sweet and full of compassion, and he identified people with this heart, even if he didn't know your label. For a while, I asked friends and family to wear name tags. The name tags were helpful until Peter began to lose his ability to read.

Peter's labels disappeared quickly along with most of his vocabulary. He found ways to cope and communicate by describing the people he was talking about with the limited words he still had. I would remind our family and friends who may be feeling sad, "while your lovely name identifies you, you are more than that. You are all the experiences and images and feelings in Peter's mind. That is what he remembers!" Until he no longer did.

ANNE-MARIE

About a year after diagnosis Peter's sister Ann-Marie was in town from Maryland. Her son, David, Peter's nephew was pitching for Worcester Polytechnic Institute. She was in town, staying with their parents for a month so she could attend David's games.

Ann-Marie invited Peter to join her for the day. Peter always loved watching David play and he was retired, so he had plenty of time on his hands. She'd pick him up at 1:30 and they'd travel together to MA, watch the game, stop for dinner on the way home and Peter would be home around 9:30.

After work, I threw on my favorite pajamas, poured a glass of shiraz, grabbed the remote, and settled into my carefree night. 9:30 came and Peter walked through the door. He announced, "Look who's here." It was, of course, his sister Ann-Marie. We chatted for 30 minutes or so and then she left to go back to their parent's house about two miles down the road.

Since Peter retired, he visited his elderly parents every other day or so. He had stopped in to see them the next morning, after his day trip with his sister.

Later that evening he said to me, "I have to tell you something." He was very serious. I stopped what I was doing and approached him. I held his hand as I knew it was important. He told me in his language that ALL DAY LONG from 1:30 until 9:30 he did not know who he was with. He spent an entire day with this person. He told me he did not feel afraid, and that "she was so nice to me. She even helped me with the tip at the restaurant." When I asked him who he thought she was he told me he thought maybe she was a friend of David's.

Peter only admitted this because when he visited his parents that morning, Ann-Marie was there, in a familiar setting. The thing that wasn't familiar was her hair. She had changed the color of her hair from dark to light. When Peter saw her at his parents' house he knew immediately who she was and it had been Anne-Marie he had spent the day with. An aha moment!

As Peter shared this with me, my knees got weak. I could barely breathe. My heart raced. I tried with all my might to not let the tears come as I looked into his eyes.

He looked into my eyes with intention, confessing, and I smiled. I held him close to me offering an excuse, "Well she changed her hair!" He pulled me away from him by my shoulders with the happiest face and said laughing and relieved, "I know! It's yellow!"

GENE

Peter and I had been discussing Father's Day gifts for our dads as the holiday was coming up and what do you get an 80-something-year-old who has everything and wants nothing but more time? "I know him!" Peter exclaimed when I showed him a picture of my father, Gene. I pulled the picture up on my phone as a cue for Peter when he asked me, "Do you have some?" meaning do I have parents?

First, I explained that my mother had died over ten years ago, and Peter was outwardly empathetic as though it was his first encounter with the news. I, of course, did not correct his memory loss, rather I too pretended it was the first time I was telling him. We then talked about my father who lives in Pennsylvania and Peter has visited numerous times. My dad has also stayed at our home in Connecticut. Peter and Gene have worked on many house projects together and the three of us have spent quality hours together. During our Father's Day conversation, Peter could not remember my father.

I showed him the image on my phone, and he moved swiftly to the edge of his seat, sitting up tall with excitement. "I know him! He's yours?!" Peter exclaimed with absolute delight and innocent disbelief. It was warm and sweet and obviously, he had lovely feelings toward my father. He just forgot that this kind man was, in fact, my father.

CINDY

While visiting my sister and brother-in-law at their home in Tennessee, we were relaxing on the porch. Peter and I were a couple of days into our trip. We sat on the couch together, my sister Cindy on my right and Peter on my left. I leaned forward to retrieve my beverage, and Peter reached behind my back with his hand extended inviting Cindy to shake it.

Peter said, "Hi! I'm Peter. What's your name?" His words spilled out of his mouth and swirled around behind me, and I wondered if he was kidding. He was not. My sister, without missing a beat answered, "Hi. I'm Cindy."

Peter asked her then, "How do you know Lisa?"

I took a deep breath and sat very still.

Cindy replied happily and matter-of-factly, "She's my sister."

Peter leaned back to his side of the couch and said "Oh," in a that's nice sort of tone. I returned to my position against the couch's back. Cindy and I locked eyes and hearts and held back our tears as we blinked through the horror. It was unbelievable and sobering. When I asked Cindy to help me recall the incident, she told me it was the first time she realized Peter's deep decline. She shared with me that she felt bad for Peter, and she felt sad for herself. I felt that way, too.

ANDREA

For as long as I can remember I heard Peter say, "keep your eyes and ears open and know what's going on around you at all times." He'd warn our children as they walked out the door or when we talked to them on the phone. He'd urge me to heed his words as I went out with a friend or met a client. Peter learned it from his father.

Over the years his warning was shortened

sometimes, but we know the rest, "Keep your eyes and ears open" and the kids would roll their eyes and respond with a "yeah, yeah."

I hope they carry on the tradition and their loved ones roll their eyes, too. Peter's cognitive ears and eyes were no longer open as he lived in cloudy confusion. His clarity was long gone when his mother, Andrea died.

Peter did not know she was ill, nor did he know she died. It's the only gift Alzheimer's offered us. Peter never had to mourn the death of his mother and Andrea never had to mourn the death of her son.

THE PHOTO BOARD

Communication was getting more difficult each day and I desperately tried to understand who Peter was talking about or what he was trying to convey. It was truly exhausting. Peter and I would often give up and as his disease worsened we simply could not connect. It was as if we were speaking different languages and this disconnect frustrated me more than anything. I feared Peter would become too frustrated and just stop talking completely.

Part of the problem was Peter's declining vocabulary, including people's names. Thinking it might be helpful and perhaps get us to the person in his stories faster, I created a tool. Using a large piece of poster board, I constructed a collage of 25 pictures. The board contained family members and dear friends and included their names underneath their photos.

Peter was napping when I constructed the photo board and I was not expecting what happened when he saw the collage for the first time. His eyes lit up and he began pointing to these people, some of whom he had not seen in a while. Peter's brain thought that the board was virtual, and they were live, as if in a Zoom call or face time. He began talking to them, "Hey! Where have you been?" Peter could not understand why his friends and family members would not respond and continued to try to connect. I suggested perhaps they had poor reception. Peter loved the board and talked to his friends nearly every day.

LISA

We snuggled into bed and when we were lying face to face, I asked Peter if he knew who I was, because I'm a glutton for punishment I guess, and his reply was, "Not really." I accepted his answer deciding right then I'd never ask him again.

I told him my name and I said as a matter of fact, "I'm your wife, and I love you very much and I take care of you and keep you safe."

Peter said, "Thank you very much," rolled over and turned the light out.

In the morning I woke up and for the briefest moment, I forgot about the conversation the night before. But then there it was, and I took one very deep breath and took inventory of my feelings. I inventoried my heartache, my options, and what was best and worst, and I made this decision.

I decided to be grateful for what we had and not what we had lost. I greeted Peter with "good morning" and started making the coffee. He approached me with a tender kiss on my lips. My face and heart smiled simultaneously. I felt thankful for the health and strength to stay present and brave and muster heaps of courage when it was called for. I was grateful for Peter's kiss and his kindness, and the memories I could tell him about. I was grateful for the smile in his eyes and his heart and his oh-so-sweet nature. I was thankful for his gentlemanly way and the way he loved me and loved me so ferociously and fiercely.

I appreciated that I was fortunate enough to be

able to have retired and spend time with Peter, caring for him and to love him. With just a little attitude adjustment, I remembered, that I was the luckiest girl in the world.

Funny what you'll accept as normal when you're desperately trying to hang on to the man you love and support him and encourage him each day. We were on our way home from our Rhode Island cottage. Peter was giving me the turn-by-turn directions helping me navigate the well-worn path I knew like the back of my hand.

"Turn here. This is my street," he told me. We were approaching our house and Peter started to tell me about it in the best detail and words he could. "It's not big." He explained to me, "but it's quiet and all the people are nice." He showed me which driveway to turn into and stopped me at the appropriate place to park.

"Right here?" I asked. And he confirmed.

He quickly got out of the passenger side and ran to open my door. He then scurried to the dark porch fumbling with a lock he hadn't been able to open for months, trying his best to show me into his home. I rescued him and he was surprised I knew the door code. He walked through the door, holding it open and Peter welcomed me into his house with a swinging gesture of his arm. He turned on the lights and started telling me about his wife, who he called "she."

Have you ever overheard your partner speaking about you, bragging about you with pride and your heart swells and maybe you feel a little flushed with a tinge of pride or embarrassment?

We stood just inside the doorway of Peter's home, our home. He pointed out a partially built cabinet and started telling me all about how hard she was working on this piece and showed me how the wood was attached to the frame. He was proud of her, and he told me she was really smart. He also warned me that she was probably downstairs working on it right now so we shouldn't bother her.

He took me to the front door and peering out he showed me her garden and told me that she was not finished yet. She'll never be finished because she loves it! And he laughed, shaking his head. He then excitedly told me about the solar lights that were glowing along the walkway. "They weren't there. She put those in." He shared with me that if we went upstairs it looks "so pretty" looking down from the second-floor porch. Peter spoke of his wife with such sweet affection and pride and devotion.

We unloaded the car together and I suggested it was a good time for our showers. I started our routine, thinking Peter would snap out of it, but he interrupted and asked me to follow him. He pointed down the hallway where the door to one of our spare bedrooms was open and the light spilled into the hallway. "I'll be down there" he pointed as if to let me know where he'd be if I needed anything. With a lump in my throat and my heart racing I took his hand and told him we'd be sleeping in here, our bedroom. Then laughing with eyebrows raised he asked, "Are you sleeping in here, too?"

I went down the hall to turn the light off and found a pile, of four of his sneakers and some clothes on the floor. He not only thought I was a guest but planned to be a gentleman giving me his room, and sleeping in the spare room. It was surreal and sad and sweet all at the same time. It was Peter through and through, gentle and kind and even if he didn't know who I was, he knew he loved his wife. I was proud of him and fell a little more in love with him watching my prince Peter shine through. Adversely, another part of me wanted to pound my fists on his chest and scream "I'm here! I'm here! It's me! I'm right here!" He was looking right at me, but he couldn't see me.

A similar situation occurred after a boisterous Thanksgiving week filled with celebration and happy chaos. "I don't know where to put myself. Where are we? Are we leaving here? Where is everyone? Who's upstairs?" These are the questions I was posed while heating our Thanksgiving leftovers for two.

The kids had spent a ton of time with their Dad and me, helping and fixing, doing and lifting, playing and staying, laughing and eating, and just being. But now the house was quiet and different than it had been for a week. So, it was confusing.

The house, over the past seven days, was precisely how I like it, how I love it. Filled with decibels of twenty and thirty-something kids and one toddler. Life was filled with laughter, fun, and catching up. I was learning things about the kids that I felt I should already have known if I wasn't so consumed by the Alzheimer's bitch.

Cooking and eating, resting and taking walks, rifling through pictures and drinking wine, celebrating life together. I often find myself just watching all of them, breathing them in, and feeling so grateful, feeling the exact opposite of lonely.

We had the conversation again, as I tried to ground Peter. "We live here, together, you and me, this is our house. We're married. I love you very much. You're so safe with me."

I held his face and kissed his lips. I made him look at me, into my eyes, putting my face right in front of his. But he wasn't looking at me, he was looking for me.

Peter had many episodes of not recognizing me during our journey. It felt like a jab and it was sharp, it stung and it hurt all while it was tender and sweet. But mostly it's a punch to the gut that makes you paint on a quick smile and breathe in all the air you can while you bite the inside of your cheek without showing it. I just kept pushing the pain of it all down as hard as I could.

The picture was taken the autumn before, on one of our many walks around the lake where we live. We normally walk hand in hand or arm in arm and this day was chilly. Our moods were soft and calm, and we strolled at a slower than usual pace just enjoying the sights of the season. We talked about the changing trees and we ran into the usual walking neighbors and remarked about the changing weather. Leaves were brightening and squirrels were busy and the air was crisp.

I decided to snap a picture of the day as it was the first winter hat day and I was feeling melancholy about saying goodbye to summer but hello to more snuggly couch time. We agreed we liked the picture and thought perhaps instead of cramming a collage of pictures onto our holiday card this year, we'd use something casual like this one. A picture that represents us well.

Peter presented me with the old holiday card wearing a huge smile on his face and my heart leaped. I could not wait to hear which part of our walk he may have remembered and wanted to reminisce about! "She's so nice, I really like her," he said so sweetly to me, as he pointed to the woman in the winter hat.

The same thing happened one day after babysitting our grandson. I was going through the tons of videos and pictures I took throughout his visit, immersing myself back in our joy-filled day. I turned the phone toward Peter and shared with him especially cute or funny videos.

We had taken Sonny for a walk in his stroller and he was getting way too somber for my taste, so I scooped him out of his buggy to tease out some giggles. I threw him up on my shoulders, but soon found I was having as much fun as Sonny!

I snapped a picture of us with our laughing smiles and showed it to Peter later. He took the phone out of my hands, pointed at my face, and said, "OH! Yes! I know her! I don't get to see her much!" I didn't ask him any questions or offer that the woman in the photo was me. I wonder who he thought I was when he didn't know I was his wife. Was it that he didn't recognize the laughing woman in the photo because I often wear a sad face?

As Peter's Alzheimer's progressed, I learned that his brain would slow down before his body. We had had a busy day together doing our usual doings of yard work and we enjoyed a long lunch on the porch, and sometimes my energy level far exceeded Peter's. Sometimes I push too hard as we've always been energizer bunnies together, working tirelessly to tackle the task at hand.

I decided to stop when I realized Peter's confusion was increasing. I made an early dinner so we could just relax in front of the TV afterward. Sitting next to one another at our kitchen island, we ate dinner per usual and Peter asked me, "Where are you from?"

As I customarily do, I repeated the question back so I could recover from the gut punch with a deep breath and a smile, "Where am I from?"

"Yeah," Peter said.

"Oh, I'm from Harrisburg. Where are you from?" I asked regaining composure.

"I don't know." Peter answered.

I put my arm around him and kissed him a dozen times until he felt grounded and smiled and I said, "Well, we're from here now."

Peter smiled and simply said, "Yeah."

Often, I had to remind myself to play along. It's just a game of pretending, and we used to play it with the kids all the time, making up stories. I had lots of practice, but this time I held my breath as it unfolded right there before my eyes. I felt panicked and completely calm and wide-eyed all at the same time.

Another day, the weather beckoned me back to the beach, and we jaunted out to do some winterizing in our RI cottage. I packed a picnic lunch to enjoy by the sea and everything was perfectly normal. Our newest normal. When we finished our chores and errands and snacks, locked up and hit the road back home. Per our new usual, Peter guided me home turn by turn, and when we were about 20 minutes into our trip home as we passed a Dunkin' Donuts. Peter asked me if I wanted to go to Dunkin' or if I wanted, I could go to his house. I took a breath and blinked my eyes and told him I would love to go to his house.

His directions became more acute, and as he guided me down the road he lives on once again. As we stopped at the stop sign in front of our home, he put both his hands out toward the house and exclaimed, "Here it is! This is my house!" I giggled with delight and told him it was lovely, and he directed me where to pull into his driveway.

As I put the car in park, Peter seemed nervous and struggled to get out of his seatbelt, so I reached over and pressed the button to release his belt. He jumped out of the car, his body and face were adorned with sheer excitement mixed with a tinge of embarrassment. He was smiling the biggest most boyish smile I've seen in years, "What's your name?" He asked.

"Lisa," I smiled.

"Lisa." He nodded grinning ear to ear, hearing it for the first time. And he showed me the way to the door of his house.

I assumed once we got inside things would click and be normal, so I turned on the TV, poured a glass of wine, and was about to sit down to relax. Peter came in and it was immediately clear that things had not clicked back to normal.

"What do you want to do?" he asked me, as if it was

his job to entertain me. I was taken aback and felt like shaking my head fiercely side to side jowls slapping back and forth to combat the cobwebs and comprehend the question. He was being such a good host to me. His guest.

"Do you want to see the water?" he asked me. I agreed with wide eyes, and off we went out our front door. My heart was beating fast as we walked down the driveway and thoughts were racing through my mind. I wanted to pound my fists on his chest and scream at him and beg his brain to remember me.

Instead, I took a very deep breath, and I made my mind push away the fear. I took another deep breath and ordered my heart and mind to open as wide as they possibly could to accept what was happening and immerse myself in this experience to make it the best it could be for both of us.

And as we walked down the road Peter told me this and that about the neighbors and how much he loves the town and the lake, and he took me to our boat launch. He urged me to feel the water and he introduced me to our lake beach and the island we had swum to many times over the years.

Afterward, he insisted we walk around the lake as he had more to show me and we asked each other questions as if getting to know each other, a sort of reset. "Are you married? Do you have a girlfriend?" I asked.

"No, it's just me."

He told me he liked to run and walk, and he did not work, since he was retired. He showed me house after house that he had worked on or almost bought and then he started asking me questions.

"Do you go to school here? What do you do when you're not here?" he wondered.

At one point, Peter eagerly offered me his coat when I mentioned it was getting chilly. I wanted so much to reach over and grab his hand and hold it but his innocence stopped me. I didn't want to scare him so I walked beside him with my hands in my pockets.

Peter was kind and cordial and interesting and informative, the most gracious guide and host. My heart smiled as I witnessed this out-of-body experience and watched him genuinely engaging this stranger, me. He was confident and curious and relaxed and happy. I watched us and with my heart and mind very open I was reminded of the man I fell in love with as we walked for an hour watching the sunset over the lake, enjoying our date.

When we got home, I turned on the TV and sat down to relax. Peter sauntered over to me with a huge smile on his face as I was sitting on the couch. He leaned down placing one hand on each side of me on the couch, his face close to mine. He kissed me and said, "This is how I kiss all the girls!"

Lisa's Lookback

It didn't matter how prepared I thought I was. I had done the research and knew what others had experienced from the stories they told me, I felt prepared. But when my husband, my lover, my friend, the person who knew me better than anyone on earth suddenly forgot who I was, it was nearly unbearable. Every day of our lives we made memories, we lived our life fully and filled it up to the brim. Peter's memory cup had a hole in the bottom, and he was forgetting all our precious memories, one at a time until he forgot me, too. Peter was the person I felt safest with. The keeper of my fears and joys and secrets. The keeper of me. I felt naked and vulnerable without him, even though his body was still with me.

Questions to Ponder

1. Can you pretend? Can you join your loved one's journey when and if they forget who you are?

2. How would you advise your friends and family members to respond if your loved one forgot who they were?

3. Could you keep a huge secret, like the death of your loved one's mother, from them to protect them?

Encourage

"Encourage:
To inspire with courage,
spirit or hope."

-Merriam-Webster Dictionary

CHAPTER 20

The Power of "Let's"

No matter what stage of Alzheimer's your loved one is in, they will require more and more help along the way. When you ask or tell someone with Alzheimer's to do a thing, they must take on the heavy responsibility so as not to disappoint if they cannot complete it. The burden is sometimes unbearable and gets in the way of completing the task successfully which leads to feelings of inadequacy.

Peter would feel an overwhelming sense of obligation as though he must get it right. He would come back to hear the instructions again and again and he would repeat them to himself on his way to tackle the job. This is stressful for the caregiver as well, having to repeat the forgotten instructions and watch your loved one struggle.

But what if we say, "Let's." Let's do the thing. Let's do the thing together. The power of "let's" is incredible! I could lead and guide and virtually hold Peter's hand as we tackled the task together and he didn't have to bear the burden of the responsibility, but he did get to feel a sense of accomplishment. You might argue that this method takes more time and energy, but does it?

Let's play out the opposite scenario. You ask your loved one, "Will you do the thing?" and off he goes and what do you do? You listen intently wondering when the appropriate time is to step in to help. Or you get frustrated when he comes back a third time to hear the instructions again, "I'm sorry, I forgot," Peter would say. Emotions are all over the place from frustration to guilt and doesn't that suck the energy right out of you? You probably end up doing the thing yourself anyway and isn't that more time spent than doing it together?

"LET'S do the thing" on the other hand allows you to remind and teach both your loved one and yourself to be kind and gentle and oh so careful with your love. And when the thing is done you'll enjoy a happy feeling of confidence from accomplishing it together. And isn't that energizing?

While it was energizing for me, I sometimes felt frustrated because my time was consumed by helping Peter and I was not accomplishing the things I needed or wanted to. I had to learn to let go of anything that was not critical and reframe my priorities so I would not resent Peter for this.

We had recently joined the ranks of those who get their trash picked up rather than taking it to the dump as we always had. It was difficult for Peter to understand what was recycling and what was trash but he knew to stop and ask me which container something went into. He would bag up the kitchen trash and then ask me, "Which bucket?"

"Green. Say green the whole way out to the can. LOL," we'd joke.

It's a short walk out the kitchen door, across the deck, and to the cans which are directly under a window. I was usually in the kitchen when he took the trash out, so I'd dart over to the window to assist. Peter would look up to the window and point to one of the cans for confirmation.

"This one?" he'd ask before depositing. This method helped Peter to be independent enough to feel accomplished, even though he needed assistance. He needed assistance with almost every task.

I had just come home from a long work day and I was tired and met Peter in the kitchen. I asked him what he had done with his day. He told me that he watered the flowers, went for a run, and visited his parents. "But I only have this much," he said concerned and holding his thumb and forefinger apart just a bit. "So, I didn't want to go anywhere."

"Do you mean gas?" I asked.

"Yes!" he pointed at me with wide eyes. More charades. Peter mentioned his empty gas tank three more times during the course of making and eating dinner. I knew he was bothered by the tank being empty.

I wanted to say it out loud, "I'm sick of this shit. You can't even do the smallest thing. Why can't you get gas yourself? You had all day!!! I worked all day and I'm tired! You've done it a million times before, why can't you do it today. I just cooked your dinner, and all I want to do is sit down and relax and watch TV! Furthermore, it's cold and it's raining! I don't feel like going out! You're such a burden!"

I did not say any of these things, but some caregivers do, or at least think them. They're pushed to the limit and don't take proper care of themselves in order to take care of others.

Your loved one has the very same feelings, if not even more intensified, that he or she has always had. They appreciate your patience and support more now than ever. I found a feeling of great pride in being able to remain calm and patient and loving. Coupled with Peter's happiness, it was all I needed to get me through some challenging moments.

Here's what really happened. This took only eleven minutes, eleven. We finished eating dinner and we were drying the dishes together. I said, "Do you want to go fill your car up with gas?"

"Oh! Yes! That would be great!" Peter said and he was so appreciative of the offer.

I grabbed the keys and we drove to the local gas

station. I was faced with more choices upon arrival.

Peter and I got out of the car and met at the pump. I could have easily and hurriedly filled the tank for Peter. Instead, we accomplished the task together, calmly. Together we found the Visa card in Peter's wallet, read the prompts on the screen and I guided him through the steps helping him to decipher whether to push yes or no. I showed him the numbers to push that made up our zip code for credit card verification and helped him to select the fuel grade and where to insert the nozzle in the car.

I felt it was always vital to find the balance of helping Peter but not enabling him by doing everything for him. If he was able, I wanted to give him every opportunity to be challenged. When doing things together, we were both happy instead of frustrated or upset. Patience and kindness win every single time! I firmly believe if you do the work on yourself you can more patiently help your loved one as these unexpected changes in ability occur.

It's unknown until it happens. I expected that Peter could do a thing just as he always had been able to and then he couldn't. He would become confused and ask questions repeatedly about something simple he knew or remembered before. Peter, being the sweet soul that he was, would sneak out early in the morning while I was fast asleep and surprise me with a cup of Dunkin' coffee when I stumbled out of our bedroom.

There are many, many steps to the Dunkin' run that we took for granted. Peter reached a point when he could no longer handle the task on his own. Dressing in appropriate clothing for the day was confusing, finding the keys, driving a car, finding Dunkin', remembering the order, handling money, and finding his way home.

Peter's decline was rapid and many things that used to be easy were becoming too difficult. When Peter's mind was sound, he was an engineer with an engineer's mind, and he could design and create anything his wonderful mind could conjure up. Always looking for a solution to anyone's problem, he would not only find that solution, but it would exceed all expectations because Peter held himself to a very high standard. He hated "hack" work and felt strongly about doing his best every time.

Peter owned every hand tool and power tool you can imagine and loved working with wood and his mind, building or improving anything he could. He would spend hours in the basement absorbed in his imagination and he was the handiest and most helpful person I've met in my life.

Peter asked me to come to take a look at the door that leads outside to the back deck. He shook the door handle to show me that it was loose. "Oh, it just needs to be tightened," I said and asked him to go get a Philips screwdriver, wondering what he would bring back. A few minutes later Peter appeared with an adjustable wrench and a garden pruner. He approached the door handle with his inappropriate tools, and I joined him at the door. "Hey, I'm not sure that's the right tool for the job. Let's go find a screwdriver."

We held hands and together went to the big red tool chest and there in the top drawer was every size Phillips screwdriver you could ever need. I chose an appropriate size and handed it to him and took the wrench and the pruner. We went back upstairs, and I left him in charge of the task. He tightened the doorknob perfectly and then put the screwdriver back in the drawer downstairs.

It was miserable for me, watching my love, seeing his talents disappear. He had so much to teach, and I have learned so much from Peter. What an absolute horrific waste of such a beautiful mind. It was eye-opening and frightening and it sucked and I wanted to scream, "We've been robbed!"

Peter's sharp declines were coming more frequently, and I compared it to a staircase. The top of the staircase represented our old perfect normal. Each step down in this mammoth staircase was another new normal with a decreased level of cognitive awareness and an increased level of confusion.

The simplest of tasks seemed to spin Peter into a fog as though he had never experienced them before. It started in the morning and I had gotten up an hour or so before Peter and scurried around the house doing this and that after brewing our coffee. I expected him to be up long before he was and had prepared his yogurt and fruit and poured his coffee. It was quite a while before he woke up and the coffee got cold. When he took his first sip, I asked Peter if his coffee was cold and he said it was.

"Put it in the microwave" I suggested, and I watched to see how far he could get, knowing I would most likely need to help. Peter stood up, walked to the refrigerator and carefully placed his mug on the top shelf, and closed the door. I must admit that I giggled because I couldn't help it. Peter looked at me quizzically and I explained the problem and he laughed, too.

He stood in front of the microwave and said, "What do I do?"

"Open the door," I said.

"How?" he questioned.

"Push the button on the bottom right" I instructed. The door flung open and I could hear the cheering in my head, success! He placed his mug in the microwave, shut the door then looked over his shoulder at me, waiting for my next instruction.

"See the round knob? Turn it to 45." I knew this was the end but tried to wait it out just before he became frustrated. Peter looked at me confused and I got up and turned the knob for him. Then, like instructing a toddler

I said, "Push the big button."

Later the same day I was washing dishes left from the night before and I asked Peter to dry them. This is one task he could do well and still feel capable. I wash from right to left, stacking clean dishes on a mat on the counter. Peter dried all the dishes leaving one wooden spoon lonely on the mat. "Would you mind drying that wooden spoon?" I asked.

"How do I do that?" Peter replied.

I handed him the drying towel and said, "Just rub the water off of it like you did the other dishes." He started drying the spoon and asked if this is what I meant as though he had never dried a dish in his life.

That evening I was cleaning up after dinner and asked Peter to feed the dogs, something he had done hundreds of times. "How do I do that?" He asked.

"Just feed the dogs. Put food in their bowls." I reminded as the dogs pranced around excited about their dinner.

"Where is it?" he wondered.

"The food?" I asked and he confirmed, gesturing. I escorted him to the cupboard and told him to feed each dog a cup of food and walked out of the room. A few moments later he was in the kitchen with the two dog bowls and he said, "What should I do?"

How could this be happening? I thought. My brilliant husband, my love, their father, their stepfather their brother, their son, their friend.

Getting ready for bed, I was in the bathroom brushing and flossing and doing all the before-bed things. Peter joined me at the sink and started unbuckling his bulging toiletry bag where he now kept his every little thing. He carried this travel bag from room to room for months.

He found the toothpaste and unscrewed the cap and as I watched in disbelief, he raised the tube to his lips

225

and started squeezing toothpaste right into his mouth.

I gently handed him his toothbrush interrupting his minty snack and said, "Here's your toothbrush, brush your teeth."

Peter replied, "I already did."

I took two flossing picks out of the bag and put his on the sink in front of him while I started flossing, watching him out of the corner of my eye. He finished brushing his teeth and promptly picked up the flossing pick and started shaving his face and trimming his ear hair with it. Gently and slowly I guided his hand to his mouth and showed him what I was doing so he could mimic me, and he did.

Another day, Peter and I were in the backyard of our home, Peter sweeping the deck and moving things around, I was weeding and planting some new flowers in a bed that needed some love. When I finished, I was putting the tools away and said to Peter pointing, "I'm going over here to put these tools away. Do you want to come?"

Peter said, "yeah" but kept on sweeping and looked back down. He was busy and safe, so I quickly walked up the path on the left side of our house to put the tools on the potting bench. While I was closer to the front of the house, I noticed a few other things that needed tending and scurried to finish them so I could get back to Peter. The elapsed time was maybe three minutes.

In that time, Peter panicked and could not find me and did not remember that I told him where I was going, of course. He promptly went in through the back door of the house frantically searching for me inside and could not find me, so he went to the front door. For his protection, the front door has a deadbolt, doorknob lock, a slide lock at the top, and a childproof handle cover.

Peter could not open the front door and he was unaware that I was just around the corner. That became very apparent when anxious Peter started frantically knocking on the inside of the front door. I rushed to greet his face peering through the glass and saw his expression of fear and so I grinned the biggest grin I could and waved assertively. Peter grinned, too, and put his hand on his chest, relieved.

I could not get in the front door because of the locks, so I calmly told him I was going to go around, motioning with my hands. "Go outside, I'll meet you on the deck" I smiled, knowing he wouldn't understand. I hoped it might distract him for a few seconds. Jolting down the path, I dashed up the deck steps and then slowed to saunter through the back door to find Peter still looking out the front door. "Hey, Mister! Did you miss me?" I joked to lighten the mood as I snuck up behind him.

Peter swung around surprised and said, "I couldn't see you!" He dove towards me, wrapping his big arms around me so tight.

I was beginning to feel concerned for his safety as he was becoming more and more glued to my side. One morning, Peter came out of the bedroom dressed in a golf shirt, cargo shorts, sneakers, and a ball cap. He stood tall, his voice was deep and he confidently announced in a rather loud tone, "I'm going for a run."

It was so unexpected that I started laughing and said "Oh! Are you now?" This may have been ok if we were in Connecticut, as he's run those roads forever and I wouldn't worry. However, we were in Rhode Island, where we were next to a major road and Peter didn't know the roads.

"Where are you going to run?" I quizzed calmly.

"I'm just gonna go," he said.

I suggested I drive him to the beach, and he could run along the water, or perhaps he could run several laps around the neighborhood, but he didn't like my suggestions. He started backing out of his plan and I could tell he was upset and felt defeated.

We were expecting some of the kids within the hour, so time was critical. I marched him into the bedroom, helped him into his running clothes, and put him in the car. I knew of a long country road about four or five miles away that would be perfect, and I wasn't taking no for an answer! This run was going to set his mood for the entire day!

When we arrived, I pulled over on the side of the road and said, "Ok! Get out and start running! Go straight and I'll follow you!" He laughed, got out of the car, and off he went. I followed behind him slowly, passed him a few times, and pulled over to wait for him to catch up. When Peter had had enough running, he got in the car. We drove home with full hearts, wearing our happiness on our faces, windows down, breeze blowing, and Peter was so grateful.

As caregivers, we are constantly reacting and evolving and adapting and adjusting to the pranks of the Alzheimer's bitch. I decided to let go of house cleaning and lawn mowing and sheet changing and all that minutia to focus more on lingering longer in the sweet moments of life. I learned to ask for help as it was becoming clearer as Peter declined that our remaining time was limited and precious.

More hand-holding and blueberry picking, and lake jumps and beach walks. More time with friends and family and certainly more kissing and dancing and yard games like corn hole and ladder ball and washer toss. More cuddling and lake walks and hikes and less screen time.

I committed to focusing on what Peter could do independently and the rest we'd do together. Let's fill the birdfeeders, let's do the dishes, let's water the garden, let's sweep the deck, let's go get the mail, let's take the trash out, let's do it together.

I woke up fresh and energetic after a rare good night's sleep. I was getting dressed and going over my to-do list in my head. Peter started talking and I couldn't understand what he was trying to say, and this horrid thought entered my mind that I had never felt before.

I could feel the energy drain as my shoulders fell slightly forward and my eyes dimmed a bit and my step turned not so springy. *No, not this again,* the thought begged, and I felt the morning wind come right out of my sails. It was so deflating and exhausting. But I knew I had to continue to inspire courage and confidence in Peter, so he didn't give up.

When we did connect after a big round of charades or I understood a word from Peter's made-up vocabulary, it was rewarding. One morning I was on my laptop and Peter came up behind me and kissed the top of my head and said, "I luck you."

I looked up at him and said, "I luck you, too."

We laughed.

Lisa's Lookback

This method of encouraging Peter took practice, but over time it became very clear that it was the only way to exist. Doing everything together, the constant interruptions and popping up from what I was doing, was draining, but it was also rewarding. I knew it was the gentlest way to keep Peter engaged, spend time together, and get things accomplished. I likened it to caring for a toddler who is learning new concepts and enjoyed a feeling of pride when Peter felt successful. This period diminished too, and ultimately Peter could do very little, even with help. I have no regrets, knowing that together we forged through the hardest of times.

Questions to Ponder

1. Are you able to replace feelings of resentment and anger with kindness and patients to guide your loved one through the most basic of tasks?

2. How do you keep your emotions in check and not lash out as your life is being consumed by helping your loved one?

3. What are you doing for your health to keep your energy level up as your loved one needs more and more help?

FAST Scale Stage Five

*The happiest of people
don't have the best of everything,
they just make the best of everything.*

CHAPTER 21

FAST Scale Stage Five

The slightest thing triggered the daily tears as I watched Peter disappear. Stage five is defined as needing assistance choosing the proper clothing for the day, season, or occasion. Peter was losing other skills and abilities as well. We had arrived and like quicksand, Peter was powerless against the relentless grip of the Alzheimer's bitch.

I watched in disbelief as Peter read a paper printed with instructions out loud to himself. They were upside down. This was the day's emotional trigger and Peter noticed the sadness leaking out of my face and came to me as he always has. As he rubbed my back, I allowed myself a rare and freeing cry burying my face in his chest and he so clearly assured me, "We still have time." I wanted so badly to believe him.

Peter was sitting firmly in stage five according to the FAST scale and the loneliness was creeping into our love. I was watching my partner fade away and my emotions were volatile. Some moments I was angry and others, just sad or devastated at the thought of my lonely future ahead.

After Peter retired, I continued to work for a year as I felt Peter was still safe alone. Each day I would leave for work Peter would stand on the porch and hold his arm high waving our "I love you" sign above his head. When we were out of earshot, we would signal to each other. With an outstretched hand, thumb holding middle and ring finger down, forefinger and pinkie standing tall, we'd wave our "I love you" to each other. He would watch me pull away and my heart ached to wonder what he was doing all day.

I wasn't able to contact him because he couldn't remember how his phone worked and most days we couldn't find it. Peter kept himself busy throughout the day and I tried to work from home as much as I could, minimizing the time away.

When I would arrive home from work, Peter was always sitting on the porch if it was warm enough. If not, he'd be waiting at the front door peering out. My heart would leap when I saw his big apple cheeks smiling at me, offering to help me carry anything I may need help with. Together again. Content. It's the place we always loved most.

I decided exactly one year after Peter retired, that it was my time to stop working too. Not knowing how much time we had left I decided the timing was right, and I wanted to make sure Peter was safe. One of the things that led me to make this decision was the lack of balance. I was trying to do too much and the pressure was getting to me.

The following paragraphs are snippets to give you a glimpse of how encompassing the deterioration is. Stage five seemed to last forever and while I never wanted to lose Peter I found myself starting to wish the disease would speed up. I had already lost the husband I married and I felt myself just wanting to get it over with, for both of us.[5]

Here's a blog post on *Oh Hello Alzheimer's* from the month before I made the decision to retire.

"I'M JUST SO SICK OF IT
Most days, I can breeze right through this new normal,

---

[5] I've spoken to many caregivers who allow these words, and thoughts, to pass over their lips in pure honesty. I'll speak about this more in a future chapter.

and leap over the hurdles and what keeps me going is that I made it through a difficult moment without getting impatient and I feel like I've conquered the Alzheimer's bitch once again.

The bitch is rearing her head more often and I'm so very desperate sometimes, like now. When you read this, I'll be fine, sleeping next to my incredible husband at five am on Saturday but right now it's Friday night I am far from fine. Far from using any sort of coping skills I have learned.

Sometimes it just surrounds me, sneaks up on me so fast I don't know where it came from and I feel so panicked and desperate knowing there isn't a fucking thing I can do to make this stop. I want our life back. I want my husband back. I want to argue and banter intellectually with him and play backgammon for hours or solve any problem together or beat him at Yahtzee and laugh while he's whining, but those days are gone now.

No matter how positive my attitude, no matter how hard I try to shrug things off or to let go of all the small stuff that just doesn't matter, I'm always just a bit sad. Even on the very best of days, there's a sadness, but I keep it cloaked very near to my heart so that the world will know how very strong and brave and remarkable I am.

But I'm not. I'm not strong or brave or remarkable. I'm human and right now I don't want to do this anymore. I'm just so sick of it. I want to scream so loud and kick and punch and take it from him. But I can't.

I share this pity party with you so you can share it with others who are caregivers. It's not pretty but it's real and I give myself permission to feel this way as long as I get back up and recover quickly."

I often felt panicked and afraid and I shared my emotions with Josephine Alexander, a remarkable woman I met through the blog. She offered this, "Sit with your fear. Show it who you are. It will slink away." Josephine Alexander told me in a message when I confessed my fear of my lonely future. I cried as we chatted. She is wise and brave and worldly and she is on the other side of this grotesque journey. I wrote this passage about my conversation with Josephine during this dark period of my life. I was afraid of death, fearful I could not be courageous, and panicked by the thought of loneliness.

She is colorful but she has shivered through the winter, the cold dark, gray, lonely winter of the end of Alzheimer's.

I am colorful. But my winter is coming.

I am strong. But will I be strong enough?

I am afraid. I am so afraid. I AM SO AFRAID. HELP ME. I'M SCARED. I'M SO SCARED!

An intense panic overwhelms me sometimes in the middle of the night and I leap from my bed and dart out of our bedroom trying to escape it. But I can't. I can't.

I want to forever feel his hand in mine and lay my cheek on his chest feeling his big hands covering my back, his lips on mine, and his heart beating in my ear.

I cannot sit with her.

I want so badly to be worldly and wise and see and show a bigger picture to those who will follow me and Jo. A vision of gratitude for my life and its lovely treasures but I feel only grief and the worst is yet to come.

I hate you. I hate you! I HATE YOU! I HATE YOU SO MUCH!

Every obvious decline was another shot to my heart. As he deteriorated, I worried about Peter's driving. When would it be time to take the keys for Peter's safety and for the safety of other drivers?

It was a Tuesday night and the house was quiet. Peter was golfing. I expected him home any minute when I received a frantic call from Chris Larsh, his golf partner. Chris was following Peter and his headlights weren't on and he was navigating his way home on the dark country roads.

I tried to reach Peter on his cell but he didn't answer. He was driving my car because his car was in for service and his phone wasn't hooked up to my bluetooth as he rarely drove it.

Chris was in a tiny panic and was worried for Peter's safety as was I. We chatted quickly about a future solution and Chris offered to drive Peter to golf on Tuesdays and I would pick him up at the golf course when he was finished. I just needed to sell that notion to Peter.

I knew I needed to curb Peter's night driving and when I told him he was furious. He stayed mad at me for 24 hours. This is not at all like him and it's extremely rare for him to be mad at me or anyone for that matter. Peter and I were on the deck and we were up later than we should have been soaking up the moonlight and soaking up another beverage we probably shouldn't have had. We were attempting to reconnect after the 24-hour bruising, he on his rocking chair, me on mine. I was treading lightly to gain access to his unhappy ego trying yet again to explain why he shouldn't drive at night or drive long distances.

"It's not the end of the world, I'm not taking your keys." *I'm just taking his pride,* I thought. "You can still drive locally and during the day, but you prefer me driving you to unfamiliar places like races, don't you?" I prodded.

He softened and regained a bit of eye contact and we sat quietly for a bit, and I knew he felt a little better. Sometimes silence was fine, and we could just be together and be peaceful, but not that night. The knife stabbed my heart and I didn't know what to do or say, hadn't prepared or imagined his question coming at me so sharply.

"How long?" He said in this hateful sort of slow monotone accusatory way and he glared at me deep in my eyes. I did not recognize this attitude and knew it was coming from the Alzheimer's bitch.

I immediately feared that I indeed knew what he was asking but I bought myself some time by pretending that I didn't. I didn't buy much time at all though because his next words came sharply, "Until I'm dead!" In that lucid moment, he knew he was dying.

I tried to use humor to distract him and said, "Well I'm not in charge of all that," but he wasn't interested in my antics, and he wanted a real answer, the truth. I rocked and he didn't. His arms were crossed. I took another sip of courage and thought back to the pages of articles I've read over the past few years and in those few seconds, all these images of our life came rushing into my brain. Peter glared at me so intently. What was I supposed to say?

"You could live another 20 years." He wasn't even phased by my answer and spewed back, "Or?"

"Or maybe you won't live that long."

"AND?" he said a little gentler.

"Absolute worst case. Five years. Or we could get hit by a bus tomorrow." Peter looked away and let that sink in for a bit then he reached his hand over for mine and started rocking.

As I reflected on Peter's driving over the past few weeks I realized that there had been several instances when I felt less than comfortable in the passenger seat. Peter seemed less and less confident about the rules of the road. For instance, more than once, when the light turned green and he asked, "I can go, right?" There were also times when he would drive 45 or 50 mph on the highway.

Another time, he was so confused about where to do a U-turn because he had turned right instead of left. I tried and tried to explain "turn here in this lane with the arrows, over one lane, right now." Peter just couldn't comprehend and nearly came to a stop on a busy road with cars coming up behind us.

The difficult driving decision sat firmly on my shoulders, another unfair nuance of this disease. I knew what I needed to do for Peter's safety and the safety of everyone else on the road. Fortunately, Peter had an appointment with his neurologist that week and his doctor announced, "Peter you should not be driving." The chore had miraculously been taken off my plate.

In an effort to not nag and let Peter figure things out on his own I would wait to see who prevailed in the seatbelt game. Most of the time the mysterious lady's voice won reminding Peter, "Please fasten passenger's seatbelt." He would grumble some expletive and reach for the seat belt and click it. Other times, when Peter would click it before the voice sounded, he would smile and punch his fist in the air as if to announce, "I win."

The seat belt continued to get more difficult to manage, especially if we were in someone else's car. Peter would look down to find his seatbelt instead of looking for it over his shoulder. While in Tennessee in the back seat Peter became frustrated and started pulling dog leashes out the compartment of the door. He became very focused on the leashes and grew upset so we quickly pulled over and I jumped out to buckle him up.

Another challenge we faced during this stage was hoarding. Below is a blog post I published on *Oh Hello Alzheiemer's* during this time.

Peter hides and hoards and collects and protects his treasures fiercely and I have not found all his hiding places, specifically the one where he hid his wallet months ago.

Friday is laundry day and also the day I reorganize his drawers again which over the week have acquired a new collection of prizes. As Peter looks for his things and moves them around and touches them and fiddles, he takes the clothes out of the drawers and unfolds them. If they make it back in the drawer they are rolled in wrinkly balls smashed in with extra clothes like single socks and hidden dirty underwear.

His bedroom drawer collection consists of rocks and sticks and socks and spinners and hats, shoe inserts and photos, golf tees, and golf balls. Sometimes there are unwrapped loose baked goods in this drawer as this is the main collection spot and Peter covets baked goods.

There are other different locales throughout the house like the family room end table drawer collection which is ever-changing. Currently, there are four pairs of gloves and two baseball hats, sunglasses, and of course rocks and sticks as well as a few golf gloves.

Sometimes there are shipping labels ripped off boxes hidden here.

The collection site in the office, is hidden behind a chair and is mainly a pile of sweatshirts and shoes, always a sock or two and spinners, rocks, and a pair of rolled-up jeans.

There is a new collection forming in the shed as the weather becomes cooler and this one is strictly large sticks and larger rocks that wouldn't fit in his pocket along with clumps of long grass Peter has ripped out of the ground.

On Fridays as I sort through the collections looking for dirty clothes and refolding the wrinkled things, I'm careful not to disturb the assortments as they bring Peter comfort and he visits them often throughout the day to rearrange them or simply check on them.

He's protective of his things and as I flit around the house picking up and straightening up and putting things away it's not uncommon for Peter to follow after me and say, "Hey! That's mine!

The bedroom became cluttered with Peter's clothes. Piles upon piles of clothes, mostly running shirts folded neatly around the room, in front of the dressers, and on the dresser tops, many of the drawers were empty. Peter would get frustrated, often trying to find something to wear, digging through the piles looking until he settled on what to put on.

Something had to be done. How could I help him to be organized and feel less frustrated? I decided while Peter was having a day with friends I'd clean out every single drawer and fold, organize and label the drawers.

The newly-organized room gave me a sigh of relief, but Peter was not overly thrilled. If he couldn't see his clothes, he couldn't find them, even with the labels on the drawers. The labels were effective for a few weeks, but eventually, Peter became confused about what clothes to wear for what season or occasion and I chose his clothes for him.

One morning I rummaged through his drawers to retrieve his outfit for the day. When I started pulling shirts out of his drawers I found the most quizzical thing. There was a neatly folded bundle of four shirts, one inside the other, inside the other as if he had been wearing them and just took all four of them off at once, then folded them as one. I realized with one whiff that these shirts were not fresh so I un-bundled them and put them in the hamper.

As I continued I found four more bundles identical to the first, coveted and carefully folded and put back in the drawer after running or working outside. The top layer of most of the bundles was adorned with dirt and mud from splitting wood or raking or other yard work.

Peter had gotten more confused about clothing and it was imperative that I gave myself extra time to get wherever we needed to go because there was always adjusting to do. Shirts inside out, backward, or tank tops layered on top of long-sleeved shirts. Peter would wear two ball caps, two coats, or different shoes. These new styles were the new norm, as were layers of two or three pairs of underwear or socks.

One afternoon we were heading out the door and I did not leave that extra time and so I was the anxious one while Peter jested and laughed with Reflection Ralph in the mirror. A tiny part of me wanted to let him wear his shirt inside out and what the hell, wear the two hats. He had recently started a new phase of picking at a mole on his chin. The mole was bleeding. If I didn't make the usual adjustments maybe someone, anyone, would hear my silent screams for help today. But then again, perhaps someone might hurt Peter's feelings today, too. So, I picked one hat, turned his shirt the right way, cleaned up his chin, and off we went all put together seemingly perfectly normal.

In conjunction with dressing difficulties, hygiene practices were changing. If I didn't gently remind Peter to shower he would forget; it was a common suggestion I made every two to three days to keep things from getting overly ripe. Peter almost always complied immediately and during this stage didn't need help in the shower except he may forget how to adjust the water. I had my son turn down the temperature on our water heater so Peter would not get burned.

I checked on him after his shower. He was still in the bathroom, wet, and had put on his dirty jeans from working outside. Peter was forgetting to dry off after his shower.

I helped Peter out of his dirty jeans and said, "Here are your jeans, put your foot in." I held them out for his step. I then handed him his shirt.

"How do I do it?" he asked.

I needed to take a deep breath.

I dried his chest and back and arms off with a towel explaining as I went and then helped him put his shirt on, over his head and then one sleeve at a time like a toddler, blinking hard and breathing deeply at the realization of what was happening. His brain was forgetting how to dress.

I started gathering Peter's dirty clothes while he was in the shower, replacing them with a new outfit, so he wouldn't get confused about what to put on. Peter was relieved the first time I laid out his clothes and I didn't realize how stressful that part of dressing had become for him.

The reality of these new hygiene changes was irrefutable the next time Peter and I made the trip to the clinical trial. The doctor began questioning me as usual. I remember one particular question that stayed with me and previously I felt relieved that we hadn't reached this stage, secretly thinking we never would.

"Peter needs to be reminded to shower. Never, rarely, sometimes, usually."

The answer had always been "never," but the answer had changed from never, skipping right over rarely and sometimes, to usually in just three months' time.

I wanted to scream, "Wait! Please wait! I'm not ready for this!" Who could ever be ready for this tragedy, this poisonous thief robbing us of our life? In my proactive nature, I had prepared my home for these changes, but not my heart.

The new cognitive dips were coming faster and faster and my heart was getting bruised over and over. There was nothing I could do to prepare my heart.

Peter needed to be reminded to shower, he needed help adjusting the water temperature and that expanded into not turning the water off at all. He simply forgot one day, and never remembered again. This included any faucet he turned on. To avoid a flood, I removed the drain plugs from every sink and bathtub.

When Peter would leave the water running, I found the easiest solution was to simply walk over and quietly turn it off. When this new behavior started, I used to say things like, "Oh, the water is running," or "turn off the water," or "are you finished with the water?" But why? If he remembered to turn off the water, he would have. Reaching over quietly and turning it off saves him the angst and still accomplishes the job.

The speed of Peter's decline was remarkable and most days I felt like I needed to buckle in and hold on tight as I never knew what to expect. It's strange and interesting to watch the different obsessions that the Alzheimer's brain will dwell on. Peter received an electric razor as a gift as his shaving skills had declined. His obsession with preening his face and head would fade in and out. He could stand in front of the mirror for an hour or more shaving his head and his face and tweezing and trimming and picking and checking.

One day Peter came downstairs after a preening session. He was plucked and smooth and looked Mr. Clean fresh but I couldn't help but chuckle as I noticed he had taken the electric razor to his eyebrows and now he wore only half of them.

Alzheimer's is unpredictable. One morning a person can do a thing and that afternoon they can't. Later the same evening they can once again accomplish the task. It's the only bit of kindness this unforgivable disease has. It offers you a tiny glimpse sometimes, of what's to come, laughing at you, knowing there's absolutely nothing you can do to stop it.

There is a sudden gut-wrenching feeling that overcame me when Peter suddenly couldn't understand something he previously could. Just when I thought the newest normal was stable, we would jolt into another unfathomable and unforeseen vortex. Imagine suddenly being shocked by new information but you must remain absolutely calm and keep your emotions completely in check while trying to help your loved one comprehend.

From the day I met Peter he wore the same type of casual watch, a $10 Casio. He owned beautiful dress watches and he proudly wore them to work and on many a date, but he loved his Casio watch. His watch stopped working and it was probably a battery, but it was an excuse to buy him a brand new one and an easy birthday gift idea.

Peter was thrilled with his new watch and put it on his wrist as soon as I set the time for him. Later I asked him, "How's the new watch?" He wiggled his arm to adjust the watch in place on his wrist and he shook his head. Looking at me he questioned, "Something's wrong with it." I got up from my seat to see what the matter was, and it happened.

Gently, I unhooked the strap of the watch and turned it around, so it was no longer upside down. Closing the clasp again I said, "There! Fixed."

Calculating time and distance was the next skill to disappear. Understanding how much time was between 11:00 am and 4:00 pm was a blur. For instance, when his friend was picking him up for golf at 4:00 pm, he was dressed by 10:30 am and already pacing. Peter was robbed of calculating time, so he paced and then sat on the porch obsessively looking at his watch for it to read 4:00, but he had no idea how much longer that would take.

At this point, Peter was terrific at finding tricks to help himself, and one day I came home to find him wearing two watches on his left wrist. When I asked him about it he explained that he wanted to see how much time he had left. If only a simple watch could tell us.

Lisa's Lookback

I reflect on the conversation I had with Peter about not driving at night. His lucid questions about how much time we had left, haunt me. I believed my answer when I told him the worst-case scenario would be five years. Peter was gone two and a half years after that conversation. This stage lasted the longest and although these behaviors were shocking, they prepared me for the unpredictability of stages six and seven. All these behaviors, made me marvel at the complexity of the brain, the exquisite and effortless brain function we take for granted as healthy adults.

Questions to Ponder

1. How will you handle the decision to take the keys from your loved one? Perhaps having a conversation with your loved one's doctor before an appointment so they can deliver the news?

2. Are you taking steps to keep your loved one safe like turning the water heater down?

3. Can you be proactive to help ease your emotional and physical workload? Such as easy steps like collecting your loved one's dirty clothes while he's in the shower, replacing them with clean ones, or removing drain plugs?

CHAPTER 22

The Vow Renewal That Went Global

There were so many unexpected treasures and pleasures, surprises, and delights during the planning and attending of this event that even now, I cannot blink away the tears. Now, after Peter's death, some tears are joyful for having had this magical experience. Other tears are still tears of grief and disbelief.

Peter was wavering in his lucidity. Some moments I felt that he knew I was his wife, and other days he seemed to be courting me as though I was his girlfriend. I tried to instruct my heart to hold on to the fact that either way, he loved me.

Isn't that all that matters? My heart didn't always heed my warning and the cruelty of the Alzheimer's bitch would seep in and clutch my breaking heart. Sometimes, I would let her. I would let her squeeze my bruised heart so I could feel all her viciousness and I would cry or scream into a pillow in utter disbelief.

As you've read, I was always a proponent of meeting Peter wherever he was, joining his journey, and playing the pretending game. This night was no different. I heard his words and delighted in them, flattered, and at the same time, I wanted to run out of the room horrified. I chose to be delighted.

We were watching an episode of the TV show *New Girl* and a certain couple was getting married. I was crying and letting some of my pain stream down my face. Peter would always tease me when I cried during a show or movie to lighten the mood. I caught him laughing at me and I laughed, too, and blew my nose and told him to shut up. We laughed together and I said, "It's so beautiful. I'm really happy," I reassured him so he wouldn't be afraid of my tears. "Isn't this nice?" I asked Peter, pointing to the TV wondering if he understood what was happening.

Peter was sitting on a different couch to my right and there was a table between us. Peter leaned in, over the end table putting his chin on his hand. He had a devilish look on his face, boyish almost, and he looked right into my eyes and said, "Let's do it!" with this huge inviting smile!

"Do what?" I asked and Peter pointed to the TV. "Get married?" I asked and his grin grew so wide!

And he said, "Yes."

Shaking my head in disbelief and joy I asked him, "Are you asking me to marry you?"

He smiled and chirped loudly, "Yes! It's gonna be a lot of work!" and he laughed from his belly, as he closed his eyes and shook his head.

"Yes, Peter, I'll marry you," I answered.

I knew this was a special moment I would cherish for the rest of my life, so I grabbed my phone and started recording. I recorded my sweet Peter who appeared to be a younger version of himself and I have watched this one-minute video hundreds of times. The personality I captured was that of a timid man in his twenties. Unsure, and wondering what I was thinking, I watched as he pondered his next question.

The recording begins with Peter saying, "Go ahead, go ahead," as though he had interrupted me, asking me for my thoughts.

I laughed in delight and said, "I don't know! I wasn't expecting this, so I'm very excited. I didn't know that you were going to ask me to marry you today."

"We're putting together this," he said nervously.

"We're putting the wedding together?" I asked.

"Yes," Peter said and then he paused for several seconds. I watched as his eyes darted and his brain spun with apprehension. His knee bounced and finally, he looked in my eyes and nervously asked, "Do you like me?"

"I like you so much, I love you so much," I said, elated.

Peter laughed and breathed a sigh of relief. His grin grew.

"Do you like me?" I asked.

"Yeah. Yeah. I do, too." Smiling ear to ear, nodding in agreement.

"Oh, that's so nice."

The conversation ended shortly afterward, but that recording will remain forever. It is absolutely priceless to me. My heart was happy and full of the notion that my husband forgot we were married but loved me so much that he asked me to marry him all over again.

I didn't give Peter's proposal another thought other than to share the precious video with our children. Our daughter Sarah is a wedding and event planner and very passionate about her work. She is connected to the kindest of people, and vendors in the wedding community.

After I sent the video to the kids, Sarah immediately responded with, "We're doing this!"

I laughed and said, "we're NOT doing this!"

The thought of planning a ceremony was overwhelming on top of everything else I had on my Alzheimer's plate.

Peter asked me to marry him (again) on December 12, 2020. I held firm to my notion of not having a vow renewal and Sarah kept nudging me. She reminded me of my mantra, "no regrets" and I immediately changed my mind. I knew if I didn't do it, I would regret it for the rest of my life.

Sarah owns a wedding and event planning company, Sarah Brehant Creations. She is extremely talented and connected in the wedding world. She surrounds herself with people she admires, can learn from, people who understand and appreciate her style, and her passion to serve love of all kinds!

She sent this post out to her community and the response was overwhelming.

As many of you know, my mom who is the author of the blog Oh Hello Alzheimer's *and is the caregiver for my stepdad who suffers from Alzheimer's. Most of you have met her at styled shoots because she was always there to help until she couldn't be anymore!*

My stepdad often shows my mom photos of their wedding because he remembers her from their wedding day, about ten years ago but doesn't know her as his wife now. He also recently proposed to her again during a lucid time. I had an idea that I could plan a styled ceremony to do a vow renewal for them to give her a timeless gift! If anyone would be interested in collaborating on this, I figured I'd put it out there to the creative community first. ❤ "

I was lying in bed and opened my phone to find comment after comment from florists and photographers, videographers, bakers, officiants, and jewelers. Hair and makeup artists and a stationer, too! These amazing professionals were offering to donate their services out of pure love.

Renewing our vows with the help of these incredibly kind humans was suddenly a reality. I could not have been more committed to promising Peter my unwavering love once again, in sickness and in health for the rest of our days. Due to Peter's rapid decline, the window of opportunity to have the ceremony was short. Sarah and I decided on a date. April 26th, which gave us just six weeks to prepare.

The upcoming day, the ceremony, was hard for me to think and dream about as I had mixed-up emotions. It all felt surreal to be marrying my husband again, but I also felt a bit like Cinderella thanks to my daughter. I felt as if I needed to hold on tightly to my heart and keep it caged as Peter could easily not understand any of it. He could be confused or paranoid and I needed to keep my expectations low. I hoped only that our hearts would connect and we would feel love. I was fully aware that we would be making these memories for me. This day would one day help me heal and get through the grieving process after our journey's end.

I wanted the details of the vow renewal to be as close to our original wedding as possible. My wedding dress was dusted off and I was determined to get that zipper zipped! I planned on wearing the same jewelry I wore back in August of 2009. Each piece had been carefully chosen by Peter during our courtship. I asked my long-time friend Darlene if I could once again borrow her prized Swarovski crystal and pearl hair pins. She put them in the mail the next day.

Sarah took care of every detail. I did not have to lift a finger. We chose MILL 1 at Open Square in Massachusetts to be our gracious hosts and this gorgeous facility was adorned with the loveliest of flowers in my favorite shades of orange arranged by It's So Ranunculus. Owner Leah went over the top choosing the perfect varieties and the most delicate and luxurious bouquets and arrangements. My bouquet will be cherished for years to come and I will think back on this day and breathe in the scent of her flowers from memory.

Several photographers jumped forward to capture our precious day. The summer after Peter was diagnosed, we were the recipients of a photo session with the lovely Cait Fletcher (Cait Fletcher Photography). She captured Peter when he was healthier and tan and witty and still mostly himself, and I love her moody photography style.

Our son-in-law Dan Brehant (Dan Brehant photography) was very close to our journey and only a heartbeat away when I needed him. Dan has captured many precious memories of Peter and me along our journey and was more than excited to offer his talent for the day.

Irma Garcia is the owner of Earth + Sun and I connected with her the moment I met her. She's an incredible videographer and was absolutely thrilled she would be recording the memories we were preparing to make.

These lovely human beings were donating their time and talent to make this happen and I knew they would be looking through their lenses with the utmost love and care, capturing every precious moment for me to hold dear for the rest of my life.

We were blessed to have the musical talent of Saxophonist Jeff Ladd, a gorgeous balloon installation by Pink Flamingo, Yen from Transcendent Studio would be my professional makeup artist and Drew from For Goodness Cakes would be creating and baking our cake.

After a few weeks, Sarah and I decided I should cut myself some slack and be realistic about fitting into my original dress. We took it to a seamstress, and she took out the zipper in the back and installed a corset back which made it fit perfectly.

It seemed that more and more generous vendors were jumping on board every day. Pencil and Ink designed lovely vow books and an invitation to our event. Refined rentals graciously offered their rental services including furniture pieces and table dressings. The aura of the space would not be revealed to Peter and me until just before the ceremony in Sarah's gracious and quiet grand style.

I had literally done nothing for the entire event except get my dress to the seamstress and buy a sweet little ring on Etsy for $17. A simple band adorned with cubic zirconia to stack next to my wedding rings was all I needed.

Peter's ring was a different story. From the time I met Peter his right hand has adorned his college ring. To my knowledge, he had never taken it off until he took it off. One night while we watched television, he fiddled and tugged and twisted for twenty minutes until it went clunk on the floor. My mouth dropped open in disbelief. He was never able to get the ring off his finger and it was bent flat from all the hard work he's done since 1987.

Peter didn't want to put the ring back on and so I put it in my jewelry box so it wouldn't get lost or hidden, never to be found again. Peter seemed to not miss it and never asked about it after wearing it for all those years.

I was a little concerned he might follow suit with his wedding ring from our original ceremony, but he had developed a huge callous just above the ring that prevented him from slipping it off. Then one night he stood up, came over to me with a frisky smile, and held his wedding ring between his fingers presenting it to me like a prize.

"For you," he said with his eyes and lips grinning.

Again, I was shocked and afraid if I gave it back to him, we'd never see it again and so, I decided to wear it for him. It was big, but I wore it on my thumb behind a special thumb ring I wore every day.

During the ring ceremony portion of the vow renewal, I slipped Peter's ring back on his finger. He wore it for one day and then in the same fashion, returned it to me as a gift. I believe he knew it was special and he didn't trust himself to keep it safe.

We were one week away from the vow renewal when my daughter called to tell me she had one last surprise and she could not wait another second to tell me. Here's my blog post on *Oh Hello Alzheimer's* about her phone call.

There are 2 women in my life who are stronger and wiser than me when it comes to my own wellbeing. These women continually give me permission to do things for myself that need to be done to preserve my health.

Sarah Brehant pushes me to take more respite, find a therapist, join the monthly massage club, find another caregiver, and she keeps opening my eyes to the reality of what's actually happening when my head is in the clouds. She is real. She is honest. She is my beautiful brave daughter, refusing to be anything but herself. What is her secret?

Sarah has planned our entire vow renewal, quietly coordinating all the vendors and preparing the mood (board), the timeline, and every single detail of the day while I do literally nothing but show up. She is giving us a gift I will never be able to repay.

Adrianne DeVivo (whom I mentioned several times, dementia specialist with Hartford Hospital) sat patiently in her office for over three hours while I asked questions and shared stories and she offered her dementia expertise. Meanwhile, my brain insisted Peter and I did not have the kind of Alzheimer's she was describing, but thanks all the same for your time. Buh Bye.

Well, Adrianne was right and she's right every single time we chat which has been about once a month ever since that November. Adrianne has a way of being brutally honest and showing me the upcoming months in the softest, kindest way and even if we're not there yet, I believe her every word. We have formed a very unique and sacred bond that I trust and will hold very close to my broken heart for the rest of my life. We are forever connected, as she holds my hand and guides my heart through this trek.

These women have impacted my caregiving journey in such a tremendously positive way they are easily responsible for the wellness of my current and ongoing mental health.

"I have one last surprise for you, you awake? I'll text it to you." Sarah texted one night as we were planning the vow renewal.

"YES! What???" I eagerly responded.

"Adrianne is officiating your vow renewal!!" She replied.

It was so unrealistic to me that I replied, "Shut up! WHAT?!! MY Adrianne?!?!"

And it was true and I was overwhelmed with joy, I burst into tears at the beautiful tenderness and irony of it all.

Everything was in place and I opened my eyes the morning of the vow renewal. The kids had flown or driven in to attend and I was ordered to be at the venue early for my makeup to be done. The kids would stay with Peter, Sam would help him get ready and they would ensure he arrived on time.

I'm still weepy thinking of the magic, the moments, the unforeseen surprises, and just how normal everything felt for just a little while. It was incredible how Peter's brain rallied as if the adrenalin had him on high alert and he remained lucid for most of the day.

Tucked away in a little dressing room upstairs, butterflies fluttered in my stomach when Sarah announced that Peter had arrived. Feeling a bit silly, I sipped, one more taste of champagne from my glass and grabbed the tissues I knew I would need. We hurried down the stairs to the long, beautiful room where way at the other end stood Peter and our daughter, Sarah Marshall. Slowly and quietly, I strolled up behind Peter as Sarah kept his attention on her face. Peter turned toward me. His first look.

From that moment, and throughout the day Peter was so very present.

"Who are you?!" Peter exclaimed! And then he whispered in my ear, "You look good."

We kissed like everything was right and for a few

hours, it was! Peter could not take his eyes off me. I'll never forget the elated look he wore on his face all day. We walked together arm in arm down the long wooden and brick room, our faces beaming, our hearts brimming, preparing for Sarah's big reveal!

I had not heard the words "grand reveal" until they slipped wistfully into my ears as my daughter spoke them and I knew instantly what they meant. The culmination of the hard work of extremely kind and generous and talented people who are eager to share their labors of love.

These incredible souls were literally waiting with praying hands over their mouths, holding their breath for our reaction. I hope we did not disappoint! Overwhelmed with the beauty of it all, Peter and I tiptoed in slow motion gobbling up every detail we could, appreciating the hard work of so many to create this memorable day. Soaking in the colors, the fabrics and the florals and the scents and sounds and the warmth and love that everyone had donated for our day.

As we browsed, the guests and vendors mingled, and saxophonist Jeff gave us the gift of his delightfully rich music. Our hearts were light and we felt embraced by so much love. The venue was filled with glorious music and full hearts!

Adrianne arrived and all the guests were seated. But before they were, Adrianne spent time with Peter so that he would feel comfortable. She offered something like, "Peter, wanna come with me? We're gonna go over there and wait for Lisa."

Just then, the most glorious moment of the day appeared. Peter kissed my lips, then leaned in close to whisper in my ear, "Thank you for staying." Those words were all I ever needed to hear and I clutched them near every day after.

I exited to the back of the room with Anh, Sarah's coordinator, and watched my beautiful daughter's lighthearted bounce as she approached us, completely in her element. Just then, Anh asked, "Sarah's walking you down the aisle?" A detail we had overlooked. My mind scurried for a split second and then I smiled and I knew as I blinked the tears away.

"Will you walk me down the aisle?" I asked Sarah when she approached Anh and me and Sarah asked, "Maybe (grandson) Sonny should walk you down the aisle?

"Well, that would be a shit show," I assured her laughing, imagining a two-year-old bouncing around noisily, and she laughed, too.

Sarah smiled widely, agreeing to be my escort, we fumbled on how to intertwine our arms, and then the music began. The sax belted out Nat King Cole's "Unforgettable." Anh cued us to start walking.

I was so focused on watching Peter, wondering what he was thinking, feeling, doing. Was he overwhelmed? Did he understand what was happening? Was he happy? Was he watching? Flashbacks flickered of our wedding day when he was nervous. I was so focused that I did not know until the next day that Cait Fletcher had captured this timeless photo of my daughter and me.

It's easily my favorite of any photo I've seen of the day. Her heart bursting with pride from all that she had given, worked so hard to plan and bring to fruition. Her love for me shining so brilliantly. All along I knew Sarah was incredible at planning and designing weddings, being an empath, she feels every emotion of the day. What I did not understand was the intense love she gives and the care she takes of her brides. A queen. I felt just like a queen.

We approached Peter and Adrianne. Sarah and Peter hugged and I held Peter's hand. I gave my flowers to Sarah. Peter and I faced each other and held hands waiting for Adrianne's words. And she began.

"The world spends a lot of time showing us things we are supposed to need. Today is a wonderful reminder that the things we need most are often not things we acquire, but things we create, nurture, and invest in. Peter and Lisa's love story, their journey to this moment, perfectly exemplifies that. We see that nurturing and investing in the people and relationships standing here in this room with some of their most trusted loved ones.

We are missing those who weren't able to be here today, most notably oldest son Thom, but also siblings, extended family, fathers, and friends. We are glad that some of you who could not be here in person are able to join us virtually. Including some of the loving online community that has cheered Peter and Lisa on from near and far.

It is an incredible honor to join two people in love, to stand with them as they promise to support, encourage and love each other. Sometimes the circumstances make unions even more meaningful. Today is one of those days.

Love is the great unifier. Marriage is not just a tradition or a system, it's a covenant. A relationship that hinges on your ability to consider each other before yourself. It takes love, respect, trust and understanding, friendship, and faith.

It is not often in life that we get to witness people love each other through the full breadth of their vows. In sickness and in health in good times and in bad. It's not often we see a relationship pushed, challenged, made to redefine itself only to emerge with a more renewed commitment to patience and seeking understanding.

Love and, in turn, marriage is not always easy. It is not made up of the fairy tale moments. Although, your story does have its fair share of those.

Love is forged in a fire. It is made up of trials. It is built and built more resilient in the unthinkable moments. The moments we can't anticipate and hope not to know. Love is built in the moments of showing up when showing up seems hard and heavy.

I recently talked with Lisa about this, about the need to commit and recommit in hard times to love and to marriage and she shared that she doesn't feel that, at least not at this point. She just shows up, loving Peter for who he was, who he is, and who he may become. And in loving Peter so fully and without any reservation, there is no need to recommit or be reminded of the commitment, that piece comes easily because the love comes first.

Kahlil Gibran eloquently said, 'Love has no other desire but to fulfill itself. But if you love and must need to have desires, let these be your desires. To melt and be like a running brook that sings its melody to the night. To know the pain of too much tenderness, to be wounded by your own understanding of love. And to bleed, willingly and joyfully. To wake at dawn with a winged heart and give thanks for another day of loving. To rest at the noon hour and meditate love's ecstasy. To return home at even tide with gratitude and then to sleep with a prayer for your beloved in your heart and a song of praise upon your lips.'

Today we celebrate a couple who exemplifies loving willingly and joyfully, that knows all too well pain that can accompany tenderness and understanding. How fortunate we all are to witness a love as dedicated and unwavering, a love that knows when to dance in the kitchen and cuddle in a cry, a love that embraces incredible grown children, celebrates fully in the joy of watching them through seasons of adulthood, dancing at their weddings, celebrating graduations and sharing in amazing meals with them.

A love that has known distance, physical and otherwise and prevailed, a love that has known trials and successes, a love that has celebrated career wins, and rejoiced when those chapters closed.

A love that has known the excitement and sacrifice of weekend commutes to be together, and that now knows there is such a thing as too much togetherness. A love that knows the joys of travel and exploration and the coziness that exists in a small cottage on a quiet lake. It is clear that you both bask in the love and sweetness and joy that sweet Sonny brings to you.

We know that nothing wonderful comes without complexities. Your love serves daily as a reminder to all who know you that when we fight for the things we love, that when we hold tight to our people we can do unimaginable things.

We come now to the words you've waited to hear. You've decided to recommit yourselves to one another's hearts, to continue sharing in life's incredible and unbelievable moments. To continue keeping each other warm and looking for reasons to laugh.

Do you Lisa, promise to continue dancing with Peter, leaving chores undone to relish in the moment, all of the moments, big and small?"

"I do."

"Do you Peter, promise to continue dancing with Lisa, continue sharing with her your hopes and fears, and a glimpse into your world?"

"Yup."

We're going to slip this ring onto Peter's finger. This ring symbolizes the love that I have for you, as I place it on your finger, I give you all that I am and ever hope to be. Peter, you're going to put a ring on Lisa's finger. And we're gonna say, This ring..."

"Yes?"

"Say this ring..."

"Yes?"

"How 'bout this? Lisa, I love you."

"I love you."

"A marriage needs support, it needs encouragement and love. Will you, family and friends, promise to support them in their marriage, loving them, encouraging their love for each other, and pushing them to seek respite when needed?"

"We will."

"Before I say what you've all been waiting to hear, I want the two of you to just look around for a minute. These people and so many others who are not here today, support and encourage and love you fiercely. Because that's what this is all about, love, support, and encouragement.

Let all that you do be done in love. By the powers vested in me by the American marriage ministries, it is my honor and delight to pronounce you once again, husband and wife, Peter you may kiss your bride."

"Ooooooh!"

"I'm proud to once again introduce to you, Mr. and

Mrs. Peter Marshall."

We did not pick Adrianne to officiate our vow renewal, she chose us, and I'm so grateful. She knew us, knew Peter and my love and our joy and the pain we suffered. There really was no one more appropriate to take some quiet reflective time to write the perfect words, deliver them and make Peter feel comfortable.

Peter was more present that day than I had seen him in months. His smile was infectious. When he saw me, he was enamored, it was so beautiful. We vowed to continue to love each other. It was perfect.

The vow renewal was covered by media outlets around the world raising awareness of Alzheimer's disease. Interviews and appearances and stories were told and caregivers from around the globe found *Oh Hello Alzheimer's*. The blog connected people who felt alone and offered a safe place for people to go and feel connected to a community of others who are going through the same thing.

While writing this chapter, I was astounded, and several times went back to look for dates to confirm the truth. Peter and I renewed our vows just three years after diagnosis, but more surreal is that Peter died exactly eight months later. I thought we'd have more time.

Lisa's Lookback

I knew I would cherish the memories we made leading up to and during our vow renewal. However, it was not until after Peter's death that I realized the breadth of this gift. I liken it to having a first child or first grandchild. I was certain watching the videos would be spectacular, but there truly are no words for the splendor I feel when I immerse myself back in the magic of that day. Remembering Peter's happiness overcomes me emotionally every time I recall his expressions. I can never express the full capacity of my gratitude to Sarah, and all the talented vendors, friends, and family who celebrated our love that day.

Questions to Ponder

1. Will you have regrets for not doing something you could still do? What's stopping you?

2. How will you celebrate the love you have with your loved one either together or with family and friends?

3. Are you taking the time to record the memories as gifts for the next season of life?

FAST Scale Stage Six

Oh Hello Alzheimer's Blog Post

Each night we brush our teeth and I help Peter put on his pajamas. I pull the covers back for Peter to climb into bed and he may or may not surprise me with a big jump onto the bed like a five-year-old and we laugh. I pull the covers up to his chin and lay on his chest for a minute and I always have the same feelings. I miss who you were. I love who you are. I cannot help but cry, mourning him as I listen to the heartbeat of a child under my ear.

Wiping away my tears, I assure Peter each night with lots of kisses that I love him so much and I'll be right outside the door in my bed when he wakes up and then I scold him, "Don't wake up too early" and we laugh.

CHAPTER 23

FAST Scale Stage Six, Safe and Busy

I learned early on in my life to choose my battles. While dealing with the daily struggles of Alzheimer's I needed this coping tool more than ever. I simply asked myself two questions.

1. Is Peter safe?
2. Is Peter happy?

That's it. Life is that easy and nothing else matters at all. Shoes on the wrong feet and clothes, inside out or backward, pajamas underneath pants, long shorts underneath bathing suits, mixed-up words and thoughts, and long-winded stories? So what!

A grown man walking around in public with stuffed animals? Good for him! We should all feel so free! Who cares? For a few weeks, he sported a one-eyebrow look. These are battles that I chose not to fight. There would be battles I had to fight, whether I wanted to or not. I saved my strength for those bigger battles: the battles of stage six. This was the longest and most exhausting stage of our journey. There were so many unpredictable and constant changes that I'll describe stage six in three separate chapters.

It was important, as Peter's disease continued to confuse him further, that I kept a constant eye on him for his safety. Like a toddler, once on the move, he needed constant supervision to keep him safe as he didn't know he could get burned by touching the stove or that a knife could cut him or a million different things. We protect a little one by locking and blocking and putting things out of reach because a toddler will need to learn to keep himself safe, hopefully not the hard way. A child will learn his boundaries as he grows and has new experiences and becomes more mobile.

Peter was forgetting his experiences and becoming more immobile. Peter was no longer responsible for his safety. I was. He had leaned his back up against the stove when a burner was on, opened the door when the car was moving, and ate things that were not to be ingested. Peter had psychotic moments which I'll describe later. Alzheimer's is extremely unpredictable.

While Peter did not have a habit of wandering and did not show aggression at the beginning of this stage, I chose to be proactive in his care. I kept all medications, supplements, razors, knives, corkscrews, matches, and the good chocolates, locked up. All outside doors were triple locked just in case and there were bells on his bedroom door so I always knew when he's out of the bedroom. I installed three outside cameras and five inside cameras, all of which alerted me to movement so I could make sure he was ok. I always wanted to be proactive with our safety rather than reactive.

All of our outside doors and the door to the basement had two locks and a child safety doorknob cover. I had to update the child proof doorknob cover because Peter could figure out how to remove it. The old version simply cracked open at the seam like an egg and he could figure that out. The new improved covers had a dual lock. The same two pieces covered the doorknob, but there was a second piece that screwed on the front of the knob. This was too complex for Peter to get off the door.

Peter was young and full of energy, even if his mind was wilting he needed to be kept busy constantly. Over the three years of our journey, I purchased plenty of fidgets and stuffed animals for Peter's comfort, brain games, toys, puzzles, and gadgets that I thought would interest Peter. Some were hits immediately, some were never touched and some he discovered later.

Peter's pockets were always swollen, full of his favorite things, whether he actually fidgeted with them or not, they seemed to bring him comfort just having them. His very favorites were spinners and golf balls and most days you could find three or four of each in his bulging pockets.

Peter had a fidget cube, several actually, but he was never really interested in them. He did, however, LOVE the little zipper box that one of the fidget cubes came in. He loved zippers and drawstring bags, and I sometimes would stash a few toys inside a little bag and leave it out for him to discover.

His favorite stuffed animal was a dog toy and he loved it so much! It was the happiest little plush monkey and Peter would talk to him and laugh with him and sometimes sleep with him. "Monkey" was always out on the sofa or the counter offering his smile to Peter.

The task of emptying Peter's pockets at bedtime when changing him into pajamas was easy at one time. But as time went on, Peter would declare, "That's mine!" or "I want that!" so I simply put the pants in the hamper after taking them off of him, pockets full. When the laundry basket made it downstairs to the laundry room, as I loaded the washer, I would have Peter empty the pockets to discover their contents. Peter was joyful as he unpacked the pockets and one by one rediscovered his treasures.

I've always been the tidy sort—a place for everything and everything in its place girl. But I had to let that go. Peter had a million fidgets and gadgets and pictures and spinners, and hats and stuffed animals and so I created an organized activity center along the dining room wall to house them all. Keeping him busy and content was the biggest struggle. His area also had play dough, his putting green and putter, his tennis racket, picture books, coloring books, toss across, ring toss, and a basket full of things he could touch and feel and look at. Peter would visit the area and entertain himself sometimes for hours with the precious prizes and I would watch him smile as he thumbed through old photos, finding them for the first time again.

Peter would take out his things, and he would spread them out all over the counters and tables and every open surface. He wanted his treasures to be out on display. His pockets were packed full of his prizes and his arms were sometimes full, too. At one point, he called me over to show me his wife in her wedding dress and another photo of his wife and children and he was beaming! Peter recognized himself in this picture which was taken almost 17 years ago. Not shocking, as Peter thought of himself as a much younger person than 55.

He had trouble reading the captions in a memory book I gave him and so I would come up behind him and read the ones he focused on. He spent an hour browsing the book one day, and even put a paper clip on a page he particularly liked.

"Peter's peacefulness overwhelmed me in the most delightful way and the contentment in our home is uniquely and incredibly lovely today." I wrote on the blog. That feeling is foggy as most of my memories are of trying desperately to keep him occupied. To the point of exhaustion.

Peter always loved music and enjoyed the classics like big band and Frank Sinatra, which I call the "twirly dancing songs." He also loved some country music as I worked in the country radio industry for almost a decade. He had his beloved Christmas favorites and the '70s were also a big hit. He especially enjoyed "Supercalifragilisticexpialidocious" or anything Mary Poppins sang!

He was a toe-tapper and leg-shaker and dancer, a finger snapper and a whistler and I've heard over and over that people with Alzheimer's never forget music, and the familiar tunes will elevate a mood. Our cousin, Sherri, urged me to get some headphones and I shrugged it off at first but as I was creating lists of Christmas gifts for people to buy for Peter I added them.

In the meantime, I watched Peter and asked his closest circle of friends to do the same. If we saw him reacting positively to a song, we added it to the playlist so it would be ready when Christmas came!

Sarah Brehant presented him with the headphones and they were a huge hit! He absolutely loved them and his ears were filled with his songs and the room would fill with his loud whistling. He even burst into song sometimes! I knew they would be a fantastic tool when anxiety or moodiness set in.

Sometimes, I would reach out to Adrianne or she checked in with me after reading something I wrote just to make sure I was coping ok. She was amazing at giving me the very best advice and I always felt so prepared and grounded after our chats. She didn't sugarcoat anything, she was blunt but careful and kind and I think that's the way I prefer all of life to be.

When I asked her one of the hard questions, for instance, what I could expect next, she told me the truth. Sometimes it hit me right in the heart, but I needed to know the answers. I wanted to prepare for the next thing, so I could react properly for Peter.

When I shared with Adrianne that I was struggling to keep Peter occupied, she offered these caregiver tips, which proved to relieve some self-inflicted stress.

1. **We don't have to occupy their every minute.** Pacing is ok. Peering out the window is ok. Putting something non-violent on the TV is ok. She gave me the permission I needed to relax a bit and realize that sometimes it's okay to just be.

2. **Have him clean the windows.** Genius. Truly. I assigned this task and Peter was happy to do it, he did as much as he wanted to, he was busy, he had a purpose and he remained in a lovely productive mood that entire day.

The days are grueling and exhaustive for caregivers and on many days I kept a constant watch on the clock counting the hours until I could go back to bed. Most days I felt like I was dragging my body through the twilight zone. On one of these days, I walked into the family room and I stopped. I couldn't decide if I should laugh or cry as I stood looking around at what had become our normal, most of which I didn't even find strange anymore.

I could hear the water running in the bathroom, the faucet happy to oblige. I looked up at the ceiling and thought how the electric company must be loving us as I counted twelve lights on. The front door offered a lovely breeze as it stood wide open to the world. The typical huge ball of socks sat proudly on the island housing some seven or eight baby socks inside. Peter's daily collection of stones and twigs piled neatly on the cocktail table.

Peter was in his own world, where he often was, on his hands and knees crawling along sweeping the dog hair off the kitchen floor with a small broom and dustpan. His socks were mismatched, and his shoes were, too. His shirts were layered, one long-sleeved then two short-sleeved shirts on top. He was wearing his pajama shorts.

I decided to laugh, and I closed the front door, turned off some of the lights, and turned off the bathroom faucet again. This was the day I decided to remove all the drain plugs from the sinks to avoid a flood. I looked for the positive and soon realized Peter had picked out his clothes AND he had dressed himself. The bathroom faucet was running because he had remembered to wash his hands, and he used the toilet himself. Triumph! The door was left open because he was carrying the dustpan outside to throw the dirt in the garden. He was cleaning the floor after all, and he needed all that light to see the dirt! It truly was like living in the twilight zone, so surreal some days.

What happened to our beautiful life? How did we get here so fast? I thought to myself watching Peter scooting along the floor. Never sure of what we'd be faced with each day, we could only approach each moment with a very open loving mind.

These unfathomable moments were happening more and more often and simply going with the flow, was the easiest approach for me. Some days, sometimes, life was agonizingly eye-opening for me. After Peter's mother passed, Anne Marie, Peter's sister gifted him the lifelike baby boy she had given their mother. The baby is lifelike and looks a bit like our Sonny Bunny and it was love at first sight between these two. Peter was gentle and kind and caring and sweet and why would I ever think he'd be anything else? I do believe the baby gave Peter purpose and something important to care for and he felt comforted with the baby in his arms.

Recalling images of elderly people with baby dolls I remember thinking how sad it was for that to happen to a person and it had now happened to my person. I missed my husband desperately, even though he was right in front of me.

Behaviors were changing and along with hiding and hoarding came thievery. Peter would pocket anything and everything and I had to be very careful to keep track of my own items. My phone or the car keys, anything of importance. Several times Peter pocketed my phone and I'd have to pat him down or ask him to empty his pockets which did not go over well. Peter's thievery and hiding and hoarding were uncontrollable for him, and the most important things are behind locked cabinet doors, so he is free to klepto on!

Peter always loved the holidays, especially Christmas and I decided that it would be too stressful to decorate a tree during this time. Precious sentimental ornaments could be broken or lost. Peter could get hurt from broken glass. It felt like a nightmare until it didn't! During one of my three am brainstorming sessions, I invented the fidget tree!

Thanks to our dear friend Jim Hilliard, who lugged the artificial tree down from the attic, I was able to put the idea to work. Adorned with fidgets, and attached with pipe cleaners, the ornaments on Peter's tree could be taken off and pocketed without fear of breaking them and getting hurt! When I showed him the tree his face lit up and he recognized some of his fidgets that were displayed.

As things evolved and changed and spiraled into scarier days, it was helpful to look outside of my perspective and into Peter's to try to understand each situation more fully. Peter had started waking up in the middle of the night and wandering downstairs. I would hear him get out of bed and use the bathroom in our room and I would stay awake until he came back to bed. If I didn't hear him come back to bed or if I fell back to sleep, I'd go investigate. I'd find him downstairs pacing around or in the bathroom or sometimes he'd be lying on the couch.

From my perspective, I thought of how tired I was and how I couldn't get back to sleep and what a pain and why can't he just stay in the bedroom? But what was Peter thinking? He was confused and perhaps scared, and maybe he couldn't find the bedroom or the words to tell me what happened. By taking his feelings into account instead of mine, it became easier to be kind, guide him back to the bedroom and tuck him safely back into bed.

One night I was particularly tired and slept better than I had slept in a long time. I didn't hear him get up. In the morning, I grabbed my phone to look at the video clips from the cameras I installed around the house a few weeks before. I watched him leave our bedroom at 2:58 and wander downstairs, pacing back and forth from the bathroom to the family room until finally, he laid down on the couch until 4:20. He got up went to the bathroom, and then back to the couch until I came downstairs. He wandered around for over an hour, confused, but he was safe.

It would have been easy to focus on all the things that the Alzheimer's bitch had stolen from us, but I chose to focus on what remained. I consider myself one of the luckiest ones as I have a bank filled with the loveliest of memories that I can pull out when I need to remind myself of our love story.

Peter seemed tired one afternoon and so I suggested that he take a nap. He was hesitant and asked questions like, "Where will you be? How long?"

To which I answered, "I'll be right here, downstairs. You can wake up whenever you want." Closing the blinds and turning on the white noise machine I wanted him not to be disturbed. I took off his shoes and pulled the covers up and kissed him.

Again, Peter asked, "Where will you be?"

"I'll be right downstairs. I promise I'm not going anywhere. I always tell you if I'm leaving, right?"

"Ok," Peter responded. "Please don't leave me. I just wanna make sure I have everything I need"

These new feelings were an egotistical phase. Peter was very focused on his basic needs, as a child would be. Feeling safe would become his priority.

Sleep was sparse and I would grab some when I could and most days I felt like a zombie. My eyelids were heavy, my body and heart heavier. Peter had developed night tremors or twitches or flinches called myoclonus seizures. The condition is not harmful and is common in Alzheimer's patients. Unfortunately, this was a new sign of deterioration of Peter's brain.

Precisely like the twitch we sometimes feel when we fall asleep, these seizures lasted all night long. The bed bounced as Peter twitched and my sleep was constantly interrupted. Peter's was not. As he vibrated and jumped, he talked and mumbled and occasionally snored, all of which contributed to my decision to head to the couch most nights.

Sleeping in one of the three empty spare beds was not an option as Peter would not be able to find me and could panic. I learned this lesson the hard way. One night I retrieved Peter from downstairs at 4 am and tucked him back in bed. I decided to sleep in the spare room for a few hours. I woke up with a stretch and a yawn and reached for my phone while tuning my ear, wondering where Peter was. He was snug in bed and I relaxed and put my face in my phone for a sec.

Scrolling through the events of the night from the camera footage, my heart sunk, my energy fell, and guilt overwhelmed me as I watched clip after clip of Peter wandering around in the night for more than two hours while I slept. He was looking for me. He finally collapsed on the couch just before 4 am. Just before I barged in and woke him up. He couldn't find me.

After that I decided sleeping on the couch was a better solution. I knew he would find me if I was on the couch as he usually headed to the family room first when he woke up. I shoved earplugs in my ears and snuggled in and fell asleep.

Late one night I was on the couch and something caused my eyes to open. I sat up immediately as the dark figure stood over me just inches from the couch. The scream was so primal and loud that my throat hurt. I knew instantly that it was Peter, almost mid-scream but by then he had already landed. The guttural scream that flew out of my body startled Peter so forcefully that he stepped back and plopped down on the couch as though my voice blew him over.

Our eyes were huge trying to adjust to the darkness and I heard myself yell, "Holy shit Peter you scared me!" and realized Peter was very afraid. I did the only thing that made sense, I burst into loud laughter, got up, and hugged him trying to diffuse his fear. He grabbed me tight and started laughing too. After a few calming breaths I walked Peter upstairs and tucked him back into bed and returned to my nest on the couch, this time without the earplugs.

I spoke to Peter's neurologist about his seizures and we started an anti-seizure medication. When Peter first started taking the new drug he was a zombie and could barely keep his eyes open. I cut the medication in half and gave it to him at lunchtime and bedtime, perfectly timed for his nap or overnight.

Not only did Peter's tremors stop, he no longer woke up several times a night wandering around the house. Some mornings he was still lying beside me in the bed.

Instead of waking up worrying and wondering where my husband was, I could just roll over and snuggle up against his warm shoulder. What a lovely way to start the day! It made me feel so grateful for something I forgot to be grateful for!

Unfortunately, the relief was short-lived and the seizures returned and so the dosage of medication was increased. All was well until it wasn't. I decided to make my newest middle-of-the-night bed on the futon in the office just outside the master bedroom door where Peter would see me. I would hear him if he wandered out. But the futon was uncomfortable, and I wasn't getting enough sleep.

I loved that spare room bed. The difficult decision was made to turn my office into my new bedroom. The futon was swapped with the spare room bed so I could be cozy and know if Peter opened the bedroom door. Peter could be safe and secure knowing I was right outside his door. I hung a string of bells on the bedroom door to act as an alarm and notify me if Peter opened the door. Peter was taken off the seizure medication. The seizures were not harmful and Peter was not bothered by them so we discontinued the drug. I missed sleeping with my husband.

Peter was always an early bird, waking before me. Typically, he would go downstairs and make a nest on the couch, cover up and wait for me. Or he would just pace for an hour or more, or perhaps chat with Reflection Ralph in the mirror.

As this egotistical phase progressed Peter began coming back upstairs and standing next to me watching me sleep waiting for me to get up. One morning, which turned out to be the first of many, I was awakened by his breath on my face. As I opened my eyes, there he was, leaning over the bed, elbows resting on the bed, chin in hands, like a child, inches from my face.

I blinked, startled, popping my earplugs out, and I said, "Hi. What's up?"

And Peter in the sweetest, most childlike way answered, "I wanted to talk to you."

The decision to move out of our bedroom was a difficult one and I often just wanted to climb in and snuggle next to Peter when I tucked him in at night. As per usual I was longing for something I could not have. My husband's body was right in front of me, yet I grieved him and the things that were already gone. What I longed for was to climb in bed with Peter and feel his response to my body. I wanted him to touch me, caress me, feel me, and satisfy me. None of those things were realistic as this physical body that appeared before me housed the brain of a small child. I was mourning Peter even though he was still living. Ambiguous grief.

Each morning when Peter came out of his bedroom, he would walk toward me with squinted eyes and furrowed brow, hunched over, stepping carefully and slowly, confused. I would greet him with a sleepy smile and a soft, "Good morning!"

I love to snuggle under a lot of blankets and keep my room as cold as I can, and Peter approached me with his arms wrapped around his body trying to warm himself. I realized the first time that I had a snuggle opportunity right in front of me and threw back the covers as I scooched over to make a place for my prince. He giggled and climbed in, and I cuddled on his shoulder and wrapped myself around him, trying to feel some

279

normalcy. The body jerks immediately reminded me of why we sleep separately, but the morning routine sweetened as Peter remembered to climb into my warm bed for 20 cozy minutes.

We've always been affectionate and whether we're celebrating or snuggling, or Peter is a bit gloomy, I've found that incredible kindness will win each and every time.

Specifically, and precisely, one dozen kisses. Bedtime became a vulnerable time once Peter was alone. He was usually tired early and possibly grumpy, usually emotionally distant. Tucking Peter in, was one of my favorite times of the day, pulling the blankets up to his chin and making him feel safe, promising him, nose to nose, I'm just outside and I'll be here in the morning. Coaxing him to relax.

And then I'd plant the kisses. I waited for his coy little smile, and then his boyish giggle with the push back as though that's enough kisses already! One dozen kisses. It worked every time.

Lisa's Lookback

This chapter was the hardest for me to write so far. Peeling the scabs off such fresh wounds is painful and I found myself needing frequent breaks to complete it. Watching your loved one become a child is horrifying. I counted on Peter and relied on him to join me in exciting news or help me work through problems. He was my rock and at this stage I was cuddling a six-foot-tall child in my arms, reassuring him he was safe. I'm not sure how any caretaker is supposed to be able to manage these feelings and emotions. The disbelief of it all was excruciating and filled me with a desperate, lonely sadness. The sadness then was for me. As I wrote this chapter there was a clear shift. My sadness was for Peter and others who have suffered from Alzheimer's. I sobbed through it thinking, how can this happen to such beautiful, brilliant minds, these people we cherish so dearly?

Questions to Ponder

1. What measures will you take when your energy is consumed by keeping your loved one busy? Can you let go believing they don't need to be occupied every second?

2. Will you be able to adapt emotionally to your loved one becoming a child to ensure they feel safe?

3. What conflicting adjustments will you make to take care of yourself, such as making the difficult decision to move out of your bedroom as I did?

*You can't explain what it's like to mourn
someone who's still alive
unless you've
experienced it firsthand.*

CHAPTER 24

FAST Scale Stage Six, Personal Care

When Peter was whole and he was my partner, I could rely on him. He was dependable. I could count on him and ask him to do sweet things for me and he would run to the store for that one ingredient I forgot or perhaps jaunt out to pick up a bottle of wine. Peter was always the one to run out to get something and he was truly happy to do it. This generous characteristic was particularly lovely if I came down with a cold or a stomach bug. Peter would gladly make the trip to pick up whatever I needed.

When he could no longer handle this task I came down with a terrible cold. I was run down, fatigued from caregiving and my body was insisting I take a break. I had taken his generosity for granted and I missed it dearly as I lay in my bed. I wished for cough medicine and the soft tissues, the kind with the lotion. I wanted a throat lozenge desperately.

If I wanted those things I would need to go get them. That meant getting Peter dressed, fed, taken to the car, and buckled in. When we got to the pharmacy, I would need to unbuckle him, physically guide him out of the car, open the door, and coax him out, holding his hand to show him where to go. I would need to keep an eye on him in the store while I tried to clear the fog in my head and find the items that would make me feel better, purchase the items, steer Peter back to the car, guide him to sit down in the passenger seat, and buckle him. All of which I did not have the energy for.

Fortunately, I have amazing children who came to the rescue and brought me what I needed. However, after that experience, I decided to prepare an emergency kit. In the event that I came down with a cold or flu or stomach bug, I would be prepared. Here is a list of what I had on hand so I would not need to go out or ask someone to bring them for me.

Emergency Kit

Tissues with lotion
Vicks Vapor rub
Toilet paper
Cough drops
Vitamin C
Zicam
Frozen orange juice concentrate
Nighttime cough medicine
Daytime cough medicine
Frozen meals
Canned chicken soup
Tums
Pepto
Imodium
Band-aids

Dressing was becoming more and more challenging. Not only did Peter need help to choose his clothes for the occasion or season, but other nuances of dressing were also incredibly difficult. Here are a few examples of the difficulty Peter was having at this point.

We were in the bedroom of our vacation home getting dressed after enjoying an outdoor shower together to wash off the sand and sun. In our life previously, a shower like this one would perhaps be sensual and naughty, but now? Just necessary. Peter needed help understanding how to wash his body.

I had laid Peter's clothes out on the bed and he fumbled trying to put his bathing suit back on instead of his clean shorts. He then held his shirt out in front of him and stepped into the sleeves like pant legs.

Offering some guidance I helped Peter put his shirt over his head and held his shorts open for his step. Peter accomplished getting his socks on and was down on one knee beside the bed. He had gotten one shoe on his right foot and the left empty shoe was in front of him. He felt around the bed lifting his bathing suit and dirty beach shirt and I asked him what he was looking for.

"The other one," he replied. I pointed to his empty shoe in front of him and he grumbled, "I know where THAT is." (How silly of me!) I picked up the bathing suit and beach shirt to allow for less confusion and he stayed in his knelt-down position looking for the other one.

When he turned his body to look behind himself, he found it. His left foot.

There were many moments when I would jump in immediately to rescue Peter from frustration during dressing. He may have been painstakingly wriggling into a second pair of jeans tugging the pants over his feet which were already clad in sneakers. He often struggled to pull his jeans up over the cargo shorts he already put on.

There were moments when I was paralyzed, completely motionless, frozen, and in awe, watching time stand absolutely and silently still as I watched in horror. My friend, my husband my lover was struggling with the most basic of tasks. How truly exhausting it must have been for him.

Early one morning, Peter had come downstairs before I woke up. He had been wandering during the night and I pulled him back to the right floor, the right room, the right bed in the wee hours and then lay there blinking and thinking about how excruciating life had become.

In the morning, while I caught up on lost sleep, Peter worked on dressing. I watched the camera footage later in the morning and discovered the challenges he had experienced. He slept in flannel pajama pants and a white T-shirt but his clothes from the day before lay on the floor and he gathered them. He took yesterday's clothes along with his work boots to the family room and worked tirelessly on the day's outfit.

Leaving his pajama pants and t-shirt on he added yesterday's sweater and then put on his socks and work boots. He still had a pair of jeans on his pile of things so, of course, they needed to be worn and he stepped into them.

He pulled. And he pulled and he pulled until he needed to rest as he could not get the jeans up over the boots. He leaned back on the couch until he caught his breath and was ready to begin again. Peter walked around the house holding the loose leg of his jeans in his hand and then sat down and tried, again and again, to get that boot through. He never did.

When I woke up I went to Peter and my heart sank to see the expression on his face. Imagine this feeling. The frustration of not understanding the order in which to put your clothes and shoes on. Watching Peter's disease progress was the most heartbreaking thing I've ever witnessed. I've never grieved harder, I've never grieved longer. I missed my husband.

On another morning, the rain was pounding on the metal roof of the upstairs porch just a few feet from my head. The patter was lulling me back into a sweet slumber and I had not slept so deeply in months. I smiled and rolled over breathing deeply, enjoying the white noise and darkened room.

No dog noises. No cameras clicking from motion. No bedroom door alarm. No hot breath in my face whispering, "Hey. Hey. Hey." And then in an instant, it was back to reality as Peter approached without even looking at me to see if I was awake or asleep or dead. "Can you help me?" He said as he crouched down on the floor. He had laid two beer koozies on the floor. They were the kind of koozies that slid over a bottle rather than a can. The koozies were identical except for the logo and each had a zipper closure. Peter knelt on the floor and proceeded to try to fit his feet into the koozies to wear them as slippers. And so, another exhausting day began.

During this stage, zippers were becoming more difficult for Peter to tackle. Buttons became cumbersome and then impossible, as did belts. Pants with zippers and buttons were replaced with elastic waists, shoelaces were replaced with velcro when he could no longer tie his shoes.

Peter's skin became very sensitive and I had to be extremely careful helping him dress. His feet were the most sensitive, particularly the bottoms of his feet. Putting his socks on took precision and care or I might find myself on my ass from a swift reaction!

When Peter was healthy and well he was meticulous about his hygiene and grooming. When he landed firmly in stage six, his habits changed. He was confused about hygiene habits he had practiced every day of his life.

We had finished up some yard work and I reminded Peter to wash his hands and he started walking into our mudroom. I reminded him again and he said, "I'm going," pointing to the mudroom.

"We don't have a sink in the mudroom," I said and

gently guided him to the kitchen sink. He stood at the sink staring down at it as though it was foreign and I prodded once again, "Wash your hands."

Peter responded, "I don't know how."

My heart beat faster and I tried to remain calm and remembered my theory of "let's". With a quick comforting kiss, I pumped some soap in his hands and then in mine, turned on the water, and lathered up my own hands. Peter rubbed his soap around in his hands without water so I added water to his hands for him. He's washed his hands in this sink a million times and later in the day had no problem washing his hands in the very same sink.

I found this to be a trend, knowing and not knowing, remembering and not remembering. He would fade in and out and some moments were bright and lucid, some not.

It seemed Peter's hygiene skills were failing in all areas. We sat together relaxing on the deck when I reached to hold Peter's hand. As I picked up his hand, I noticed his nails were long and I teased him about it. In twenty years, I had never seen Peter's nails this long as he was thorough about trimming his fingernails and toenails.

"You need to cut these nails!" I joked.

Peter replied, "I don't know how?"

With a lump in my throat and an ache in my heart, I instructed him to go get his nail clippers. I was uncertain if he could find them or even remember the task once he left the deck. He returned a few moments later with his deodorant. Together, we fetched the tool and I encouraged him to give it a try. He remembered what to do and trimmed up his fingernails. Knowing his toes were probably in similar shape, I asked him to take off his mismatched shoes to reveal the situation underneath his socks. Peter cleaned up his toenails. This was the last time he was able to manage the task.

With each new fumble, I was reminded of our reality. I could feel the Alzheimer's bitch giggling at us in the corner. I knew she would win in the end, but I constantly found new ways of doing things to make the tasks easier.

When I began taking care of trimming Peter's nails, it was awkward to find the right position. Peter also became fearful that the nail clipper would hurt, so in addition to finding a comfortable position, he needed to be distracted.

For his fingers, I positioned Peter behind me at the bathroom sink, bringing his arm underneath mine. I could easily trim his nails over the sink right in front of me while Peter was distracted chatting with Reflection Ralph in the bathroom mirror! Peter could not see what I was doing so he was less anxious about the task.

For his toes, I had Peter sit on the bed and I sat on the floor, leaning back against the bed. I would drape Peter's leg over my shoulder so his foot was resting in my lap. He was not distracted by the mirror, but he could also not see what I was doing. He was not as nervous about having his toenails trimmed.

New hygiene deficits continued to appear, and the next was Peter's hair. Peter's whiskers on his sweet face had grown longer than stubble and I just assumed he had decided again to grow a beard as he has many other winters. I rather liked him in a beard and told him so and he wholeheartedly disagreed rubbing his face.

"No, I gotta get this off," he winced, "But I can't."

I've gotten used to trimming his fingernails and

toenails. It's just love, it's just gently taking care of your loved one, and he was so appreciative. He felt better afterward, and that was always my reward.

And so, the beard had to go but Peter could not remember how and before today I had never shaved his face or anyone's face. Nervousness set in but I reminded myself I had never trimmed fingernails or toenails before I did the first time, except those of our children. I nudged myself to be brave and mustered up the courage to learn the new duty.

The hair on his face was long so I trimmed it first and I was fumbling and lacked confidence but Peter was very patient. I used the electric razor to trim his beard as close as I could before using the razor to get the cleanest shave, learning as I went. And as I did, I softly rubbed each spot I had just shaved and I found myself melting into the task, easily slowing down, caressing his face to make it last just a little longer. This was my new way of making love to my husband, reminding myself how very much I loved this man.

I had never shaved a man's face before I shaved a man's face. Just like everything else, one day he could and then he couldn't. Like fingernails and toenails and taking out trash and feeding dogs and getting the mail, Peter's abilities seemed to dissipate, like smoke.

It turned out not to be as scary as I thought, nor was it as time-consuming as I expected. I switched from Peter's regular soap to lavender-scented baby shampoo for his shave and shower. It lathered nicely, had a relaxing scent, and didn't sting Peter's eyes if I accidentally dripped.

Our shave and shower brigade went smoothly most mornings, but we had to adjust things along our journey. Constantly trying to adjust to the Alzheimer's bitch and her challenges, I moved forward, committed to outwit her when I could.

As the disease progressed, Peter needed more and more instruction and guidance, and hands-on help. While some tranquil music played in the bathroom to keep him calm, I would instruct Peter to take off his shirt. Most days I had to physically help him to understand the instruction. "Ok, come in here. I'm going to shave your handsome face." I'd say, taking his hand and guiding him to the sink.

While I warmed up the razor and lathered up my hands, Reflection Ralph would keep the mood light. The boys would joke around while I worked on Peter's face and head. Peter tolerated the face shave very well for a long time and there was lots of kissing as we were face to face in a small space. The mood needed to be light so the transition to the shower was easy. Peter was becoming less fond of the shower with each day.

Next came the head shave. This step needed to be adjusted as it became more and more difficult for Peter to understand my direction. He had always been easily guided to sit on the toilet, so I could see the top of his head for a close shave. But as time marched on, it became too confusing. Peter associated the toilet with going to the bathroom so he would take his pants down, pull them back up, open the lid, and put the lid down. He would get frustrated not understanding what I wanted him to do.

After his face was clean-shaven, soft, and smooth, I simply got out the step stool from underneath the sink. Stepping on it, I could stand taller so I could see the top of his head. Peter understood with the guidance of my hands when to turn, and continued to play with Ralph while I quickly finished the task.

Eventually, Peter's skin became hypersensitive and he could no longer tolerate the tug of a razor on his face and head. He would wince when I started his shave and so, another adjustment needed to be made. I decided to only use the electric razor. The shave wasn't as close, but it seemed to be enough to keep Peter comfortable.

In the long run, I got a little lazier and decided that it would be easier to let the hair on Peter's head grow a bit and just trim it every week or two. I also let his goatee grow out as shaving just his cheeks was far easier and less time-consuming than maintaining his entire face and head.

My sweet husband reached a point where the shower was so confusing he no longer knew what to do behind the curtain. Additionally, I didn't know how much cleaning he was doing behind the curtain. Thinking it could be a new routine, I decided to get in the shower with Peter. He enjoyed when I washed his back but otherwise was either a giddy school boy feeling embarrassed by his nudity or was anxious when I tried to wash anywhere else. I tried to instruct Peter to wash those private bits but he could not understand my direction.

I was concerned he might get sore as I was certain he was not cleaning his undercarriage properly. Peter was also becoming hypersensitive to the water pressure and the water temperature. The time came when I thought a bath would be more beneficial. I imagined the warm water would be soothing and it would hopefully loosen fecal leftovers. Peter would not let me wash his private areas no matter how gentle I was or how slowly I tried to explain what I was doing.

In the end, when bathing Peter, it was important to be slow and gentle and the water couldn't be too hot, the air couldn't be too cold, and my hands and washcloths had to be warmed as well.

Life was becoming extraordinarily exhausting. In speaking with other caregivers, they too felt a level of fatigue they had not fathomed. Peter needed help with everything and even though I was in the throws of it every minute, there were still surprises.

For instance, I remember applying sunscreen to

our children when they were young. They would seldom sit quietly and allow me to gently apply the sunscreen to their little faces and ears and let's not forget their sweet cheeks and feet. They'd tug and pull and whine and want to get moving on to their fun in the sun. Until stage six I didn't have to worry about Peter's skin. I'd just toss him the lotion along with the motherly look of, "put it on" and he would.

Things were different, one of those lessons learned the hard way. It was the end of a lovely beach day and the sun had shone brightly all day and we enjoyed several hours in the sun. I had tossed Peter the sunscreen along with the look but not paid much attention after that.

After the sun had dimmed and Peter got out of the shower, I saw that we needed a new sunscreen plan. Blotches of red where he'd missed applying lotion popped out alarmingly on his legs and arms and ears and the tops of his feet. Moving forward, similar to when our children were small 20 or 30 years ago, I gently covered all his exposed skin before we left the house, so he was protected from the sun. The good news is Peter was much more cooperative than our children ever were!

That was one of the easier changes that occurred. However, I knew the hardest changes were coming and I did as much research as I could to ready myself for the incontinence portion of our journey. There is no amount of readiness to prepare you for this part.

In telling our story, I continue to want to preserve Peter's dignity, even after death. But at the same time, I have set my intention to help others learn and provide a glimpse into a world they may not be able to fathom. Peter's words ring in my ears today as I approach one of the hardest topics. "It has to be done, it has to be you," he reminded me. And I will tell it all for the sake of others. This is Peter's gift.

The first experience with incontinence caught me

by surprise as it was nothing like I imagined. I can honestly say I have never seen Peter in a panic as he was more of a cool as a cucumber kind of guy, while I'm the high-energy one, but our roles were reversed one morning.

I stumbled downstairs to meet Peter who always got up earlier than I did. The dogs were crying to go outside and be fed which is usually first on the daily task list. Normally, Peter is lying on the couch waiting for me but this morning he stood statuesque in the kitchen arms folded, ankles crossed.

"Good morning!" I greeted him cheerfully and he came toward me and said in a panic "I need your help. It's upstairs." That was the clearest thing he had said in days.

He started up the stairs and took me to a laundry basket of clean clothes and began rifling through the folded clothes which I noticed had been refolded inside each other like little packages. Words were few and energy was frantic. Peter told me he "couldn't find something" and "they took it."

I felt a calm come over my body and we unloaded the basket together looking for something he said he lost but he forgot what it was. I had not yet had my coffee and was foggy. He kept trying to explain but the words were mostly gibberish and nothing made sense to me. Still in a panic, he took his shoes off and pulled his pant legs up simultaneously looking to make sure he had two socks. I assured him he had everything he needed, socks included. He started unbuckling his belt and ordered, "Go over there" and pointed to the bathroom so he could have privacy.

There was no calming him down, so I decided to try distraction. "Let's go make the coffee," I said, and I took his hand and led him downstairs. He wandered around the family room and the bathroom looking for the thing he lost that he couldn't remember and telling me again that "they" took it.

I didn't argue. I knew not to argue. I leaned in belly to belly and stood on my tiptoes and I kissed him trying to calm him, and he melted down onto my shoulder and apologized. He was physically shaking. I assured him everything was ok, and the lost thing would turn up.

He ate his breakfast and drank his coffee and after about an hour and a half he was himself again. I've not seen or experienced an episode like this before and I felt like the proverbial duck; calm on the top of the water but paddling like hell underneath.

All I can say or recommend is to stay calm and lead with every ounce of love and gentle kindness that you can muster. Don't try to understand this enemy, this Alzheimer's bitch, you never will. Don't waste a second trying to understand her, instead use that energy to cherish the leftover scraps that she hasn't taken yet.

Peter's dignity is my utmost priority and I weep now while I write. As repressed memories like these reveal themselves to me, they play back in slow motion, thankfully, so I have time to breathe and take them in without panicking.

The mysterious thing had not been found, but it seemed to be forgotten and it was time to take our showers before heading to a small birthday celebration for Peter's 81-year-old father. I jumped in the shower first, after laying Peter's clothes out on the bed. He was waiting for me with a big smile when I came out of the bathroom wrapped in my towel. Peter was dressed in just his underwear and he nodded his head with pride and said, "I figured it out! I found it!" He was very excited.

He raised his hand, palm facing me as if to tell me not to come any closer. I was to watch this gloriousness from afar! Peter was grinning from ear to ear. He slipped off his underwear, stepped carefully out of them, and picked them up to show me the prize he had been looking for. He had soiled himself.

My friend Adrianne, dementia guru, and I had a detailed discussion two weeks prior as I quizzed her about what to expect and how to react. How best to prepare me to take very special care of Peter's feelings and his dignity. I wasn't prepared. She told me I wouldn't be.

Her advice rang through me at that moment so loudly and clearly that I knew just what to do.

"Oh, that's ok, Peter. That happens." I said as carefree as I could, and he asked me what to do with it? I told him I'd throw them away and he should get in the shower. I had just moments to collect my thoughts while he showered. My skin was suddenly freezing and then I was hot and sweating, although maybe that was a hot flash? And then the calm. I knew what to do because Adrianne and I had talked about it.

I ran downstairs, my legs were shaking, and my hands were trembling, and I was still dripping and wearing a towel and I pushed those selfish pity tears away and I got to work. I went to the closet underneath the stairs and I pulled out the box of disposable underwear and I grabbed a handful and I paused asking myself outloud, "Is this right?"

I decided it was the right thing to do and I flew up the stairs and replaced the cotton underwear on the bed with the disposable ones. And then I waited. I got dressed and brushed my hair and started my makeup and I was shaking so hard anticipating what Peter's reaction would be, but I had my words ready.

He went right to the bed and picked them up, put them right back down, and then started putting on his shorts.

"Don't forget your underwear," I reminded, and I held my breath as he picked them up.

"These? Are these mine?" he asked.

I said "Yes, they're new!"

He giggled and said, "Are you sure?" He unfolded the foreign paper underwear and told me that he hadn't ever had underwear like these before.

I said, "Well, now you do!" with a smile. I held them out and he put one foot in and then the other, almost gleeful as he pulled them up.

"These feel funny, are you sure these are mine" and he was still giggling. I told him to put his shorts on and he did, followed by his shirt and socks and shoes.

It had happened, the heaviest thing. I do believe every caregiver anticipates this moment and worries and wonders how and when and what the details will be? I'm so very grateful to have had the conversation with Adrianne and to know what to do even if I was not prepared emotionally. While this memory reveals itself slowly to care for my heart, the memory could have been far worse.

Unpredictability is the only consistent thing you can count on with this Alzheimer's bitch. You never know when it will happen until it happens. What I did know at this point was that Peter was not getting as clean as I would like and we were having difficulties toileting. I decided to have a bidet installed. I opted to replace the entire toilet, but there are less expensive options that require only swapping out the seat.

The bidet came with a remote. Peter could not work the remote, but he could understand when I stood outside the door and explained what was going to happen. I would tell him to stay seated and he was going to feel some warm water. I felt that at least he was getting a little cleaner with the bidet.

Peter would only allow me to wipe him for a very short amount of time before his combativeness and agitation set in, which I'll talk about in the next chapter. His skin had become so sensitive to temperature and touch that I purchased a baby wipe warmer. It's violating enough having someone in your bathroom space, coming at you to touch that area, but when the wipe is cold, I imagine that can make it even more shocking. He was more amenable to my cleaning him if the wipes were warm instead of shockingly cold.

As Peter's toileting confusion grew, he would sometimes sit down on the toilet without lifting the lid. This caused quite a few messes until I figured out how to outsmart the Alzheimer's bitch. I simply took the lid off the toilet. Peter had no choice but to sit on the seat and I no longer had to clean up the lid.

As an aside, it's funny how the dog drinking out of the toilet used to be a stressful thing. I used to yell at her to stop. At this point in our journey, I just shrugged my shoulders and thanked the universe for one less chore.

I started keeping an Alzheimer's go-bag in the car after the first incontinence event. I'm a proactive, be prepared sort of gal, so if an opportunity were to arise that I needed to take care of I was ready. I used a backpack as it was easily strapped to my back so I was hands-free to help Peter.

The bag was stored in the car in case of emergency. In it I packed an extra pair of pants and underwear, disposable and otherwise, and wipes. Peter's weight fluctuated constantly, so the pants had an elastic waist. I also included a comfy white T-shirt and extra socks.

I changed the pants to shorts when the weather turned warmer and added an extra sweatshirt in the fall. Individual-sized hand warmers were a good idea as body temps fluctuate. Other items I included were a stuffed animal and a few fidget toys and photos for comfort. Two doses of Peter's medication were added and some nonperishable snacks along with two bottles of water. The water would come in handy for drinking or if the wipes should get dried out over the season. A towel is always handy for easy clean-up or modesty should a restroom be scarce.

During the last few months of Peter's life confusion cloaked Peter's brain and no amount of medication or prodding would ever lift his fog. I met him in his bedroom and most mornings cringed to think of what I would probably find. Peter could no longer make it to the bathroom during the night and if he did he most likely would not remember what to do. Sometimes he forgot where to urinate and would relieve himself on the bedroom or bathroom floor. Other times his pull-up collected the urine and he didn't get out of bed.

I learned that no matter if I bought the brand name adult diaper or the generic, it never kept Peter dry. I added a guard, which is simply an insert that looks similar to a maxi pad. This piece fit nicely inside the front of the diaper and stayed in place with the adhesive strip, like a maxi pad. The extra layer of protection usually did the job of keeping Peter dry, along with whatever surface was next to his skin.

One particular morning, I met Peter in his room and he was drenched and shivering. Carefully undressing him, I drew a warm lavender bath and helped him sit down. I knelt on the floor next to him in his bubble bath concerned only with making Peter feel safe and loved after a tormented night. I continued pouring the warm bubbly water over his back, slowly and gently, washing him. He kept groaning about how good it felt. He soaked for longer than I expected, and I was glad.

When he was ready, I helped him get up, step out and I dried his body. Peter was not able to dry or dress himself at all and could not understand any of my instructions. The work was hard, but the heartbreak was harder.

I dressed him in the comfiest of his comfy clothes and guided him downstairs gingerly. My arms were full of soiled bed linens and pajamas and wet socks and shoes for the washer's hot cycle. In my hand dangled the little garbage bag that was showing up more frequently.

Later I made the emergency trip to purchase a carpet and upholstery cleaner to tackle the remaining evidence of Peter's difficult night. The machine came in handy many mornings.

Peter's decline from this point was alarming and

scary and I was constantly on high alert. I could no longer handle Peter's personal care alone and needed someone experienced to help us maneuver the rest of our journey. I hired a nurse who came to our home 30 hours a week. Peter loved her and trusted her more than any other caregiver I had hired. Although he would not allow her to help with any of the personal care at this stage, it was a relief for me to have her expertise and I knew Peter was in excellent care and I could take a break knowing he was safe.

One morning before Miss Nurse came, Peter walked out of the bedroom door and his eyes were blank, they blinked so slowly and fog surrounded his brain, the thickest I've seen. He moved so sluggishly. I slowly eased out of bed and went to him rubbing his crossed arms and kissed him and kissed him again. I pointed my eyes right into his, searching. But he wasn't there.

I guided him to the bathroom and kept my eyes on him as I squeezed out the toothpaste and handed him his toothbrush. He forgot what to do. Trying to meet his eyes I grinned showing all my teeth and scoured mine so he could relearn, but he didn't. I brushed his teeth.

After bathing Peter, I handed him his towel, but his empty eyes told me he didn't understand. I dried his body. Peter could usually manage some of the dressing on his own, but not this morning. He didn't understand when I said, "push, push, push" referring to his arm through the sleeve hole. He couldn't comprehend putting his feet into his pants. I dressed my beautiful husband.

Placing a bowl of yogurt and bananas in his breakfast spot, I directed Peter to sit down on the stool, but he walked behind it and didn't understand the words floating in the air and couldn't figure out how to sit on it. I guided Peter on how to sit on the stool and helped him to eat his yogurt.

And then, at nine in the morning, I guided Peter to

the couch. He slept for over two hours. When Miss Nurse arrived I sprang out the door, I dialed my sister and as I spoke, tears spilled from my eyes. I passed neighbors who knew me as I walked, and I couldn't look up and my face felt hot and red, and I felt vulnerable and naked and so very, very frightened.

I felt my Peter's impending death. Little did I know that we were just a few months away from the end of our agonizing journey.

Lisa's Lookback

Many of my memories from this stage and through the end of Peter's life have been repressed. As I read through my notes and journals the emotions associated with these memories come flooding back in a way that I can express now. Tears, horror, empathy, grief. As I uncover these memories, I am overwhelmed and often sob at my desk managing them. When I was emersed so deeply in the everyday chores, I could not fully express these feelings. Stage six, particularly the end of this stage was the scariest for me. It was long and grueling, exhausting both mentally and physically. Trying to dress a six-foot man who is uncooperative or not participating is difficult and on many days I was tired before breakfast. Witnessing the hollowness of Peter's beautiful mind was unbearable, but the worst was yet to come.

Questions to Ponder

1. Have you thought about if you will be able to provide complex personal care for your loved one or if you will need to place your loved one in a memory care facility?

2. Have you considered talking to a therapist to help you manage your feelings as your loved one declines?

3. Are you preparing for ambiguous grief, grieving someone whose body is still alive yet their brain is deteriorating and you no longer have their companionship?

Perspective

When you are frustrated with me
because of the things I cannot do,
Just imagine how frustrated I must be
because I'm not able to.

CHAPTER 25

FAST Scale Stage Six, Behaviors

Alzheimer's literally consumed me every single day. It was always on my mind or I was talking to someone about it or writing about it. There were no days or hours or minutes without Alzheimer's.

The air around us was constantly thick with the fervent breath of the Alzheimer's bitch and she was relentless and proud. She persisted day and night, night and day. No matter how tired I was, I could not sleep more than a few hours most nights, and I roamed the days with burning eyes and a breaking heart.

My heart ached as I thought of the dreams we once had. After a day at the beach, we walked to the parking area to leave, and I noticed them. They were professional beach goers and had a lifetime of experience. Their tired saggy skin was already leathery brown and it wasn't even mid-July. They sat on their old beach chairs with a cooler in between them, he in his red faded trunks, her in her visor and a skirted floral suit. Each of them had a handful of playing cards and their table was a little blue cooler between them.

Their cooler seemed to have as many miles on it as they had, and it was large enough for just a few items but small enough to manage. They brought only what they needed and sat just off the parking lot as it appeared their tired bodies couldn't walk far. They were content and happy and old, and they were together.

I smiled as I saw them and a moment later a lump swelled fast in my throat and my heart ached and I longed for this. This future Peter and I had dreamt of but would not have. I longed to play setback or oh hell or gin or yahtzee or backgammon or anything at all as we used to so fiercely, before Alzheimer's. We were competitive and it was fun, and these were our plans and dreams and we had been robbed.

My feelings towards Alzheimer's became more callous and I was disgusted and hurt so deeply by this point. I was experiencing such intense exhaustion that I felt like a gust of wind would knock me over. The blog post below sums up how I was feeling a few months before Peter's death.

Please bear with me, endure this with me, without judgment as I explain it to you all, to let you into my very real world, and allow you to follow our journey, truly and honestly. But, not only my world but the hellish environment of many a caregiver who is on the precipice of falling to the floor in a tantrum.

I packed a few clothes and dog food for the pups, and food and a cooler in preparation for a one-night trip to RI to clean our Airbnb, change sheets and do lots of laundry, and try to relax a bit. As I packed, Peter rifled through the bags unpacking and unfolding and digging for his things telling me "this is mine" and quite frankly I'm sick to death of the undoing he does. I love helping him but please stop undoing my work so I have to do it again! I do NOT have the energy or the strength to do your things, my things, and then my things again.

Peter no longer understands the concept of unloading the car in several trips and so I lugged all the bags up the beach house stairs myself while he talked to Ralph in the bathroom. He met me with the delightful news about Ralph as the door slammed against my back and did not offer any help with the bags.

THIS IS NOT MY CHIVALROUS PETER. This is the horrific ugliness of the Alzheimer's demon. I MUST, above all remember this is not Peter, but it doesn't make it any easier, I promise you.

Imagine sitting on the couch after an exhausting day and your significant other is in the kitchen and you call out, "Hon, can you bring me a so and so?" Or "Would you please turn the light out?" OR "Throw me that blanket" or "Hey, grab the chips while you're in there." These are impossible tasks in our house. Peter has lost the ability to understand the simplest of tasks.

Please be grateful for the things you can ask of each other, be so grateful. I'm an optimist. Through and through. But I'm human too and I'm tired. I'm tired of doing it all, or maybe just sick of it. Every bit of everything, and the jumping up off my ass ten million times a day to smile and help and coax and assure and redo. The arduous task of searching for something he's hidden has gotten on my very last nerve.

This is an exhausting job, no matter how in love you are with the person that no longer is. Some days just suck. Some days you're just sick and tired of it all. And that's just the way it is. Fuck you Alzheimer's. I hate your guts.

Peter's cognitive decline had been steady and fast and I tried to shield my heart, but I found myself crying more often to release the ache. He didn't know who I was, but he was very comfortable with me and he would kiss me and hold my hand and scratch my back. Such a pimp.

He would talk to me about Lisa and deny that we are married with boisterous laughter. *Who am I, then?* I wondered. *I am just someone. I am no one.* I was losing my identity in Peter's mind. The lovely layers of our relationship had been peeled away and discarded. I clung to the thought that at least he felt safe and loved, and that was all that mattered.

His speech was jumbled, and he often repeated words in the middle especially the word "there." He would get stuck and would say something like, "it's over there, there, there," as though his record was skipping. If only I could have lifted the needle for him.

He comprehended little and forgot much. I didn't

need to hear my own words, but I felt they would comfort him, so I cheerfully explained the chores and errands of the day as though he understood.

I found myself talking to him, telling him things that fluttered past his ears as if he could respond in any meaningful conversation. Although we were together constantly, our relationship got hollower each day and I was lonely without him. The days were long, but far from silent, as Peter sometimes rambled on and on incoherently, and in my exhausted mind I thought, "Please. Please, shut the hell up!"

These feelings are real and I am transparent to help those of you who are caregivers feel less alone. I offer this raw reality to others to help them see more clearly how difficult this disease is.

Eating was becoming more and more baffling for Peter every day. We were still able to go to a restaurant if it wasn't too noisy and we didn't stay too long. When we did go out, I wanted Peter to enjoy his favorite foods rather than change his diet because of his limitations, so I asked for accommodations. He loved a good steak, but he could no longer cut it, so I asked if the kitchen could cut his food, whether steak or salad, into very small bite-size pieces. They were always happy to accommodate.

I wanted Peter to feel normal and enjoy the things we used to, so we would go to places where people knew us. I always said, if I take the emotion out of it and look at our situation scientifically, the brain is so complex and interesting.

Imagine not remembering how to eat a dinner roll and trying to cut it with a knife and fork. Or cutting pizza or a hamburger because you've forgotten how to pick it up. Taking apart the turkey sandwich you've been eating for years, eating it layer by layer.

We were in the middle of the COVID pandemic and I had been sick for four days. Worried I had covid, I went to the closest Urgent Care. COVID test was negative and I was diagnosed with something viral. Disappointed I did not receive the miracle pill, we left the doctor to head to the pharmacy for the secret recipe, Flonase and Robitussin DM, and juice. I was deflated and still sick as I drove up to the light remembering to use the hand sanitizer. I grabbed it while the light was still red, squeezed some in my hand, and rubbed them together.

"Hold your hand out" I directed Peter and he did, and I squeezed a dollop of the red hand sanitizer into Peter's palm. The light turned green and off we went. I took a quick peek at Peter as I turned into the pharmacy, and he still had his hand held out holding the gel in his palm. We locked eyes at the precise moment that Peter popped his hand to his mouth and sucked up the glob like an underdone Jell-O shot. I can't make this stuff up.

Another new deficit Peter started experiencing was losing his peripheral vision. I noticed first when he sat down for breakfast, seeing his yogurt bowl as he approached the table. Once he was seated and his face positioned more above the bowl, he could no longer see his breakfast. Just another thing we take for granted. Simply pulling the bowl back to me and giving it to Peter again from the front alleviated any further struggle.

I was standing to the right of Peter, very quietly responding to a text message, and Peter facing forward, said, "Where is she?"

I pivoted on one foot around to his face and said, "Peek a Boo!" and he smiled in delight!

One time in the bedroom, we were in the midst of our normal morning routine and while I dressed and dried my hair, Peter chatted with his reflection friend, Ralph. When I finished getting ready for the day, I realized that Peter's feet were bare. Standing behind Peter and Reflection Ralph I met eyes with Peter's reflection and said, "Come here Honey, we need to put your socks and shoes on."

Peter looked at my reflection in the mirror and trying to comply with my request, bent his knee and began climbing up onto the dresser to come to me. He did not understand that I was standing right behind him.

Approaching the end of this stage, Peter's ability to communicate using the words he had left had diminished. His word bank was reduced to just a handful of sensible words. Peter was napping every day now, sometimes three times a day. He no longer fought me when I took him upstairs for a nap or guided him to the sofa. Sometimes after I pulled the covers up and kissed him a dozen times he smiled and said, "Thank you."

He tired more easily and he walked more slowly. Physically, he looked older, frailer. I found myself gesturing more to communicate or guide Peter where to go. Tapping his foot to take off a sock, physically turning his body to point him in the right direction, or holding his hand or arm to lead him.

I tried to speak at a slower pace, and I knew he understood inflection, so sometimes I tried exaggerating my tone to help him comprehend. It didn't help. When I smiled, he smiled. If I laughed, he would laugh. Sometimes I would catch him staring at me if I wore no expression. If he looked unsure, sometimes scared, I offered an emotional cue, like a smile, to comfort him.

Peter was always a quiet person until this stage. He talked constantly in his language and eventually continued talking overnight. The unfortunate reality was that Peter was rarely understood. Sometimes, paying attention to his body language and gestures could help, but not usually and so I would pretend. I interjected the appropriate head nod or gesture or phrase with eye contact to make him feel understood and part of a conversation.

Our grandson Sonny was born a year and a half after Peter was diagnosed. The pair became buddies as Sonny became playful. I would babysit Sonny every Sunday for about eight hours. Peter was a natural teacher and loved showing Sonny how his toys worked and they often played with Peter's fidget toys together. Their relationship changed as Sonny grew cognitively and Peter declined.

Peter continued to regress and become more like a child with each day. Peter was the exact opposite of our grandson Sonny who was a sponge soaking up and learning everything he possibly could at lightning speed.

Peter was losing the ability to understand something every week. Instructions Sonny could follow like, close the door, open the door, turn off the light, take your socks off, let the dogs in. These were all becoming extremely difficult instructions for Peter to comprehend. I wondered when Peter and Sonny would reach the same age? When Sonny would outgrow Peter cognitively? When Sonny was two I had the pleasure of keeping him overnight. He was cheerful and polite and sweet and kind as he was every Sunday, but things were different this time. Peter's decline caused more stress for all three of us than it did before.

The usual fighting over toys and space was still apparent, but Peter's level of jealousy had increased. He was jealous of the time Sonny stole from him and seemed to feel neglected. Like a child, Peter became pouty and angry. Sonny's toys often ended up in Peter's pockets and caused a disruption that needed to be extinguished.

Sonny understood, even at the age of two, that Peter required special care. A two-year-old, even on his very best behavior is a tornado of energy and even a gleeful squeal was harsh on Peter's ears. Sweet Sonny often repeated his loud word softer after realizing it was too intense.

"Come on, Poppy", or "Poppy, kiss," Sonny would invite, pursing his lips in front of Peter, but none of it made much sense and Peter would just stare at Sonny.

Peter had had enough by the end of the day and as I tried to get his pajamas on and enjoy bath time with Sonny the tantrum began. Peter refused to put on his shirt, sat down on the bed yelling at me, arms folded, and finally picked up the shirt and threw it across the room at Sonny who was fiddling in the closet. It should have been a silly fun bubbly bath time, but instead, I bounced my attention back and forth from the bathtub to the bedroom making sure they were both safe.

The morning came and I realized there was no way I could shower, leaving the two together. No way I could shave and shower Peter, leaving Sonny on his own. And dauntingly, no way Sonny could spend the night again until our journey ended. We never did get those showers and spent the day in our PJs while Sonny tried his best to comfort his Poppy and coax a smile.

It was daunting watching our grandson progress and my husband regress simultaneously and that time I knew would come, did. Sonny surpassed Peter cognitively and while my heart swelled for Sonny's milestones, my heart ached for Peter's decline.

We sometimes perched up on the second-floor porch as it's like a giant playpen for them, and I get to rock and take a deep breath. Sonny would pick up all the fallen flower petals and load them in an old, blue, wooden wagon. He enjoyed carting it back and forth and finding more treasures for cargo. My two boys often did not see eye to eye by this point, as Peter didn't understand what Sonny was trying to accomplish.

Sonny would try to get through a tight space that Poppy was standing in, and he would say, "Que me!" (Excuse me) and Peter would physically stop Sonny's wagon. The pair would yell, taking turns to be the loudest and I would carefully and gently redirect them.

During one of our second-floor porch sittings, I witnessed the most beautiful moment and saw Sonny's integrity shining. Sonny had worked very hard picking up all the flowers, back and forth, back and forth.

When Peter felt the need to stop Sonny he knelt down and started unloading the wagon's freight and Sonny knelt down, too. I held my breath for the explosion but as I looked at Sonny, we locked eyes and I smiled at him, "Thank you for being so nice to Poppy."

Sonny smiled, put his hands on his lap, and sat patiently waiting for Peter to finish his undoing. Sonny squelched his frustration, replacing it with understanding. Later he took Peter's hand and said, "C'mon, Poppy," guiding him to our next activity.

Peter was intelligent, one of the smartest people I knew. He was generous and kind, empathetic and helpful, and completely selfless. I didn't know this person in Peter's body. Peter's moods began to change and often he would sulk like a child who didn't get his way.

He would mope because he had lost his independence and could do little on his own. He was not mourning his loss of independence, but posturing because he was not getting the attention he desired from me. It was impossible to entertain him every minute of every day and I prayed for the day he started to nap so I could rest my daytime mind.

Peter became increasingly withdrawn both emotionally and physically. He stood behind a chair and wouldn't talk to me while I cooked and wouldn't come to dinner without an incredible amount of coaxing and continued this behavior after dinner, which he didn't even finish. While we usually sit down together and watch TV in the evening, Peter decided to stand in the kitchen, arms crossed by himself, sulking. This was the first day of his paranoid and angry period.

I suggested maybe he should go upstairs to bed after questioning him about what was wrong and why he wouldn't talk to me. Peter was adamant that he had done something wrong but he hadn't and that's when it started. He was very outwardly angry.

Peter yelled and pointed at me. He was big and I was afraid of my husband for the first time. Peter decided to leave and he ran out the door and down the road. I went after him in the car to try to persuade him to get in and come home. Peter continued his yelling and pointing in anger. He was delusional.

I called our son Sam, and he jumped in his car and went to find him. Sam scooped him up and brought him home and I tucked Peter in bed, and he slept for 13 hours. He was exhausted. It was a frightening experience for both of us. The level of patience and kindness required for this new moodiness and sulking was incredibly taxing. I learned quickly that this was just the beginning.

Adrianne, my dementia specialist, advised me, "You're going to want to curb the violent criminal shows and movies and the news and anything scary or controversial at all, because one day Peter will become delusional and think that these things are real and happening in his world." What? Seriously? To be proactive, I toned the shows down from murder docs to love stories.

It had been a very stressful day and Peter was moody beyond moody and no matter what I did I couldn't pull him up and out and I was emotional. I took the trash out just to walk very slowly down the steps and across the driveway to the can and let a few tears leak out for a little release, but it wasn't enough.

After dinner, I knew Peter would 'do' the dishes and I had been texting my sister, so I snuck downstairs to feed the dogs and chat for five very rare private minutes and I lost it. I needed to. I cried and cried, and the words weren't important. It was the release that was so critical. If I hadn't had that critical release, I may not have been able to deal with the next ordeal which was just around the corner. Peter had joined me downstairs as I knew he would. Peter began to warn me about the group upstairs and he was whispering and extremely concerned about them.

I hung up the phone so we could investigate the concerns upstairs. He was tiptoeing and whispering and nervous about this group in our living room and I tiptoed behind him wondering who they were. We got to the top of the stairs and I inquired about this group and he pointed and whispered, "They're right there, those two!" pointing at the TV.

The characters on the TV had become real and they were talking to Peter. I explained that it was just a show, but he wasn't understanding. I decided maybe the medical documentary we were watching was too heavy so we should watch something else, so I changed to an old movie, *The Help*.

As soon as the actor began, Peter shushed me and said, "She's talking to me." I decided a walk was a better option than trying to convince Peter of something outside his perception, his reality.

The movie *Love Guaranteed* is a playful and comedic love story. There are a few court scenes that are light and humorous, but as Peter watched he grew more and more anxious. He had inched forward and was sitting on the edge of his seat. There is a court scene in the movie and I realized after a bit of quizzing that Peter was concerned he was going to need to testify. He physically and emotionally relaxed after I told him we didn't need to go to court.

Another example of Peter's reality TV world occurred when we watched the Steelers play. The game was less than thrilling for most, but for Peter it caused concern. He inched closer and closer to the edge of his seat as the game progressed when finally he asked me, "Do I have to play?" He relaxed and sat back when I told him the coach wasn't going to put him in.

In keeping with the no-violence theme, I decided the Tom Hanks movie, *Turner and Hooch* would be a good choice, but I forgot there are some scary scenes. Peter was triggered by them, and growing more concerned he stood up. I was ready to turn it off when the scene changed. The people on the TV could instantly become real to Peter and it could be very frightening to him.

Peter settled back into his chair as the scene changed and relaxed and laughed again as Hooch is a slobbery pooch and Peter found the movie hilarious again. Until Hooch got shot.

Tom Hanks picked up the dog and rushed him to the vet. Peter was on high alert and as Tom Hanks carried Hooch, struggling through the door to the vet, Peter jumped up out of his chair and said to Tom Hanks, "Do you need some help?" Peter's core, his soul, his everything was so kind and helpful and giving, even in his delusions.

There were many times I grabbed Peter's headphones and without saying a word, placed them on Peter's head. Peter's delusional behavior began with leg shaking and whispering and Peter would invite, or rather urge that I join him in another room to tell me about the secret thing that was happening in his brain. Peter was relatively easy to redirect, refocus and distract.

The headphones usually did the trick to redirect him, but every time was different. My entire body sighed with relief when Peter immediately started to smile and snap and clap and whistle. These mood swings were not always so easily managed, but the headphones and playlists were a wonderful tool when he began traveling down a scary road of delusions.

My head was perpetually turned in Peter's direction, my ear leaning toward the sound of him, one eye constantly on him. Exactly like my two-year-old grandson is now. *What is he doing? Does he need to be redirected?*

Previously, there was some notice and the storm brewed slowly, giving me time to batten down our hatches, but no more. The Alzheimer's bitch shocked and stunned abruptly now without notification. From mood to mood in the snap of a finger.

Peter's outbursts and agitation and aggression became more common than his smiles and whistles. He was now more difficult to soothe. Constantly unsettled, talking to someone in the room that wasn't there, instant anger for seemingly no reason.

I felt permanent exhaustion that never ceased, no matter how much sleep and rest or respite I got. My eyes burned, my neck ached, and my body dragged. I continued to find joy, but the work was heavy. The tension was thick and uncomfortable when Peter's mood became angry or aggressive, and these moods were happening regularly now.

But I hated it. I hated it because I'm an extrovert and communicating and taking the temperature of the world on a minute-by-minute basis is my jam. And I nurture, that's what I do. I nurture and make things right, but I couldn't fix this or change his mood.

It wasn't like Peter to be down and it was difficult to watch and deal with quite frankly. It was lonely because he wouldn't or couldn't talk to me and Peter seemed mad at me and I felt very alone.

Peter's morning routine had evolved from waking up and wandering around the house to quietly watching me sleep. It was alarming when I opened my eyes to see his face or feel his breath on my face. One morning, he was not his usual patient self and he pushed on my sleeping shoulder. His face was close to mine and I could feel and smell his breath.

"Hey," he said as my eyes opened in slow motion.

"Oh. Good morning." I answered rubbing my eyes. "Do you need something?" I quizzed.

"I want you to get up," he said sternly.

"Is everything ok, do you need something?" I asked again as I came to.

"I want you to get up. Seriously. Get up." Peter demanded.

Now, this mood is rare and not Peter's norm at all and so I got up and I plunged into our routine at 5:45 AM. (We would typically get moving around 7.) We brushed our teeth and slipped into slippers, I put the dogs out, made the coffee, and prepared Peter's breakfast while finding safety in the usual *Animal Planet* show.

Peter's mood remained the same through breakfast and shaving and showering, dressing, and finally getting on the bus to school. (Peter's understanding of his adult daycare program). Impatient and rude and just plain mad. His moods would never again be predictable.

As the disease progressed, Peter would forget where he was. He'd ask me things like, "What is this place" when we were sitting in our home of nearly 20 years. Or he'd look at me with the youngest most honest eyes and ask, "Where is Lisa?"

When he felt this way, scared and panicked and things were unfamiliar we both felt anxious. Imagine yourself as a child and think about something you were afraid of and how that made you feel. Comfort. Safety. These are the two things Peter needed when he felt this way. Reassurance that he was safe and that he had everything he needed.

I say the words to him, the safety words, the reassuring words, and he reacts as I cover him with a weighted blanket and kiss his face and rub his hand.

"Ok. Ok. Ok. Ok." He repeated the word over and over telling his mind to hear the words and feel their meaning. He rocked in the chair as I change the channel to something about puppies or babies or zoos or exploring. These distractions were tools and tricks I've learned to help him cope, and cope with the panic of the bitch's deeply embedded nails.

As I looked at my husband and his worried forehead, I squeezed his hand under his heavy blanket, and I smiled at him as if nothing in the world was wrong and he leaned over with a kiss and a thank you. But you see, everything in the world was wrong, and I could not, no matter how very desperately I tried, I could not fix it.

An entry was posted on the blog. One of the last times we took our walk around the lake. This would be Peter's last spring.

We took a big pause on the front porch as we walked out the door to take the usual three-mile walk around the lake and the air felt crisp and fresh in our lungs. Our heads, at least mine, cleared out and let in some joy and peacefulness, happiness for spring and I felt my shoulders drop and relax.

We walked and Peter rambled on about this and that and I pretended to understand our chat, and I feel lately as though I'm not trying so damn desperately to understand anymore. He responds the same whether I actually comprehend or just show inflection and some good intention.

But I mostly drift off and see a squirrel and smell the air and hear a bird and Peter rambles in the background....noise. It sounds terrible, doesn't it? It sounds so mean, but there is only so much chatter a mind can take before it turns to something manageable and not so numbing.

I snapped a picture as we paused on the big hill after the dam and we laughed at how funny we looked in it. We held hands and we were at about mile marker two when his crying began, and Peter kept stopping at every house asking if it was mine trying to drop me off. He was lost and didn't know his way and he didn't know my part in his life. I told him who I was and that he was safe, and I was not leaving but his eyes continued to weep. Was it the picture I snapped? What was it that triggered this emotion? Why? What? I always ask.

By the time we reached the front door, Peter's breath was sharp and fast, the tears were flowing, and he was bent over. Worrying I might need to call for help, I held his body tight as we walked the last quarter mile. My arm around his waist, holding him firmly, reassuring, I thought he may fall over in the street, and curl up like a child.

I took him to the couch and got the weighted blanket and the headphones, and put on his relaxing playlist. We sat side by side on the couch and I spoke slowly and softly and kindly, but it wasn't working, and he threw off the blanket and the headphones and stood up abruptly, and again I was afraid.

Peter no longer recognizes me as his wife, but he tells me about Lisa with such sweet endearment that I feel his love so deeply and truly. I often wonder who I am to Peter and I've happily decided that I am his favorite caregiver.

Anxiety blankets him some days and he tries to pick and pace and physically scratch away at it to rid himself of the panic. The Zoloft helps but nothing works like my touch. He responds so beautifully to a kiss, locking eyes until I feel him relax, or a nice long back scratch when he's drifted off somewhere far away. Simply joining him, sitting beside him, and holding his hand will calm him. It's just absolutely marvelous and I hoped he would always respond this way.

When Peter's words are completely gone, I will still feel his beautiful heart. I'll cherish every one of these sacred moments I get to bring him back to me.

Peter's decline is startling and steady and swift, and the bitch's evilness leaves me breathless sometimes. I've written about the real people in the TV and Reflection Ralph and these things are very prevalent in our house to the point I barely think they're odd.

They are our new normal. Yet another new normal. The new normals are coming faster and faster at such an astonishing rate I can hardly keep from batting my lashes to see and comprehend all the changes.

Peter hears voices now and thinks that I have spoken when I have not. He will answer the question that he heard or ask me what I've said at least six or seven times a day or more. Sometimes I tell him I didn't say anything and other times I just make up a question that he might be able to answer.

By the end of stage six, Peter suffered from SEVERE separation anxiety and his mood swiftly changed as soon as I walked out the door leaving the nurse with a six-foot angry toddler. Peter would even get nervous when I left the room.

He was agitated, angry, anxious, combative, and inconsolable most of the time. No amount of redirecting worked, soothing and calming fell on deaf ears, and he paced. He would ball up arms full of things and try to get out the door. He complained to the mirror and would scold his nurse. There were times the nurse would call me and I would have to go home to help her manage Peter.

We tried increasing his anti-psychotic medication. We increased his anti-depressant. We changed his anti-psychotic medication several times. It was as if we were throwing darts at a bullseye we could not see. Peter's nurse and I were constantly reacting, redirecting, and trying to soothe him.

I had the tool of being able to lovingly comfort Peter with a kiss or a hug or a back rub, but Miss Nurse could not rely on these tools. I felt I had a little bit of an advantage, but it was a curse and a blessing being the only one who could calm him sometimes. The only one who could bathe him. The only one he would allow to help him in the bathroom or get dressed. He was so modest and it was magnified as his disease worsened.

When I would leave Peter in the nurse's care, he would fixate on the front door, which was concerning. While I installed three locks on every outside door, Alzheimer's is unpredictable, and humans are human and things happen.

While visiting adult daycare centers, I was introduced to this incredible concept! Simply covering the door with a decal sticker that appears to be a set of bookshelves completely deterred Peter from the door. After installing the sticker, Peter no longer recognized the space as a door and stopped fixating on getting outside. There are lots of choices online!

So we had arrived at the place where people on the TV were real, and the slightest hint of violence evoked fear. Peter heard voices in his head. He would hide in the corner next to our curio cabinet sometimes to feel comforted by three walls.

All of his reflections were his friend Ralph, and Ralph was everywhere. Sometimes I was summoned to chat. Peter was delusional. Peter was paranoid. He was aggressive and combative and bigger than both me and Miss Nurse.

Above all else, I needed to keep me and our family safe. There was always the chance that Peter may have brought a concerned expression to the mirror, an emotion he had never seen before and he may have become frightened because he didn't understand Ralph's expression. Peter was unpredictable and aggressive.

He may have heard something he felt he needed to protect himself from. Peter could easily have thought I was a threat. There are many different devastating scenarios that could and often do happen with this horrid disease.

Since the Alzheimer's bitch arrived, my practice was to be proactive, rather than reactive. Every knife, every corkscrew, and every pair of scissors was locked in a secure drawer that Peter could not open.

I was afraid of this man who looked like my husband. I wanted to love him like I always loved my husband. My husband was gone and I cared as gently as I could for an angry, confused stranger in my husband's body.

Lisa's Lookback

Every day I focused. I woke up and I set my intentions to care for Peter as I would want to be cared for. I reminded myself that he was extremely confused and tried desperately to make him feel safe. Busy and happy were no longer relevant. By the end of this stage, Peter was not interacting much with the outside world, he lived in his own world. Napping, sitting sorting shoes and socks for hours, or chattering on and on in his language. My heart was black and blue, and my soul was crushed, but I felt better nurturing him and caring for him. At least I felt as though I was doing something to console him. I knew I would never give up. It became very clear that taking care of Peter was my purpose.

Questions to Ponder

1. What measures will you take to protect yourself and your family should your loved one become aggressive and combative?

2. Will you be able to separate the disease from your loved one, knowing that it's not who your loved one is, but the effect of the disease?

3. Have you considered hiring a nurse or several caregivers should you decide to keep your loved one home until the end of your journey?

FAST Scale Stage Seven

*How lucky I am to have something
that makes saying goodbye so hard.*

CHAPTER 26

FAST Scale Stage Seven

Stage six lasted the longest and was a memory in an instant. Overnight we were sitting very firmly in stage seven, our final stage, and I was scared to death. Or scared of death.

Stage seven has six subsections, a-f and they are described as follows:

7a: Severe dementia, speaks 5-6 words during the day.

7b: Speech is limited to the use of a single intelligible word in an average day.

7c: Ambulatory ability lost (Can't walk without personal assistance).

7d: Ability to sit up without assistance is lost (will fall over without lateral support).

7e: Can no longer smile.

7f: Can no longer hold head up.

Peter flew through stage seven in 20 days.

Before I detail those twenty days, I'd like to backtrack and share with you the lack of medical support I felt during our last year. I wasn't sure why I continued to take Peter to his primary care physician for checkups. Furthermore, why would I put either of us through another annual Neurological exam? Looking back, that answer is crystal clear, which I'll describe.

Peter's PCP has always been a kind and thorough doctor, allowing plenty of time for concerns and discussion. He's gifted with a fun sense of humor and a sweet giggle and we liked him. Still do. The problem lies in the training and the lack of hands-on experience, and

I'm not sure where the deficit lies, but more training is vital.

I decided to discontinue Peter's annual exams with his primary doctor after he advised me to "continue to tell Peter the time, date, year and season to keep him oriented." I actually thought he was joking in some sick sort of way and cracked a smile. When I realized he wasn't, I just took a deep breath and felt very alone and unsupported by the medical staff there.

That feeling was exacerbated when I took Peter to his annual neurology appointment. Again, Dr. Neuro has always been wonderful, and as I shared in chapter one, he delivered Peter's diagnosis with the gentlest of care and respect. He knew what was coming. This visit was a little over a year before Peter died. I had researched and read and scoured books and websites and was hoping for an intelligent answer, a slice of medical wisdom I had not been introduced to.

"What can I expect in the coming year?" I quizzed Dr. Neuro.

"Progressive decline."

No shit Sherlock, I thought, and my mind whizzed back to Peter's PCP visit. I was deflated and dumbfounded by his lack of detail and empathy and willingness to share what was ahead.

For some reason, I felt compelled to take him back a year later. Peter had indeed experienced progressive decline and I had been in touch with the office and had been counseled by a different Dr. Neuro in the practice. New Dr. Neuro adjusted Peter's anti-psychotic medication and his anti-depressants as Peter was more combative, aggressive, and agitated than ever. Miss Nurse and I were fearful for our safety and weary of our ability to keep Peter safe. His medications were adjusted several times, but these powerful drugs had side effects that made Peter lethargic, so the balance was difficult to attain.

Below is a series of blog posts outlining our experience with Peter's neurologist.

TOO NUMB TO BE MAD

The horror of it was so unrealistic that I couldn't react. Current me is regretting not speaking up right then but I think I was just so dumbfounded by it all that my mouth felt stapled shut. Utter disbelief.

The exam room was furnished with two chairs in front of the desk and an exam table off to the side. Miss Nurse and I sat on the chairs, Peter on the exam table, and the physician's assistant asked probing questions and was diligent in her note-taking. Miss Nurse and I were eager to be heard, sitting upright and focused on getting answers.

After we expressed our concerns about Peter's current behaviors, and medications, and made our request for hospice assessment, the PA left to get Dr. Neuro. I got up from my chair and went to sit with Peter on the exam table as he felt very far away. I stayed seated on the exam table when the PA returned with Dr. Neuro. I introduced Miss Nurse, with a quick explanation of her role, PA and Dr. Nuero sat down behind the desk.

Peter's medication had been adjusted three times over the past three weeks by a different Dr. Neuro who was on vacation and not able to be at our appointment. Dr. Neuro immediately suggested we reconvene in a week when he returned from vacation and meet via video appointment.

Miss Nurse and I pushed to discuss the items on our task list and Dr. Neuro briefly answered our questions and again talked about rescheduling. When I pointed to the insurance form I brought for his signature, he said they would have to mail it as they are really backed up today. It was only 9 am.

The room went quiet, and it became awkward. The PA and Dr. Neuro did not stand up, but it was clear our appointment was over.

Wait for it...DR. NEURO DID NOT ACKNOWLEDGE

PETER ONE SINGLE TIME. NO EYE CONTACT. NO HELLO SIR. NO EXAM. NOT A SINGLE GLANCE IN HIS DIRECTION. NOT AN OUNCE OF HUMAN DECENCY.

It took two grown strong women to guide Peter to and through this appointment, driving over 90 minutes, putting Peter through the confusion of it all and he was treated as though he didn't exist."

The next entry is an email I drafted to the clinical nurse administrator after cooling down a bit.

Dear Clinical Nurse Administrator,

Good morning. I write to you to escalate an experience my husband, his nurse, and myself had yesterday. The letter I wrote to Dr. Neuro, copied below, should suffice in summing up the accounts of yesterday's visit.

I'm writing not to have anyone reprimanded, I'm hoping Dr. Neuro's conscience is handling that for him, but rather to nudge a little change. Perhaps a change in training, a lesson in compassion for the staff.

No one should ever be treated the way that my husband was yesterday and based on the nearly 600 comments on my blog, this is a chronic problem. I did receive an apologetic email from Dr. Neuro as well as a lovely phone call from his nurse, whom I've had a fantastic relationship with over the years.

Here is the letter I sent last evening:
Dr. Neuro,
After our visit today I feel compelled to reach out to express my thoughts.

I author an international blog called Oh Hello Alzheimer's. *I am a megaphone creating awareness about Alzheimer's and a fierce advocate for my husband. We have been featured on The Today Show, CNN, CBS NY, The Washington Post, and many many more media outlets. (Google Peter Marshall Alzheimer's if you are the least bit interested which I doubt you are)*

The care from your office continues to disappoint me and today your behavior takes the cake. I wanted to make sure I wrote you right away, although based on best practices I've experienced from your office, you won't read this for a few days.

When I wrote last night, a post that was launched at 4 am today, I worried that the 'white coats' would not include Peter in their conversations and I was concerned the Drs. would do the typical TALK LOUDER TACTIC so the demented person could understand as if their hearing has been compromised.

You have absolutely no idea what it took for the three of us to coordinate getting to your office by 9 am. Worrying about Peter's stress level, confusion, incontinence, etc.

We were met with your complacency, and lack of empathy, and felt pushed aside because you were "really backed up today". What we wanted was to feel heard and have our concerns acknowledged and come up with solutions.

I trusted you to help me preserve Peter's dignity today and help us on this journey with a little human kindness. You could have easily taken the four-five seconds to pause, make eye contact with Peter, and make him feel respected. You never even looked at my husband, never a glance in his direction or an exam of any kind.

Perhaps a bit of self-reflection is in order on your part, perhaps you should be doing research in a lab not dealing with vulnerable human beings who deserve the respect of the people they trust and are supposed to be so highly educated.

How would you feel if one of your family members was treated the way Peter was today? Please. I beg you to truly contemplate that question thinking of your own family members and don't make another person feel the way you made us feel today.

Shame on you.

Today's post reached nearly 17K followers. The consensus is unanimous, your behavior unacceptable. I didn't mention your name or the name of your practice. Don't you DARE, don't

you DARE send me a bill for what you did NOT do today!
So Sincerely,
Lisa Marshall

SOUL SOOTHING

The day after Peter's annual checkup I decided to just take the day and do what felt good. Have a soothe my soul kinda day. To be perfectly fair, just over an hour after I wrote the email to Dr. Neuro he personally responded with an apology. His ten pm words were heartfelt and sincere and I'm certain that he was riddled with thoughts of us the next day. I do believe that he cared for his patients more tenderly for the remainder of the week.

Additionally, after reading the letter the next morning, Dr. Neuro's nurse, who I adore, reached out with a personal phone call. (I had copied and pasted my letter into Peter's patient portal for all to read) She has always treated me with the utmost respect and has been a person I never needed to follow up with. If she said she was going to do something I could very confidently cross it off my list and hang up the phone feeling closure. She was kind and compassionate, shared my feelings with staff members, and agreed that she should also slow down.

I fought back the tears of satisfaction until the call ended and felt very heard by both of them, and for that I am grateful. I wasn't looking to punish anyone and believe that Dr. Neuro's conscience would do that work.

The day continued with me committing to begin again, my yoga practice, and once on the mat, I had much to be thankful for. All of you. And so much more.

A LOVER AND A FIGHTER

Vivid memories come to mind when I think of the few arguments Peter, and I have had over the years. I love fiercely and therefore fight fiercely, too, both purely out of passion. More than a few times recently people have said something to the effect of, "Boy I wouldn't want to piss you off!" Well, I make no apologies for my passion when they evoke positive change that profoundly affects people who cannot help themselves.

I feel intense gratitude for being blessed with both passion and a big mouth. I posted several updates about our experience with Dr. Neuro on November 15th and I'm overjoyed to report the following news from the leadership team:

As we discussed the nursing support in neurology is undergoing some restructuring effective 1/10/22 which will improve patient care in all sections of neurology. We will begin a team approach that will include two-four nurses per team and one clinical admin who will work closely with our social worker and the physician to ensure patients' needs are met timely and efficiently. With this approach, complex patients' plans of care will be discussed during weekly meetings with the attending physician and fellow to ensure all needs are met. Additionally, the team model will allow patients'/caregivers' concerns to be addressed more readily in the event the assigned nurse is on the phone, a nurse from the team who is also familiar with the patient's plan of care will help facilitate. Nurses will also collaborate with their physicians to review complex patient's needs the week before the patient's scheduled appointment.

#RAISEYOURVOICE Merry Christmas Everyone. Hold your loved ones tight.

She was powerful, not because she wasn't scared, but because she went on so strongly despite the fear. -Atticus"

After experiencing such revolting medical care, and advocating for Peter and other families suffering from dementia, it became very clear why I had to take Peter to that last appointment. It was for the greater good. Like his permission to share our journey, his endurance of the visit was another gift from Peter to help others.

During the final weeks, communication was

difficult for Peter and more difficult for anyone in his presence. The conversations were filled with lots of head nods and agreeing to things incomprehensible as his words were strung together like a chewed-up popcorn string.

Fragmented thoughts trying to be words, never to become sentences again. I did not know what he was trying to say most of the day, though he talked for hours. He talked to himself and he talked to Reflection Ralph and he talked to the dogs. I knew there would be a day when I would miss his yammering. I remained patient and kind and tried to stop, looking him in the eyes with respect, but I found myself ignoring the chattering more and more.

Peter had started a new communication technique. Since his words no longer made sense, he resorted to tongue clicks and pops and finger snaps and slaps, stomps, and whistles, and anything he could to relay his thoughts and emotions.

While Peter was still mobile there was one way we always communicated without words. Dancing. We danced all the way up until the month before Peter died. He remembered the rhythm of the music and he may not have been able to recall all his dance moves, but he could recall most.

Peter taught me to dance, and like whistling it was one of the memories he held onto the longest. During our life together, no matter where we were when the first three or four notes of Van Morrison's *Brown Eyed Girl* started we immediately locked eyes and smiled.

It didn't matter where we were if we both heard it. From across the room, across the house, at a bar, in a restaurant, or at a friend's house, if we could dance, we danced! Sometimes in my apron and slippers, sometimes outside in my muck boots, it didn't matter.

Dancing was one of those precious times we got to pretend that everything was still perfectly perfect. Peter would hold my hand and before I knew it he was twirling me around the kitchen or on the deck or in someone else's kitchen or maybe down a grocery aisle.

We'd laugh when he triple twirled me or purposely pushed me a little too hard. I'd go stumbling forward and we'd laugh and laugh and try to compose ourselves. Interlocking once again and giggling, looking into each other's eyes as though it was 2001 again and life was brand new. And for those three minutes, it was.

We didn't need words, our hearts were connected. Peter didn't need to try so damn hard to communicate and I didn't need to try so damn hard to figure out what he was saying. That intense and wondrous feeling outweighed any care I may have of what anyone thought of our public shenanigans.

During one of our last dances, I felt the lump in my throat start. Peter did not glance my way, we did not lock eyes from across a room when our song began. He had forgotten our song. I decided at that precise moment that I had a choice. I could look into the future and be sad about what was coming, or I could be in this moment and be happy. I chose the latter and became very present noticing the texture of the fabric of his shirt and his soft hand in mine and the beating of his heart against me. During our dance, I felt his breath and his stubble and I planted all of it in my garden of memories. And there, they bloom.

Our dances ceased, Peter's body was withering and at the end of November, I called hospice to come to evaluate Peter. I did not expect that he would be approved for their services, but he was. The hospice nurse went over the physical things they provided like walkers and hospital beds, bedpans, pullups and diapers, and so on. She told me about the support they offered as well. The hospice team would include a nurse, an aide, a doctor for the nurse to discuss Peter's case with, a social worker, and clergy to support me. After evaluation from the assigned nurse, we would put a schedule in place. Peter would be reevaluated every 60-90 days to be sure he would continue to qualify for hospice services.

It all sounded foreign and scary and I was sure we weren't anywhere close to needing most of these services, but time would tell.

I was afraid. Of his pain. His anxiety. His fear. My grief. What will happen? Will he be afraid? I was afraid of our home being an empty house. Afraid of our empty nest, returning to our empty bed. I was afraid of too much closet space. I was afraid of the deepest, darkest loneliness I had ever felt and I was most afraid of the day I could no longer feel his warm sweet lips on mine.

I was not aware of how quickly I would be facing these very real fears. In a blink, things had taken a sharp turn. Peter was speaking only a word or two all day. Walking was shuffling, and he was very unstable, even with help. Peter could no longer feed himself or hold a cup to his lips. Pull-ups have been swapped out for diapers with tabs.

On the morning of December 6th, the hospice aide came to help with Peter's bath and he did not understand how to get into the tub. Stepping onto the inside ledge of the tub by the shower wall, straddling over the water I coaxed him into remembering. We could not get him to sit down, and in retrospect, it was a blessing. We would've had a difficult time getting him up out of the tub if he had sat down. Peter could also not understand how to sit on the shower chair. He did not get a bath that day.

After dressing him, it took three women 15 minutes to get him down the stairs as his legs and feet did not understand what to do. His legs were stiff and we patiently and carefully guided his legs, bending and supporting them from step to step. We were all nervous and sweating profusely by the time we reached the bottom, fearful he would fall and hurt himself. It would be his last time maneuvering the stairs.

We called hospice to relay the morning's events and the hospital bed arrived that afternoon. Son and son-in-law moved the family room sectional upstairs to a spare bedroom and brought my bed downstairs. They placed my bed just across the room from Peter's hospital bed. I arranged and organized and fluffed pillows and cleaned to make the space cozy for us both.

Miss Nurse and I said goodbye to our sweet hospice aide as she went on to her next patient. Later in the morning, Peter's hospice nurse came to visit. The sons had come and gone, and so had the afternoon and the entire day felt fuzzy. I wandered around aimlessly without purpose for most of it. I cried several times and just couldn't get going at all.

I decided to go upstairs and was unprepared for what I found. I found the remnants of the morning as I stood and scanned the room. The bed that Peter would never sleep in again. The bathroom was just the way we left it, the bathtub filled with cold water. We would not bathe him there again. His big, oversized beach blanket I would wrap him in after his bath, slung over the railing. The unused wet washcloth. The empty office where my bed had been for the past eight months. Those damn bells on his bedroom door. The grief washed over me. The reality was settling in.

Peter had been in manic distress those past few months, agitated and anxious and combative and angry and pacing, truly horrific to watch. He could not stop moving until he collapsed. It was exhausting for everyone to handle. I found comfort knowing he was calm now, and I breathed in the relief. And as I did, I think the house took a deep breath, too.

It was then I had the very sudden shift in my emotions that I later learned was something called radical acceptance. According to *Psychology Today*, radical acceptance is about accepting life on life's terms and not resisting what you cannot or choose not to change. Radical acceptance is about saying yes to life, just as it is.

I did not know what radical acceptance was or that I was practicing a conscious effort to acknowledge and honor the difficult situation and my emotions. Fully accepting things as they were, instead of wishing the situation were different, was a critical step in moving through the end of our journey and helping Peter die in the most peaceful way possible. Acceptance doesn't replace grief. It doesn't take away the pain. Acceptance helps you to stop fighting. That night, for the first time in twenty years, I found Peter's snoring to be comforting. The vibration of his snoring soothed me to sleep as I knew he was calm and safe across the room.

On Tuesday, December 7, 2021 I started keeping a record of Peter's meds, moods, and food. Today as I flip through the notebook, the words on those pages are haunting as Peter's impending death swirls around them. Keeping a physical log of Peter's last days was grueling as each entry forged us closer to the last entry.

I did not allow myself to wallow in the darkness of this task, rather I focused on what I was grateful for. Constantly being thankful for the beautiful gifts I have been so fortunate to enjoy in life, helped me through the final weeks. I practiced reflecting on these joy-filled memories, along with deep deep breathing to get me through the hardest moments.

"I am thankful. I am grateful. I am broken. I am weak." I thought.

By mid-month, Peter remained in the hospital bed in our family room and no longer walked. He had to be moved and turned as his body no longer allowed him the strength to do it himself. He was awake for most of the day. Some days he was full of smiles and even a few laughs. He hallucinated and reached for things in the air and sometimes threw things at someone or something we could not see. Each day there were fewer smiles and eventually, Peter stopped laughing.

Early each morning when he woke up, I climbed into his hospital bed and snuggled with him until his aide arrived to bathe and change him. He moved his arm and remembered how to hold me and one time he tried to stroke my hair the way he always did.

Peter was loving and helpful to his core and these traits remained til the day he died. During one of his last weeks, Miss Nurse sat with Peter while he lay in his hospital bed. I was running manically around the house keeping my mind busy. As I turned on the vacuum cleaner, Peter sat up in his bed and said verbatim, "Can I help ya?" He was helpful to his core and somewhere in his brain the sound of the vacuum cleaner triggered that caring part enabling him to not only physically sit up but form a sentence!

Agitation came and went and Peter seemed to sleep for an entire day or be antsy and combative all day. At this point, getting out of bed could be dangerous for him, as his body could no longer bear his weight.

Early one morning I climbed into his hospital bed. He was agitated, had flung one leg up over the railing of his bed, and was trying to climb out. I was alone and could not risk running out to the kitchen to get his morning medication to calm him. I called my neighbor Todd, knowing he was an early riser.

"Can you come over?" I asked without explanation.

"I'll be right there" he answered without question, and he was. The night before I had a strong notion that I should leave the front door unlocked. I had never done that before.

When Todd walked in I was lying next to Peter with my left leg over Peter's body, my arm over Peter's chest grasping the railing to hold him down. His body was still strong.

Todd came to the bedside and asked what I needed. I explained that I needed him to make sure Peter didn't get out of bed while I ran to the kitchen for his medication. Together Todd and I lulled Peter's mood back to a safe level. It takes a village.

The last two weeks were brutally cruel in a way that cannot be described with words. The horror can only be felt and I know the pain is so intensely sharp because I loved Peter so fiercely. How lucky am I to have loved and been loved so deeply to experience such agony?

I posted this on the blog. Reading it now, I can recall the physical sickness I felt during this last month. It feels extremely heavy as I submerge myself there once again.

It is unbearable, the not knowing when death will come, the ambiguous grief is torture. Lately, I have not been myself. My motivation falters, my body physically feels heavily weighted, and ill, and I drag myself through the sludge of the day. Other times, I paint on my face and head out the door not wanting to ever turn back.

Peter is calm and then he is highly agitated. This wavering in Peter's cognitive ability is the only constant, the constant unpredictability that one nurse referred to as psychological torture. The Alzheimer's bitch continues to torture us both incessantly. I want her to leave. I want her to stay.

Most days, I am numb. Chewing is a chore and I have dropped sixteen pounds, unknowingly. I hope only for Peter's comfort and peace, nuzzling near him, offering him all the gentleness I can muster. Snuggling sessions are precious and nothing else matters. The chores and dirt and tasks and things will be there later, the hand I'm holding won't.

Miss Nurse and I reacted to Peter's every flinch and moan and groan. He was surrounded by a sea of pillows to protect his fragile legs from the unforgiving side rails of his bed. The softest pillow was placed between the heels of his feet and the bottom of the bed. No matter how many times we boosted Peter up he always seemed to slide down to the bottom of the bed against the footboard.

The hospice aide, Miss Nurse, and I were constantly fussing and propping and changing Peter's position. Our only concern was that he was comfortable.

Peter's brain forgot how to chew and his medications were changed to liquid or suppository form or crushed in yogurt or applesauce. Those we felt he no longer needed were discontinued. Water and juice became too thin and Peter would cough so we added a thickening agent to the water which made it much easier for him to swallow. Hospice supplied a nosey cup when it became difficult for him to lift his head to drink. This special cup had a U shape cut out so the cup could fit around the nose and pouring liquid into Peter's mouth was less difficult. Hospice delivered an oxygen tank for comfort and it helped Peter to sleep at night.

One evening my daughter Sarah and her husband Dan, who is a professional photographer, came to visit. Dan and I previously had a brief and somber conversation about a last photo shoot that would be solely for me to cherish. I had decided against it after Peter's rapid decline. Dan and Sarah were ready to leave and he revisited my request which I quickly declined.

"Are you sure? Are you absolutely sure? My camera is in the car. You can always delete them." He urged and I nodded my head, agreeing to the photos pushing away the day's tears. I'm so grateful he nudged me to say yes that evening.

I visit the album when I am strong enough, or

maybe when I am just weak enough to consume their devastation. The gift that Dan gave me is priceless and I cannot imagine how difficult it was looking through the lens of his camera to get those perfect shots. While they are haunting, they are the end of the most beautiful chapter of my life.

When Peter's brain could no longer remember how to swallow, sponges were introduced. We had to give him very small amounts of water to wet his lips and tongue and mouth so he would not aspirate the liquid into his lungs. His lips were dry and cracked, peeling.

I felt as though I was dying with him. Walking was an effort, I wandered aimlessly, and Miss Nurse said I once banged into the fridge which I was not even aware of. I felt we were in limbo waiting for the end. My mind was numb with the knowledge of what was coming.

He kissed me one final time on Friday, December 24th before falling asleep one last time. I hadn't slept snuggling next to Peter for nine or ten months, but early that night after he was bathed and tucked in, I climbed into his hospital bed and nestled close, curling my body around him listening to the hum of his oxygen. I cried silently so I wouldn't wake him, my tears dropping quietly on his chest. The next thing I knew I woke up and it was after midnight. I had fallen asleep listening to his heartbeat.

Christmas day, Peter continued sleeping. His face and head were fuzzy as he could no longer tolerate any kind of grooming. His beautiful blue eyes watered. His mouth relaxed as he slept. I was alone with my love when things started changing. His body was hot, he had a fever, and he was sweating. I tried to cool him with a cold wet cloth. His respirations were very high and he breathed heavily, but he slept. He was peaceful and I don't believe he was in pain.

I kissed him often and told him how much I loved

him. I thanked him over and over for giving me such a beautiful life. I promised Peter I would be fine and told him it was ok to go. He remained asleep for the entire day and I remained awake overnight, watching him.

In the morning, on December 26, waiting for Miss Nurse to arrive, I started adjusting Peter's pillows to make sure he was comfortable. That's when I saw it and I knew that my sweet husband was going to die that day. I had uncovered his body to find that during the night he had placed his left calf over his right ankle. As I adjusted his fragile body, tenderly lifting one leg off the other I noticed it. The purpleness, the pooling blood, the mottling where his heavy top leg rested on his underneath leg. As I lifted it, I noticed the top leg, too, was purple.

Slowly, to protect my heart, I held my breath and pulled the blankets off his legs to study his skin. His knees were purple, his thighs blotchy. I looked at every inch of him and found purple splotches on his fingers. He was dying before my eyes. I gently covered him up and dropped onto the couch, howling in pain and grief and relief.

The question of 'when' after all this time, was finally being answered. It was the longest and shortest day of my life. My heart ached with loneliness, yet I felt a peacefulness for Peter, knowing his suffering was ending.

Peter's respirations were stabilized with medication and he remained asleep and peaceful all day. I had previously talked to our five children and asked them each the same question, "Do you want me to call you before, or after?" Their answers were unanimous: after. They had all said their goodbyes and did not want to remember Peter in death.

The kids and I were in constant communication throughout the day and they knew the dreaded end was near. At the last minute, my daughter Sarah changed her mind and drove the fifteen minutes to our home. She came and slowly sat down with me on Peter's bed. She spoke sweetly to him, telling him who she was, holding his hand. Sarah recognized that it would be very hard, but she came anyway to be a witness for Peter and me. Sarah had a role to play during our entire journey, often being the mother to me. She was a divine gift, guiding me, urging me, loving me. Helping me with decisions along the way, she was typically two steps ahead of me, patiently waiting with the answers when I asked her advice.

Relaxing music played, lavender was being diffused in the air and there was a calmness in the room. I slipped Peter's wedding ring off my hand and carefully nudged it on his purple finger and I kissed him, once again telling him to go.

I laid my head on Peter's chest listening to his heart beating, feeling his methodical slowing breaths on my cheek. Peter had waited for Sarah's arrival. Even in death, he protected me as he knew I would need her. Her presence on this night was her biggest gift. I had not thought about what I would do immediately after Peter's death and cannot imagine how empty the night could have been without my angel Sarah, by my side. I will be forever grateful for her bravery, integrity, and compassion in making that decision for us. Sarah helped Peter to die peacefully because he knew she would take care of me.

Moments later, ever so peacefully, his brain forgot how to breathe and his heart stopped beating. I heard his last heartbeat and felt his last breath on my face. And just like that, the Alzheimer's bitch took my Prince Charming.

Lisa's Lookback

The shift to radical acceptance was comforting. I knew then, that I had done everything I could for Peter and I regretted nothing. There was nothing left to do, but keep Peter comfortable and spend every minute I could with him. He loved me until the end. When I am brave enough I allow myself to feel his last soft kiss imprinted on my lips. His last breath tingling on my cheek and the final beat of his heart faintly tap against my ear.

Question to Ponder

1. What is your immediate post-death plan?

2. Who is your person who will be on call when you need to be supported witnessing death?

3. Who will you assign the logistical tasks of calling end-of-life professionals?

All I Ever Wanted

He's all I ever wanted, I thought to myself, all I ever wished for in a husband, and our romantic love story has been more than I ever imagined it could be. Truly, I feel so incredibly blessed and forever grateful for the gift of his love.

I wished for a gentleman.
I wished for a man to love my children.
I wished for a tender and kind soul.
I wished for integrity and honesty.
I wished to be loved completely.
I wished for him to be humble.
I wished for a partner.
I wished for someone I could learn from.
My every wish came true.

But I forgot the most important wish, growing old together.

CHAPTER 27

Life After Death, Grief

At the precise moment I felt and heard the final beat of Peter's heart faintly tap against my ear, I became a widow. The grief was no longer ambiguous. Even though I had known what was coming all along, even though I had been grieving for years, the pain rippled. The intensity of the anguish seeped through me like spilled ink.

I laid on him, secretly begging to go with him, how could I go on without him? Recalling the advice of my friend, I opened the nearest window to allow Peter's soul to fly free and I returned immediately to his face. I kissed him and caressed him as though he were still in his body and I felt a black powerful energy radiating through me that I needed to expel. I sobbed and screamed in disbelief. The vulnerability was unbearable. The reality of the instant loneliness was so potent. No amount of preparation could help me at this moment. The finality of death was so raw.

I had previously contacted my Rabbi and asked him to recite and record the mourner's kaddish, the Hebrew mourning prayer. Sarah and I stood over Peter's body, connecting his hands with ours while Rabbi Kessler's somber words whirred around us, squeezing my heart. My legs were weak, I was lightheaded and needed to remind myself to breathe. I felt crippled. I thought I would be ill.

Nothing could console my wounds and I felt desperate. I wanted to call an ambulance, go to the hospital, die. I needed intensive care now. I was so thankful Sarah had come. She was gentle with me, though she was grieving, too.

Lying on Peter's chest, I sobbed in disbelief. Removing his wedding ring, I placed it back on my hand. What an amazing marriage it had been. What an incredible man Peter was and I felt the relief wash over me. Relief for Peter, that he was no longer suffering from the torment of the Alzheimer's bitch. I would, however, suffer from her thievery for the rest of my life.

There were things that needed to be done. Phone calls to be made. Hospice was called and the nurse was summoned to make the official pronouncement of Peter's death. The funeral home was called to come. I spoke with our children. Our friends. I remember none of those calls.

When the undertaker came to take Peter's body, Miss Nurse insisted I leave the room. "You don't want to see this Lisa," and Sarah escorted me to another room. I'm sure there were papers I signed and conversations I had with both hospice nurse and undertaker but I cannot recall them.

A few hours had passed since Peter's last breath and we were all exhausted. Sarah and Miss Nurse stayed overnight. I climbed the stairs and for the first time in nearly a year returned to our bedroom and our bed. It didn't feel strange or weird, and I felt comforted there and remember getting a decent night's sleep.

I posted these two entries on the blog shortly after Peter's death. The panic that accompanied the grief nearly brought me to my knees.

THE DAY AFTER

I want to walk away from this, the day after, knowing I did everything I could and I gave him a beautiful life. My beloved Peter passed away peacefully last night surrounded by so much love. He is free of her horrendous grip, and for that I am relieved. My heart is broken, but I have no regrets. My heart is broken, but I will find Joy in our memories. I'm the luckiest girl in the world. Peter gave me a beautiful life.

THE OPEN WINDOW

It starts in my chest, and I notice my heart begin to pound, and then I hear my breaths getting louder and closer together and I feel my body moving faster and the thoughts turn to panic. I want to run or scream or hit something, I always cry. Something always triggers it, the slightest thing, a song, a smell, a memory, glimpsing something Peter loved.

Today is day two without a panic attack like that and while I came close, I was able to breathe it away and realized I wasn't quite ready for what triggered it. The trigger was a load of laundry that had been left in the dryer. Feeling compelled to stay busy I attempted to fold it, but feeling the fabric of Peter's clothes, imagining him wearing them was too much to bear. I can handle the every-single-day sadness, but the panic is unnerving.

Grief is a process that you cannot go around. You must go through it and feel all the feels. Good, bad, horrific. The emptiness accompanying grief is haunting and terrifying and cannot be described with words. I was not prepared.

The finality of the death of your soulmate, your best friend, the love of your life, cannot be comprehended until it happens. The last breath is devastating and crippling.

My next-door neighbor, Michelle, texted my daughter the morning after Peter's death, "My window was open last night when I heard your mom. I'm so sorry for your loss."

The next days are hazy and I cannot recall many of the details. I scrolled through the pictures on my phone and am perplexed by some images I captured, but have no memory of. The next day, hospice came to collect the hospital bed, the bedside commode, the oxygen, and the shower chair. I was glad to be rid of it. I gathered all the diapers and pullups and wipes and chucks and organized them in bags. Placing them by the door I planned on donating them to someone who needed them. If I pushed all these physical things out the door maybe these pain-filled memories would leave as well.

Sarah and Zachary went to the funeral home with me. Plans were made, death certificates ordered and urns were chosen. I chose one large urn for the mantle and six smaller heart-shaped urns. Peter wanted me and the five kids to spread his ashes wherever we had created our favorite memories together.

The kids showed up strong, as did the best of friends. Meals were prepared and dishes were done and I think I must have just wandered around. I'm not sure. The kids helped disassemble my family room bed and moved it back to the spare room. The sectional was reconnected, and the family room once again became a gathering space where we delighted in going through decades of pictures of Peter's life. Carefully placing our favorites in a folder to be printed out and glued onto poster boards for the funeral. I don't recall ordering the photos or picking them up, buying poster board or glue. Did I?

I walked around going through the motions, clutching Peter's monkey. During stage six Peter became attached to him and constantly picked him up off the floor. Peter carried him around, stuffing him in his pockets, and even slept with him. I became equally attached to his friend, taking over custody after Peter's death.

Three days after, I posted a video inviting anyone who would like to join me and Monkey and our dog, Mollie in a tribute walk to Peter. We would be walking the next day, the three-mile loop around the lake where we live. Peter and I had walked it hundreds of times, maybe thousands. Fifty-four people showed up. I couldn't believe it. I cried my eyes out at how people just showed up. It was a reminder that people in our lives want to celebrate and honor our loved ones that pass. Perhaps this gave them closure as well, for their part in Peter's journey.

"How are you doing?" friends asked, and the truth was that I am relieved for Peter mostly, that he was no longer suffering. I was relieved that I was no longer grieving someone who has been gone a long time, waiting for tiny glimpses of the man I married. But there were waves. They'd crash in when I least expected it. Waves of panic and grief triggered by a favorite shirt of his or a special picture or the smell of him, or a song or anything. The waves washed over me and I couldn't breathe.

I visited with the grief, allowing myself to feel it, sit with it. Then I participated in affirmations of gratitude for having been loved so deeply by Peter. Feelings of pride for having so carefully helped him through his journey. To his death. And I looked forward. Because Peter would want me to. I looked forward to time with our children and our grandson and sharing sweet memories and stories. I looked forward to our second grandson, who I had just learned would be arriving in the summer. Because Peter would want me to.

Our family was hurting in the deepest way because we loved Peter so intensely. We were blessed with an incredible amount of support and love to guide us through the worst time imaginable. During the walk, an eagle watched over us from the treetops as the walking group posed for a picture on the bridge, and then it soared over the lake. Peter was with us.

Everyone who knew Peter had grieved and mourned his tragic loss for years and I felt strongly his funeral should be a celebration. Stories were shared and jokes were made. We laughed, we cried, and we toasted to

Peter with his favorite beer. I do not recall who came and who did not. I don't remember arriving or leaving the funeral home.

The first time I walked out of the house alone, I stopped on the front porch. Feeling like things were undone or as though I had forgotten something. Leaving the house while Peter was alive required preparation and planning. The emotional impact of just leaving the house became shockingly obvious. I felt as though I suffered from post-traumatic stress disorder. Could I just walk out the door, get in my car and drive away with no guilt? No planning or preparation? No anxiety or fear?

The nights were the hardest. I was lonely and missed nurturing and caring for Peter. I missed being needed. I questioned my identity and how I would fill my time and my heart. One night the loneliness smothered me and I panicked. Without even looking at the clock, I called my friend MJ. It was nearly 11 o'clock at night. She answered and I sobbed, "I can't breathe. I can't breathe."

MJ knew what to do and instinctually I knew she was the one I needed to call. "Yes, you can. We're going to breathe together. Breathe with me, Lisa." She instructed and I gulped the air in jagged breaths with her until the fear passed. Be sure you have someone in your life like MJ who you can call anytime for any reason. Surround yourself with people stronger than you, so you can be supported by their strength.

I became a little stronger and I folded that load of laundry. I went through all of Peter's clothes and possessions. Every piece was connected to a memory. His work jeans, his work boots, that favorite sweatshirt, race t-shirts, ball caps, and slippers. I made a pile of the things I couldn't part with and tucked them away. Monkey will stay with me forever.

When I had gone through his things, I invited the kids to come to find their treasures. A special shirt or pair of shoes, running gear, whatever helped them to heal or hold on. Wherever they could find comfort.

I became manic in my urge to purge everything that reminded me of the Alzheimer's bitch. Everything my heart could handle had to go. Puzzles and games and fidgets and stuffed toys were stored or donated and I tried with all my might to push her out the door and out of my life. My cousin Sherri graciously took the dozen bags of diapers and chucks and donated them for me.

I made plans to change the master bedroom and rid the space of her. I kept purging and freshening and it felt as good as screaming or yelling or crying but there was only one thing that would truly help. Time.

Sixteen days after Peter died, I shared this news on the blog. I was still numb from my husband's death when I received the news.

THANK YOU, DEAR

Those were the last words I would hear from Peter's Father before he passed. Richard Marshall passed away yesterday, predeceased by his lovely wife, Andrea, less than a year ago. Three of the most wonderful people I have known in my life were gone in less than a year.

Rich had an infectious, boisterous laugh that made you smile along, and he filled your heart with stories you'd heard a hundred times before. Peter was a gentleman because his father taught him to be. I will miss him dearly."

"Thank you, Dear." Peter's father spoke those last words to me in our home. Rich wasn't sure if he wanted to visit Peter in his hospital bed in our family room. He wasn't sure he could look at his son and face his looming death. Peter's sister Ann-Marie had brought him but Rich stayed in the entrance as though his feet were glued there. I approached them to learn of his apprehension. I hugged him and I told him it was terrible experiencing

353

this as Peter's wife, and I acknowledged that it must also be terrible as a sibling. We all blinked back the tears. I empathized with Peter's father and assured him I could not fathom what it must be like to lose a child, no matter what age.

"Would you like me to describe what you'll see? Would that make it easier for you?" I asked my sweet father-in-law. Rich agreed that it would. I explained that Peter was sleeping and he was peaceful. He was comfortable in his hospital bed with no tubes or machines other than some oxygen to keep him comfy. He is not talking, or thrashing, or groaning, he is calm.

"He's not in pain," I told his father. Rich was brave and went in to say goodbye to his son. He visited as long as he could stand the pain and then hugged me to say he was leaving, while he wiped his eyes and nose. His familiar parting words ring like a gift in my ear, "Thank you, Dear."

Lisa's Lookback

The reality of this disease is that there's no remission, there's no stopping it, there's no slowing it down, there's no cure and there are no survivors. I knew these to be facts and prepared myself by envisioning what I wanted after Peter's death. I wanted to have no regrets. By purposefully and intentionally demanding no regrets of myself I was able to manifest joy, be as patient and loving as possible, and constantly remind myself of my goal. There was only one way I would not have regrets, and that was to not do anything I would regret. This mantra allowed me the space to research and create techniques to make our lives easier.

I'm so grateful that Peter progressed through the final stage so quickly. His quality of life had diminished and he lived with constant confusion and anxiety. The hardest thing was watching Peter suffer and now he is free.

Questions to Ponder

1. Are you preparing for your grief after death by surrounding yourself with people who can support you?

2. Do you have end-of-life plans in place, such as an advanced directive[6], and funeral arrangements, so you are not burdened with decisions while you're grieving?

3. Are there rituals you want to practice when your loved one dies?

---

[6] See this article on advanced directives by Dr. Geoffrey Hosta, https://www.washingtonpost.com/opinions/2019/11/28/doctors-are-torturing-dementia-patients-end-their-life-its-totally-unnecessary/

I want to inspire people.
I want someone to look at me and say,
"Because of you, I didn't give up."

CHAPTER 28

Hope After Death

I recall one vivid moment of our journey when Peter came to me putting his face in front of mine, so his breath was warm on my skin, and he whispered, "I'm afraid you're going to leave me."

The lump in my throat grew fast and large and I thought I might suffocate on his words but instead, I whispered back, "My Love, I'm trying to keep you as long as I can."

And I did keep Peter as long as I could. I cherish every moment and memory and every ounce of love that man poured over me. But by the time we reached stage seven, a part of me wanted the journey to end. I have come to understand that many caregivers precisely feel this way. Peter's body, which used to house his beautiful mind, was just an empty shell. I was becoming one as well. One of us had to make it out alive, and it had to be me.

I was relieved it was over, the darkness of waiting for death and the constant need to be alert and responsible. I was thankful to be done with this vulgar experience and it felt cathartic to say it out loud. I clearly remember clutching my chest and wilting with exhaustion, saying quietly, "I did it." I felt like a battered champion for having climbed the mountain and survived.

Nigerian poet, Ijeoma Umebinyuo said, "You must let the pain visit. You must allow it to teach you. You must not allow it to overstay."

Alzheimer's was not a punishment for Peter and

me or you and your loved one. I like to think it was an opportunity and the pathway to my next chapter. Our journey was a learning opportunity and with Peter's blessing, he gave the world the generous gift of sharing his story. Although it was difficult and dreadful to watch, it was necessary to teach others what to expect and to create awareness of the tragedy of this disease. We are here to teach what we most needed to learn. "Tell it all." Peter urged. And I have told it. I will continue advocating for fellow caregivers, guiding and sharing my own experiences.

My paralyzation from the trauma has lifted and I have surrendered my grief and trust in this new chapter. Surrendering and letting go, does not mean forgetting. Letting go is cherishing memories and paying tribute to them. Surrendering is another step in radical acceptance for me. Surrendering allows us to receive the grace of knowing how to accept our past, how to heal in the present moment, and how to be courageous and open to what experiences are coming for our future.

After re-entering the world I was saying yes to everything and everyone. I was no longer shackled to the Alzheimer's bitch and I felt free, almost high. Free to spend more time with family, visit with friends, babysit grandchildren, walk my dog, and travel. Help other caregivers cope, raise funds for the Alzheimer's Association, join committees and advocate to make a difference on a political state policy level. It was my time to write a book and do all the things I had been saying no to for too long. I became overwhelmed and anxious and didn't know what was next on my calendar from morning to afternoon! Once I realized how overstretched I was, I decided I needed to find balance. Like a pendulum, I swung to the other side into life, the opposite direction of when I was a caregiver.

I needed to start analyzing what I was saying yes to.

I pondered each request and asked myself if it felt good. I made sure I wasn't overextending myself causing anxiety and stress. The things I planned from this point forward were to intentionally bring me joy and peace. I promised myself to be present and grateful and I grew stronger as I healed.

As I started truly enjoying life, I gave myself permission to feel good and I chose to be happy. I am worthy of these feelings and I felt calmer as I settled into a new balance I deserved. I have never lived alone in my life and I am learning that I enjoy the peace of being alone. Being kind to myself, I was reminded of things I loved like gardening, walking, swimming, hiking, and being adventurous and spontaneous. Being present, vibrating positivity, being so very grateful for the simplest pleasure the day is offering me. I became a better version of myself.

I urge you to devise a list of things you not only can enjoy after your Alzheimer's journey but one that will help you heal. You can create a list of experiences that will help you acknowledge the trauma you've endured and encourage growth. Can you reflect on your experience and ponder ways to use your newfound wisdom to help others?

I went on a five-day vacation alone to Clearwater Beach, Florida and it was life-changing. I felt empowered getting acquainted with myself, the new, older, wiser me. I was free to walk the beach and shop, eat out, swim in the pool, and read on a rooftop all by myself. I even took my first ride in a helicopter! I became my own friend, and I like myself.

My lunches and visits with friends and family are selective as I want to be very present. I've spent so much time being a pre-occupied caregiver that now, I set my intentions to be fully present and interested in my conversations and relationships, including the time I spend with my grandsons.

In keeping with the fresh attitude of my new chapter, I decided I needed a new space. The master bedroom was riddled with terrible memories left by the indelible ink of the Alzheimer's bitch. No amount of paint or new carpeting would rid the space of her and so I gutted the bedroom, knocked down the wall between the bedroom and my office and opened up two rooms into one. My bedroom suite is cozy and soft and peaceful and it's where I wrote this book, overlooking Andover Lake. The space is mine and mine only and it feels lovely.

I took a trip to East Matunuck Beach in Rhode Island to spread Peter's ashes. This was Peter's favorite beach when he was whole. I have many beautiful memories of the Peter I fell in love with on this seaside stretch. At East Matunuck we beat our own paddleball record, we body surfed and took tumbles. We played backgammon, ran, and walked the beach. We wobble-walked the entire length of the jetty, arms outstretched. I waved to Peter's parents for the first time on that beach as they took a ferry to Block Island. We skinny dipped in the dark. We made love under the moon. I thought of these memories and more as I released his ashes and my fears into the ocean. I cried because I miss him and I cried in celebration of him. But most of all I felt peaceful and grateful for the memories.

On the other side of this reprehensible, catastrophic, and heart-wounding journey there is hope. My broken heart is healing more every day. The painful memories that fill me are softening and I am looking through a life lens that offers relief, joy, and anticipation. The memories I recall of Peter now bring fewer tears and more smiles and laughter.

We are free. And although I miss him, I miss the man I married, not the conflicted, fearful, confused man who left me. Because of this dreadful illness, I've been missing Peter for years. On the other side, I can take a very fulfilling deep breath relieving what aches and my shoulders have dropped from my ears. The lines on my face have eased, and my jaw is unclenched. Peacefulness encompasses my every cell as I throw my hands up in a glorious chant, "I did it! I have no regrets!"

Peter and I blanketed each other in the deepest of love, and I am eternally grateful for our experiences, as they have made me who I am today. I am alive and I am living life to its fullest. An incredible sense of peace has come over me and I stress over very little now. I've been through something extremely tragic and the feeling of relief is powerful. Ralph Waldo Emerson reminds us that, "The reward of a thing well done is having done it."

Peter and I were together for over 20 years. I miss him terribly, but the pain is softening, and the bad memories are fading. The old happy memories are starting to shine through the clouds of grief. I'm aware of what triggers the sadness and sometimes I just welcome the grief to wash over me and other times I push it away. Sometimes I'm a little blindsided and have no choice. I imagine grief lasts a lifetime and I cannot go around it, I must go through it to honor Peter and the love we shared. Sharing precious stories with friends and family brings me so much comfort and joy. We keep Peter's spirit alive by reminiscing about our best times together.

Looking forward, my heart is open to filling the void of companionship. My energy level is high and I want to gobble up life with someone who shares my interests. I have never felt more vibrant, more content, or more hungry. I have so much love to give, so much life to live and I don't want to do it alone. I look forward to being interested in someone, counting on someone, and sharing with and caring for someone. I look forward in anticipation to a new connection, and isn't anticipation delicious?

There is hope on the other side. I not only survived the horror, but I'm thriving. I have been reminded of who I am again. I am free of the Alzheimer's bitch and my goal now is to continue to help caregivers and families with Alzheimer's. Understanding that this journey was a big chapter in my entire life enables me to vibrate positivity, and inspire, offering hope to those who feel they are sinking. It's important to me to honor Peter's memory by sharing the knowledge I've gained with other families. And to pay attention to what I could not prioritize before, my friends, my family, my health, my happiness. Peter would want that. I am peaceful and free and I am alive. I am content knowing I did everything I could and we gave each other a beautiful life.

Lisa's Lookback

Pablo Picasso said, "The meaning of life is to find your gift. The purpose of life is to give it away." Peter trusted me with the gift of his permission to share the story of his journey with Alzheimer's. My purpose is to give it to you, to improve your experience, and create awareness. I feel proud to have accomplished the things I have and feel complete with the decisions I made along the way. I have no regrets. This disease will not define me for the rest of my life. I am looking forward, and I am anticipating wonderful things to come. I have much to offer, and much to experience and learn. Life has been patiently waiting for me.

Much Love,
Lisa

APPENDIX A:

"Running Into An Unclear Future"

By LORI RILEY

Hartford Courant

Dec. 22, 2019

One of Peter Marshall's best friends from high school came from Southington. So did a childhood friend, who went to Horace Porter School in Columbia with him and trained for the Hartford Marathon with him three years ago. Former co-workers. Neighbors. His kids. His wife Lisa's kids. Their first grandchild, bundled up against the cold rain. A friend whom he had saved from drowning drove three hours from Albany.

They all had their own memories of Marshall, who was completing his goal of running a road race in all 169 towns in Connecticut on a cold rainy Sunday in late November in Scotland.

"We were on a company trip," said David Marks, who made a three-hour trip from Albany to the northeast corner of Connecticut to watch Marshall cross the finish line of the Scotland Scoot 4-mile race. "We were both swimming in the ocean, and I got stuck in a rip current. I couldn't make it back to shore. He dragged me out of the ocean, and I was non-responsive on the beach for 17 minutes. Spent two days in the emergency room. But if he didn't drag me out, I wouldn't be here. I said, 'I've got to drive here to see the 169th race.'"

They came to let Marshall know he was in their thoughts. But Marshall's memories of them were fragmented and sometimes needed prompting. Sometimes he would light up, a broad smile spreading over his face. Other times his face would be blank. Or he would pretend, which his wife Lisa Marshall said is a common occurrence.

Or he would say, "It doesn't matter."

Marshall, 54, of Andover, was diagnosed with early-onset Alzheimer's in April 2018. A fire protection engineer who moved to Connecticut to work for a global investment management firm specializing in insurance, Marshall was the kind of guy that if you had a problem, he could usually think of a solution, often innovative.

"It's been rough, watching his good days and his bad days," his stepdaughter Sarah Brehant said, as she stood under an umbrella with her mother Lisa, waiting for Peter to cross the finish line. "He started this journey five years ago, and he was fine. And now it's like I'm not even sure he realizes all these people are here for him."

"He does," Lisa said. "We had a long talk last night when we went to bed about how he needs to tell me when he doesn't know who somebody is. He'll go a whole day and he doesn't know somebody. He's real good at faking it.

"I think he knows what's happening now."

The rain poured down. Runners started coming across the finish line, where a bagpiper played.

"It's been very hard," Brehant said. "I'm trying to support her, but I'm like, 'How are you doing so good?' I don't get it."

"I'm a mess today," Lisa said. "I can't stop crying."

"That's because it's a bittersweet ending to something," her daughter told her.

"It's like I don't want it to end," Lisa said. "Because I don't know what's next."

Lisa Brenner and Peter Marshall were neighbors in Harrisburg, Pa. Their kids, Peter's two and Lisa's three, grew up playing together. Then Peter and his family relocated to Connecticut in 2001 for Peter's job. Peter got divorced. Lisa, still back in Harrisburg, got divorced.

"He out of the blue gave me a call and he said, 'Hey, what's going on?' I said, 'Why don't you come down?' and the rest is history," Lisa said. "That was 18 years ago. We were long distance for eight years."

To Peter, she is "Tart." He cannot tell you why right now. It doesn't matter. They drove back and forth from Connecticut to Pennsylvania, from Pennsylvania to Connecticut—a six-hour drive—for eight years while their children were growing up and they needed to be with them.

Anyway, they were young, and there would be time later on for them to be with each other. They had the house on Andover Lake remodeled. Their wedding picture is on display on the wall in the front room. They're on a beach in Turks and Caicos, married Aug. 13, 2009.

"Always and all ways" is what they used to sign their cards to each other

When Peter was diagnosed with Alzheimer's, they got the saying tattooed on their forearms.

"Peter was adamant about where they were placed," Lisa said. "On our arms, so when we hold hands, they are touching."

Lisa got him into running; she had run since ninth grade. It was something to do when Peter came to Pennsylvania to visit. They ran two half-marathons together. Various aches and pains stopped Lisa, but Peter embraced it and kept going.

The night before the Scotland race, a group of friends and a few relatives gathered at the house on the lake. They were drinking wine around the kitchen island when Peter looked at Lisa.

"I love you," he said, out of the blue. She got up and kissed him and he said, "I love you" again.

"That's one thing he hasn't forgotten is that love for Lisa," said Kevin Fluke, a longtime friend who came from Washington, D.C., to run Peter's 169th race.

"I think that's her biggest fear, is that he's going to forget that love."

It's been hard for Lisa, to be a full-time caregiver, to be patient all the time, listening to Peter and trying to understand what he's talking about. One day, she was sick and as she lay in bed, she realized he was lying there, too, waiting for her to tell him what to do.

He's always been handy around the house and likes to do yardwork. But this summer, as his cognitive skills declined, he spent three hours mowing half the yard with a weed whacker before he remembered that he had a lawnmower. In the fall, they had two cords of wood delivered. Peter spent a lot of time in the basement, chopping and chopping and finally, Lisa, curious what he was doing down there for so long, discovered that instead of splitting the wood, he had chopped two cords of wood into kindling, because he just didn't know when to stop.

Lisa has a blog on Facebook. It's called, *Oh Hello Alzheimer's, F---."* If you don't like the brutal honesty of the title, she doesn't want you to read it because that's exactly how she feels. She shares her thoughts and fears, reminiscences of their life before Alzheimer's started to steal her husband. Anger. Incidences like the kindling story or how Peter would always, in a courtly way, pour her a glass of wine when she wanted one, and how one day in October, after deliberating for a bit, he poured her wine into a large pint beer mug.

"Maybe he thought I needed it!" she wrote.

Her Sept. 14 entry read: "I want our life back. I want my husband back. I want to argue and banter intellectually with him and play backgammon for hours or solve any problem together or beat him at Yahtzee and laugh while he's whining, but those days are gone now.

"No matter how positive my attitude, no matter how hard I try to shrug things off, or to let go of all the small stuff that just doesn't matter, I'm always just a bit sad. Even on the very best of days there's a sadness, but I keep it cloaked very near to my heart so that the world will know how very strong and brave and remarkable I am.

"But I'm not. I'm not strong or brave or remarkable. I'm human, and right now I don't want to do this anymore. I'm just so sick of it. I want to scream so loud and kick and punch and take it from him."

Lisa has gone to support groups, but she found that local ones are for people caring for older people, like their parents — not their 54-year-old husbands. There are other groups, but they're farther away, and she doesn't like to leave Peter by himself for a long time, mainly because he gets bored and he's always sad when she leaves.

"I keep thinking about that when you're on the airplane, they tell you to put on your oxygen mask first and then help others," she said. "But it's a little bit of a guilty feeling."

Bill Liebler of Southington drove an hour to run the race in Scotland. He worked with Peter in Hartford, starting in 2005. In 2014, the two joined the Run 169 Towns Society running club, whose members strive to reach a goal of running a race in all 169 towns in the state. He and Peter were competitive, both in racing and in collecting towns.

"There was this rivalry between the two of them," Lisa said. "Peter would come home from work and say, 'He ran two [races] this weekend and I didn't have any. Damn Liebler.'"

"The first race we did together was Old Wethersfield," Liebler said. "And he beat me. We kind of became close. He joined 169 before I did.

"At work, we'd rehash the races from the weekend. At one point, he was so forgetful, he couldn't remember which town he had done. A couple times he tried to drive to the races and couldn't remember how to get there. There were all these signs that something was not right. I knew his towns better than he did."

Liebler finished his 169th town last December. In March, when Lisa took over figuring out which towns he still needed, Peter still had 17 to go. It was once an important goal to him. It became important to Lisa now.

"He asks me every day," she said in late October. "Every single day. He woke up yesterday and he goes, 'I think I have to run today.' I said, 'Do you mean a race?' And he said, 'Yes.' And I said, 'Nope, you don't have a race today.' 'Oh, when's my next race?' Every day. 'When's my next race?' He's very, very concerned about finishing. But running isn't that important to him now, recreationally. It concerns me, almost, when this is over, what's he going to have to look forward to? It's been such a goal for so long. It's kind of like when people retire and they don't have anything to do. I don't want him to fizzle out, to have motivation, to be excited for something. He can only chop so much wood and pick up so much dog [poop]."

Peter can still run an 8-minute mile. He typically goes out fast on a run, then slows down and will walk up hills. He may not know how to use his running watch, but he knows all the roads around Andover Lake and runs at least once a week, between 5 and 8 miles. He couldn't drive to the races to complete the 169-town goal, though, so Lisa enlisted help.

Jim Hilliard, a childhood friend, was among those who helped.

"When I moved to Columbia, Peter was probably the first person I talked to, the first person who was nice to me," said Hilliard, who lives in Southington and ran five races with Marshall this year.

The morning of Nov. 24 dawned gloomy and cold and rainy, but Peter was nonplussed.

"Whatever," he said. But as everybody sat and talked at the house before the race, one leg jiggled up and down. He wanted to go.

He would sometimes struggle getting dressed for races, and wound up bringing everything, a laundry basket of clothes. Not this day, though. He wore a purple shirt that read "Alzheimer's Sucks" on the front and "Peter's Peeps" on the back, along with a blue tutu, which members of the running club often wear when they reach their final race.

There was a crowd waiting for him at the little firehouse hall in Scotland near the finish line. His father was there. His sisters, his kids. Their month-old grandson Sonny, Lisa and Peter's first grandchild, in his little carrier, with Lisa's son Zach and his wife Priscilla.

Five of his former co-workers came. Marc Scrivener, the fire chief in Willimantic who had run a race in Griswold with Peter in August, came to run with him.

So did Jill Levasseur, who went to Horace Porter School in Columbia with Peter and then to Windham High. There were about 75 kids in their class at Porter so everybody knew everybody. They kept in touch, and when Peter started training for the Hartford Marathon in 2016, he reached out to Levasseur. They ran long runs together. She got hurt and couldn't run, but she went to Hartford to cheer for him.

"I wasn't sure today if he would recognize me or not," she said. "But he did. It's hard to see someone you've known your entire life doesn't really remember who you are or what we did together, all those special memories."

Lisa and her daughter waited under the umbrella, watching for Peter. The finish line clock ticked. Is that him? Nope, no tutu. Wait — there he is! There was commotion, cellphones at the ready to capture the moment. And then Peter finished, crossing the line as his friends who ran with him whooped and held their hands in the air.

Inside the hall, it was warm and there was hot chocolate. Everybody had changed into dry clothes. People milled around Peter, a sea of purple shirts, congratulating him.

Lisa had a crown for Peter; when the 169 towns are completed, the runner becomes a king or a queen. Somebody gave him a bathrobe, like a boxer's robe, with "I ran 169 towns in Connecticut" embroidered on the back. A plastic medal with the number 169 on it was placed around his neck and so was a special bell from the race commemorating the day.

But before that, there was an awards ceremony. One name was called in the 50-59 year old age group. Then, "Second place — Peter Marshall."

Peter looked surprised. The sound in the hall swelled, clapping and cheering, and people rose out of their seats and applauded as he walked up to the front to get his award.

Lisa cried.

And though it was cold outside and rainy and dreary, a day without much hope or possibility, there would be warm memories of that day. Facebook posts. Pictures, to be framed eventually.

"After the rain and the race and recuperation, after the day was done and celebrating had subsided and we lay in bed recounting so many special moments Peter said, "I just don't understand why it was all for me?" and he cried," Lisa wrote in a Facebook post that night.

"It was more than either of us expected. ... For now, thank you, our hearts are bursting and we're clutching to each other laughing and smiling as we recall the new memories we made thanks to all of you!"

APPENDIX B:

Alzheimer's Disease Stages

The FAST Scale

The FAST Scale, also called the Functional Assessment Staging (FAST) Scale, was developed by Dr. Barry Reisberg.[7]

The summary below of the scale is excerpted from: https://www.aoascc.org/Customer-Content/www/CMS/fil es/events/EAC/FAST_Scale_HAND_OUT.pdf

Stage	Alzheimer's disease stage	Functional Assessment
Stage 1	Normal Aging	No deficits whatsoever
Stage 2	Possible mild cognitive impairment	Complains of forgetting location of objects. Subjective word finding difficulties.
Stage 3	Mild cognitive impairment	Decreased job function. Difficulty in travelling to new locations. Decreased organizational capacity.
Stage 4	Mild dementia	Decreased ability to perform complex tasks such as bill paying, cooking, cleaning, traveling, handling personal finances

---

[7] https://pubmed.ncbi.nlm.nih.gov/1504288/

Stage 5	Moderate dementia	Requires assistance in choosing proper clothing to wear for the day, season, and occasion.
Stage 6 (A-E)	Moderately severe dementia	A) Difficulty putting on clothes without assistance B) Unable to bathe properly C) Inability to handle the mechanicals of toileting occasionally or more frequently D) Urinary incontinence (occasional or more frequent) E) Fecal incontinence (occasional or more frequent)
Stage 7 (A-F)	Severe dementia	A) Speaks 5-6 words during the day. B) Speech limited to use of single intelligible word in an average day or over the course of interview. C) Ambulatory ability lost. D) Ability to sit up without assistance lost. E) Can no longer smile. F) Can no longer hold head up.

Stages of Alzheimer's

Excerpted from:
https://www.alz.org/alzheimers-dementia/stages

Early-stage Alzheimer's (mild)

In the early stage of Alzheimer's, a person may function independently. He or she may still drive, work and be part of social activities.

Common difficulties include:
- Coming up with the right word or name.
- Remembering names when introduced to new people.
- Having difficulty performing tasks in social or work settings.
- Forgetting material that was just read.
- Losing or misplacing a valuable object.
- Experiencing increased trouble with planning or organizing

Middle-stage Alzheimer's (moderate)

Middle-stage Alzheimer's is typically the longest stage and can last for many years. Symptoms, which vary from person to person, may include:

- Being forgetful of events or personal history.
- Feeling moody or withdrawn, especially in socially or mentally challenging situations.
- Being unable to recall information about themselves like their address or telephone number, and the high school or college they attended.
- Experiencing confusion about where they are or what day it is.
- Requiring help choosing proper clothing for the season or the occasion.
- Having trouble controlling their bladder and bowels.
- Experiencing changes in sleep patterns, such as sleeping during the day and becoming restless at night.
- Showing an increased tendency to wander and become lost.
- Demonstrating personality and behavioral changes, including suspiciousness and delusions or compulsive, repetitive behavior like hand-wringing or tissue shredding.

In the middle stage, the person living with Alzheimer's can still participate in daily activities with assistance.

Late-stage Alzheimer's (severe)

In the final stage of the disease, dementia symptoms are severe. Individuals lose the ability to respond to their environment, to carry on a conversation and, eventually, to control movement. They may still say words or phrases, but communicating pain becomes difficult. As memory and cognitive skills continue to worsen, significant personality changes may take place and individuals need extensive care.

At this stage, individuals may:
- Require around-the-clock assistance with daily personal care.
- Lose awareness of recent experiences as well as of their surroundings.
- Experience changes in physical abilities, including walking, sitting and, eventually, swallowing
- Have difficulty communicating.
- Become vulnerable to infections, especially pneumonia.

The person living with Alzheimer's may not be able to initiate engagement as much during the late stage, but he or she can still benefit from interaction in ways that are appropriate, like listening to relaxing music or receiving reassurance through gentle touch. During this stage, caregivers may want to use support services, such as hospice care, which focus on providing comfort and dignity at the end of life. Hospice can be of great benefit to people in the final stages of Alzheimer's and other dementias and their families.

APPENDIX C:
Practical Tips for Caregivers

Lisa Marshall's Four A's of Self-Care

Asking for help is difficult. People want to help, but they don't know what a caregiver needs. I developed the FOUR A'S OF SELF-CARE to help me enlist my army in a way I could accept emotionally.

1. **ACCEPT:** Accept help when someone offers something, anything. This will encourage them to ask again and get you in practice for saying yes more often.

2. **ASK:** Ask for help before you need it, being proactive rather than reactive after you've unraveled. When we wait too long, our thoughts become insurmountable, and we begin to feel alone and sad. Before burnout begins, enlist someone to help.

3. **ARTICULATE:** Articulate precisely what you need. Perhaps you have a personal doctor appointment and you cannot take your loved one along? Maybe you simply need a nap to recharge? Does the dog need to be taken for a walk? Does a phone call need to be made that you simply cannot get to? A small errand, like the post office?

4. **ACTUALLY:** Even after developing this theory of good intentions, It was hard for me to kick start, so I needed to somehow hold myself accountable. When someone asked, "Please let me know if you need anything" I made a demand on myself.

Instead of offering the usual empty promise, "Ok, I will", I made a difficult demand of myself. I responded differently, with just one word. "ACTUALLY." That one word caught my friend's attention, and they perked up, excited to hear how they could be of assistance. By saying, "Actually" it held me accountable to ask for something I needed. The first few times were cumbersome, and I soon realized I needed to have a mental checklist of some things that I could always use help with.

Here are a few things I always kept on my list:

- **A meal for my freezer.** Often by the time dinner time rolled around I was too exhausted to cook. Going out to dinner was becoming too confusing for Peter and too tiring for me.

- **An hour or two alone in my house.** This was by far my favorite ask. Friends would come and take Peter for a walk or a run or bowling or out for lunch. The quietness of having the house to myself was heavenly. Sometimes I would blare my favorite music and dance around. Most times I cleaned up Peter's piles of fidgets and photos and shoes and things he insisted on displaying on every surface. I prefer everything in its place, so this gave me great pleasure to clean and feel organized again. Peter wouldn't notice, he'd simply get everything out again, but I enjoyed a few hours of tidiness.

- **An hour or two away from the house**, perhaps lunch with a friend or a manicure, or a walk, anything!

- **Can you run to the store for me?** It became harder each day to get Peter in the car, to the store, through the store, back in the car, and home again. Having someone pick up a few items was incredibly helpful.

- **Take the trash cans to the street.** Early on, Peter was able to maneuver one of the trash cans and we did the task together, but eventually, he could not understand what to do and would usually rifle through the trash instead. If he did manage to pull the can to the street, I worried about the cars and his safety. Imagine trying to haul two large trash cans to the street yourself while trying to keep a child out of harm's way. Eyes dodging back and forth between task and toddler. Peter, somewhere between unaware and feeling inept.

- **Can you have a glass of wine with me and just make me laugh?** Laughter is lovely medicine.

Practical Tips and Tricks When Caring for Someone with Dementia

Labels for dresser drawers: Naming what is in each drawer

Silicone sport medical alert bracelet: With name, address, and emergency contact details

Purple Alzheimer's seatbelt cover: In case the driver becomes incapacitated. Responders will know the passenger has dementia

Memory basket: Fill with photos, fidgets, and old keepsakes

Photo board with name labels: Extremely helpful when language skills decrease and names are difficult to recall

Stove knob covers: To avoid burns

Games: Toss Across, ring toss, washer toss, golf putting green to keep loved one occupied

Blink Camera System: Options to mount on the wall or sit on surface make it easy to keep loved one safe

Puzzles and fidget toys: to keep your loved one occupied and help reduce anxiety

Tile stick-on buttons: Useful for wallet, coat, shoes, etc. when hiding begins

Child safety strap locks for drawers and cupboards: Lock cleaners, medications, sharps

Child Safety door knob cover with dual locks: This particular style not only snaps over the knob, but also has a screw on the front piece making it too complicated to take off

Childproof reinforcement locks: For outside doors, installed above eye level

Lavender bedtime baby bath: Calming for easier transition to bed

Noise cancelling blue tooth headphones: Create a relaxing and/or happy playlists

Bells on the door knob bedroom: Helped me to know if Peter woke up during the night

Electric razor and beard trimmer: Helpful when Peter could no longer shave himself

Fidget Pillow: Perfect when your loved one is less mobile, but still needs to be occupied

Weighted blanket: Helps reduce agitation and anxiety

Laundry basket filled with socks and shoes: Kept Peter busy for hours

Shower floor non-slip stickers: Helps curb slipping, contrasting colors are useful when vision starts to fail

3D bookshelf door decal: These door-size stickers deter your loved one from exiting the house or going into rooms you don't want them to

Elastic waist pants, shorts, pajama bottoms: When zippers and buttons and dressing become too much

Slip-on shoes: When tying is forgotten

Lower temperature on hot water heater: Reduces risk of your loved one burning themselves

Remove drain stoppers from all sinks: as your loved one may leave the water running and it may cause a flooding issue

Motion sensor Dog and Cat: Peter found comfort in these and thought they were real

Lifelike baby: Comforting to hold and rock and talk to when your loved one is anxious

Suction cup toddler bowls and plates: Perfect when self-feeding becomes difficult and plates and bowls slide around

Toilet hat urine collector: In the event you need a urine sample

Bidet: Easier clean up when your loved one protests personal care

Baby wipe warmer: Warm wipes are less shocking when trying to clean your loved one

Incontinence guards, for inside pullups: Pull-ups usually not absorbent enough. Guards catch overflow, meaning less clothing and linen clean up

Waterproof mattress cover: Buy two so there is always one clean one available.

Chucks Waterproof Fabric sheet squares: Invaluable for both curbing linen changes and moving LO when they become bedridden

Christmas tree decorated with fidget toys: No need to worry about ornament breakage

Nosey cup: Edge is cut out for easier drinking when loved one can no longer sit up

Mouth sponges: When drinking and eating stop

Remove the toilet lid: Helps avoid messes on top of the toilet, reduces confusion

Go bag: Keep a bag of extras in the car including pants, shirt, wipes, pullups, extra meds, fidget toys, underwear, towel, and bottled water for cleanups

INDEX

ABOUT THE AUTHOR

Lisa Marshall was the primary caregiver for her husband Peter Marshall who was diagnosed with early-onset Alzheimer's in 2018 at the age of 53. Lisa retired in 2020 from a professional sales career to care for her husband who could no longer be alone. Peter passed away on December 26th, 2021, just three years and eight months after diagnosis. He was 56.

She is passionate about advocating for support for caregivers and raises her voice to create awareness of the disease. For over three years she chronicled her and Peter's journey at www.facebook.com/ohhelloalzheimers offering an honest, realistic, and raw look at Alzheimer's disease, to followers all over the world. She is also a contributing author of *Chicken Soup for the Soul: Navigating Elder Care and Dementia.* Her chapter depicts just one of the many sad nuances of Alzheimer's.

Lisa and Peter's journey has been covered on CNN, The *Washington Post, Today.com, CBS Evening News, On the Road with Steve Hartman, People.com*, and more.

Continuing her passion, she holds virtual Alzheimer's discussions with followers, offering her insight, tips, and coping skills. Participants discuss their own unique stories and realize a sense of community together in a safe space.

She works with companies that offer continuing education credits to medical professionals helping them to understand the disease. Lisa shares tips she's learned to help professional caregivers cope which ultimately helps their Alzheimer's patients.

Lisa works closely with the Alzheimer's Association and led a team with Walk to End Alzheimer's helping fund research to find a cure. Her team was the largest fundraising team in Connecticut in 2021, raising more than $55,000.

When Lisa isn't writing, she spends time with her family. She has three grown children, two stepchildren, and two grandsons who she babysits whenever she can. Additionally, she enjoys a very active life hiking, swimming in the neighborhood lake, going to the beach, visiting with friends, traveling, and gardening. Lisa practices meditation and vibrating positive energy and love to everyone she meets. Her mantra is to find joy in life and live each day with no regrets.

www.linktr.ee/OhHelloAlzheimers

www.facebook.com/OhHelloAlzheimers

www.instagram.com/OhHelloAlzheimers

Green Heart Living Press publishes inspirational books and stories of healing and transformation, making the world a more loving and peaceful place, one book at a time. You can meet Green Heart authors on the Green Heart Living YouTube channel and the Green Heart Living Podcast.

Made in United States
Orlando, FL
16 November 2022

24640582R00213